THE NATURAL HISTORY OF NORTH AMERICAN AMPHIBIANS AND REPTILES

THE NEW ILLUSTRATED NATURALIST

THE NEW ILLUSTRATED NATURALIST

THE NATURAL HISTORY OF NORTH AMERICAN AMPHIBIANS AND REPTILES

BY

JAMES A. OLIVER

Curator of Reptiles
New York Zoological Society

D. VAN NOSTRAND COMPANY, INC.

PRINCETON, NEW JERSEY

TORONTO LONDON

NEW YORK

D. VAN NOSTRAND COMPANY, INC.

120 Alexander St., Princeton, New Jersey
257 Fourth Avenue, New York 3, New York
25 Hollinger Rd., Toronto 16, Canada
Macmillan & Co., Ltd., St. Martin's St., London, W.C. 2, England

All correspondence should be addressed to the principal office of the company at Princeton, N. J.

Library of Congress Catalogue Card No. 55-10534

Published simultaneously in Canada by
D. VAN NOSTRAND COMPANY (Canada), LTD.

PRINTED IN THE UNITED STATES OF AMERICA

To my Mother, Mary Roberts Oliver,
who encouraged and enabled me
to follow my chosen career.

Preface

There is apparent today in the United States and Canada a growing interest in the study of amphibians and reptiles. This is indicated by the popularity of the excellent handbooks and field guides that have appeared during the last decade and a half, and by the increasing attention given to the study of these animals in colleges and universities. A number of colleges and universities offer formal courses in herpetology—the study of amphibians and reptiles.

With this increased interest there is a need for a book covering, in a single volume, the general ways and habits of amphibians and reptiles. The present volume has been prepared to fill this need. It presents the basic principles of the natural history of the amphibians and reptiles occurring in the United States and Canada. This is a large subject and one about which we have only incomplete information. I have endeavored to summarize the available facts and to present them as simply as possible, along with their general implications. This difficult task demands the omission of many details, qualifications, and authentications that the scientist requires. Some herpetologists may feel that certain topics have been oversimplified and other pertinent topics omitted altogether. However, I am sure that they understand the desirability of keeping the material in a simplified form—even at the expense of documentation.

This book is intended for the naturalist and the beginning student of amphibians and reptiles. No knowledge of biology is necessary to understand its contents. The classification and names used are those of the sixth edition of *A Check List of North American Amphibians and Reptiles*, by Karl P. Schmidt. This provides a ready reference for the reader and avoids the necessity of belaboring controversial questions in a book of this nature. A few additional books are listed in the back under "Recommended References." These will provide those interested with additional details and a means of identifying native species.

For the sake of consistency with the Check List, as well as for ease of treating the subject, the geographical limits of that book have been adhered to. Thus North America, as used here, includes only Alaska, Canada, and the United States. This continent is sometimes defined as including all land areas north of the Isthmus of Panama or the Isthmus of Tehuantepec or some other region. However, the southern boundary of the United States will be considered as the southern limits of North America in this book. One other geographical matter requires mention: for the purpose of discussing the distribution of families of amphibians and reptiles, Antarctica is not considered as one of the continents, since it is inhabited by no animals of these groups. Thus the statement that a particular family has representatives on all continents means that the family occurs in Africa, Asia, Australia, Europe, and North and South America.

Specific common or vernacular names are capitalized to distinguish them from descriptive phrases. This is a matter about which there is considerable difference of opinion and the reader will find many books in which the names are not capitalized. However, capitalization of the names removes any possibility of ambiguity or misunderstanding. Thus "green frog" can refer to any green colored frog, but "Green Frog" used in this area can mean only one species—the frog known scientifically as *Rana clamitans*. Where family or generic names are employed as general designations, these, too, are capitalized.

A book of this broad scope is necessarily a compilation of the works and observations of others. Our present knowledge of amphibian and reptilian life has been gathered by the combined efforts of a great many people, including both amateur and professional herpetologists. In illustrating the topics discussed in this book many contributions could be cited, but I have selected only a few representative observations in each case. In presenting this material, I have frequently indicated the name of the individual who recorded the information. This serves several purposes and has been done as often as readability would permit.

Naturally, in the preparation of the book I have been helped by many people. It is not possible to acknowledge the assistance received from all. My wife, Elizabeth Kimball Oliver, has been a constant source of inspiration and encouragement. She helped materially in gathering some of the observations reported here and has read the completed manuscript, offering many helpful suggestions. The manuscript has been read also by Charles M. Bogert, Chairman and Curator of the Department of Amphibians and Reptiles of the American Museum of Natural History and James W. Atz, Assistant Curator of the Aquarium of the New York Zoological Society; both made numerous helpful suggestions, corrections, and criticisms that improved the manuscript materially. Lloyd Sandford has done a splendid job of illustrating the book. It is a pleasure to acknowledge his close cooperation and industry in the preparation of these illustrations specifically for this book. Most of the drawings were made from live animals, but a few were necessarily taken from the works of others, which are duly credited in all instances.

I wish to thank the New York Zoological Society for six of the photographs of living specimens. Charles Stine, Jr., generously permitted the use of four of his excellent photographs of amphibian activity. Charles E. Shaw made available the Zoological Society of San Diego's spectacular photograph of the Rattlesnake "combat dance" and Robert C. Hermes kindly provided his remarkable photograph of the Tree Frog engulfing its large meal. Lee R. Dice and the University of Michigan Press courteously granted permission to reproduce part of Dr. Dice's map of the Biotic Provinces of North America which appeared in his book "The Biotic Provinces of North America," published by the University of Michigan Press.

To these and all the others who helped in one way or another, I am most grateful. Any errors or incorrect statements are solely my responsibility.

August, 1955 JAMES A. OLIVER

Contents

CHAPTER		PAGE
	PREFACE	vii
1.	Folklore	1
2.	Economic Values	16
3.	Classification	30
4.	North American Amphibians	41
5.	North American Reptiles	51
6.	Occurrence of Amphibians and Reptiles	69
7.	Locomotion and Movements	84
8.	Activity	115
9.	Relation to Environment	135
10.	Food and Feeding	168
11.	Reproduction	209
12.	Growth, Size, and Longevity	264
13.	Amphibians and Reptiles as Pets	305
	GLOSSARY	329
	REFERENCES	333
	INDEX	335

CHAPTER 1

Folklore

WHEN YOU MENTION THE TERMS "amphibian" and "reptile" to the average person, the mental pictures called forth are usually vague and have little resemblance to the actual animals belonging to these groups. One or more of the major types may be recognized, often in relation to some erroneous or exaggerated habit. During World War II the terms "amphibian" and "amphibious" were constantly before the reading public, many of whom were completely unaware that a group of animals had a prior claim to the term.

One reason why amphibians and reptiles are more or less unknown is that their economic importance is relatively slight compared with other backboned (vertebrate) animals. Mammals, birds, and fish are utilized in large commercial and governmental enterprises involving billions of dollars, whereas the economic value of amphibians and reptiles is primarily indirect or on a much smaller financial scale. Another reason for their being poorly known is the secretive, nocturnal, or retiring nature of many of them. For example, some people live in close proximity to large populations of salamanders without even being aware that such animals exist. Finally, many superstitions and misconceptions have resulted from the fact that a few species of reptiles are harmful to man. This causes many people to persecute and shun all of them, and to make few or only incomplete observations on them.

In spite of the fact that these animals are relatively little known, they have had more than a small impact on our culture. Through the pages of history we find recurrent accounts of man's attitudes toward and uses of amphibians and reptiles. Supernatural traits are attributed to many forms; and cults have been established for the worship or placation of particular species endowed with great powers of either good or evil. The Bible contains numerous references to amphibians and reptiles—some in favorable, others in unfavorable, light. Much of our present attitude toward snakes may be traced to the story of Adam and Eve in the Garden of Eden. However, not all Biblical references to snakes are of this nature; for example, we find Solomon pondering the mysteries of the world, including "the way of the serpent on the rock." Perhaps the scope of the impact of these animals on human society and beliefs can be illustrated best by considering their role in our folklore.

The folklore of America is richly flavored with more than a sprinkling of misinformation concerning animal life on the land. Amphibians and reptiles have been—and still are—subjects of the myths, legends, and simple exaggerations that make up this folklore. Despite the abundance of misinformation included in these folklore yarns, there is often some basis of truth in them. Many erroneous beliefs are the result of incomplete or uncritical observations.

That well-known American boy, Tom Sawyer, was endowed with a goodly portion of his country's folklore. Tom tells his good friend, Huckleberry Finn, that warts on the hands are the price that one pays for handling frogs and toads. To Tom this was no serious matter as long as a supply of "spunk" water was at hand and one knew the magic words—

> Barley-corn, barley-corn, Injun-meal shorts,
> Spunk water, spunk water, swaller these warts.

The erroneous belief that the handling of frogs and, especially, toads will produce warts on the hands is an old idea that goes far back in history. It is not restricted to American folklore; it was brought to this country by European settlers. This erroneous belief is more frequently associated with toads than with frogs, probably because of the warty texture of the toad's skin. One version of this belief is that the warts are transferred directly from the skin of the toad to the skin of the handler. Another version involves a common reaction of toads when picked up. Under such circumstances many toads will promptly empty the contents of the urinary bladder. Although this liquid does have a slight odor, it is harmless unless it gets in the eyes or mouth; it does not cause warts.

It is thought by some people that warts are caused by a secretion of the skin glands of the frog or toad. This is not so. All amphibians possess large numbers of skin glands. Some of these glands secrete a toxic alkaloid that produces marked irritation when it comes in contact with the mucous membranes of the mouth or eyes, or if it gets into the blood. The secretion of these glands affords protection from would-be predators. The glands may be scattered throughout the skin or may occur in clusters, such as the parotoid gland and warts of toads or the dorsolateral fold of some frogs. Because of the large numbers of glands that occur in the warts and in the parotoid glands of the toads, their poisonous nature is widely recognized. The fact that dogs, cats, and other mammals become violently ill from merely mouthing a toad is probably the basis for the belief that toads are venomous animals. In "As You Like It," Shakespeare expresses this belief:

> Sweet are the uses of adversity,
> Which like the toad, ugly and venomous,
> Wears yet a precious jewel in his head.

Doubtless because of the toad's supposed venomous qualities, it was also thought to possess various charms associated with a "jewel" in its head that was so highly prized that it was supposed to be worn as a talisman to ward off all sorts of evil. The jewel was reputed to be a priceless stone, but exactly what object was worn as the jewel and what the origin of this strange belief may have been is uncertain. However, when the toad's eyes are shined at night with a light, they do sparkle with a gleam that would do credit to a precious gem.

Toads are frequently reported to possess the ability to remain imprisoned underground, in rocks and in trees, for long periods. Almost every year there are newspaper stories of toads being blasted out of rock during excavation operations, or being dug up from great depths beneath hard-packed clay, or even being released from within some building cornerstone. The most recent version in the southwestern United States involves the "horned toad," which is, of course, a lizard and not a toad. By burrowing into the moist ground, toads can withstand brief periods of drought. The Spadefoot Toads appear to spend most of their adult life underground, becoming active above ground only at night or during very hard rains. These toads have been uncovered under hard-packed soil. However, they burrowed under such soil when it was soft and wet. Normally, they would have emerged when the soil became wet again. This would have happened in the following rainy period. In unusually dry years, toads may possibly skip a year and not emerge until the next rainy period. Probably many individual toads could not survive that long, but some certainly would. As pointed out in a later chapter, experiments have been performed to test the ability of toads to remain confined in boxes of limestone and sandstone when buried underground. All the toads died before the end of two years.

A quite different belief about toads and frogs is that they may descend upon the earth in "rains of frogs." This is, of course, another version of the more common stories relating to rains of fishes. Some versions even have turtles, lizards, and snakes descending in the rain! A suitable setting for a rain of frogs can be found in almost any part of the country during the middle or latter part of the summer when many species are ready to terminate their tadpole stage and hop out on land. This often occurs during a summer thundershower, and the ground may become literally covered with young frogs and toads. Where did the horde come from? If one didn't know better, one might assume that the little frogs had fallen with the rain.

During violent windstorms—such as hurricanes, typhoons, or tornadoes—many forms of life get picked up and carried with the wind. Such storms are usually accompanied by heavy rainfall, and hence may result in "rains" of various sorts. Perhaps the recollection of such phenomena or the unconscious desire to witness such an unusual occurrence is what prompts the report of a rain of frogs without the violent wind disturbance necessary to effectuate this rare occurrence.

In contrast to the frogs and their purported water-soaked descent from the heavens, there is the old belief that salamanders are creatures of fire. They are supposed not only to live in fire, but to be able to extinguish it. The antiquity of this belief is shown by the nonbiological uses of the word "salamander" for the following: a person or thing that can stand great heat; colloquially, a large poker; a mass of hardened metal or slag remaining in the hearth of a furnace when the fires are drawn; a small portable stove; or a girl who figuratively plays with fire without apparently getting burned. In Paracelsus' system the nymph, the gnome, and the salamander were the elemental spirits of water, earth, and fire, respectively. The basis of this belief seems fairly clear. Many of the land-dwelling salamanders live in or under logs. Undoubtedly they are occasionally transported into the fireplace in these logs. The heat of the fire drives them out of the log and out of the fireplace. Thus they would be seen emerging from the fire; and to an uncritical observer the animals would appear to have the supernatural ability to live in fire.

The folklore concerning turtles comprises a variety of exaggerations and outright inaccuracies, mainly relating to the strength of these animals, their fecundity, and their longevity. The attribute of longevity is the one that seems to be the best known. Consequently any large turtle is generally believed to be a shelled Methuselah. This supposition is greatly enhanced if the turtle in question is a fresh-water form whose shell is covered with a mosslike growth of algae (which, incidentally, can be accumulated in a single year). Actually, as pointed out in the chapter on longevity, some turtles are the longest-lived members of the animal kingdom, but none of these approaches the ripe old age attributed to Methuselah. The greatest length of life known for any animal is somewhat more than 150 years, reported for certain land turtles. This age is based on the known length of life of turtles in captivity. Few animals, including the turtles, live anywhere near this long.

Crocodiles and alligators also figure in legends of longevity. One alligator farm in Florida advertises that some of its ancient inhabitants may approach 1,000 years in age. This is simply advertising enthusiasm that grossly exaggerates the truth. Both alligators and crocodiles actually grow more rapidly than most people realize. The maximum age definitely known is 56 years, a record reported for the American Alligator.

Perhaps the most frequently encountered bit of folklore concerning the alligator and the crocodile is the story that these two animals can be told apart by the manner in which they open their mouths. According to this yarn, the alligator opens its mouth by moving the lower jaw, as do most vertebrate animals. But the crocodile is reputed to open its mouth by raising the upper jaw. This is an old belief, going back at least as far as the ancient Greeks. Both animals, of course, open their mouths in the same way, by normally moving only the lower jaw.

Lizards suffer because of the widespread belief that many of them are highly venomous. Some are even thought to have a poisonous breath. As a result of these erroneous notions, large numbers are needlessly killed. In the southeastern United States the large red-headed males of the Blue-tailed Skink (*Eumeces laticeps*) are commonly thought to be very dangerous because of their potent venom.

The old males of this species possess an impressive appearance because of the large size of the head and its bright reddish-orange color. As a matter of fact, this lizard is entirely harmless and quickly retires from sight when it sees a human being.

One of the most interesting folk fables about lizards is that of the Glass Lizard, Glass Snake, or Joint Snake. The animal in question is a legless lizard (*Ophisaurus*) that is commonly mistaken for a snake and often called the Glass Snake. According to the myth, this "snake" will break into many pieces when hit with a club or stick. Later, after the "snake's" antagonist has departed, the pieces will reunite and the "snake," as good as new, will joyfully wiggle away. The truth is that the Glass Lizard has a very long tail that is easily broken. The tail breaks in such a way that there is little loss of blood and the piece that is broken off retains marked powers of reflex movements. Thus the detached tail moves vigorously, generally attracting the attention of the molester while the lizard escapes. If hit again, the tail may break into two smaller pieces, and each of these will exhibit vigorous reflex movements. The pieces will not unite, but the lizard grows a new tail to replace the one that is broken off.

By far the most colorful of all amphibian and reptilian folklore is that pertaining to snakes. The fact that a few species possess powerful venom has led to the belief that most snakes have a venom of some sort in addition to numerous supernatural qualities. A favorite among the snake stories is that of the Hoop Snake. Reputedly, this snake has a powerful stinger in the end of its tail: one stab with this organ and the victim is dead. The Hoop Snake is said to take its tail in its mouth and to roll along like a hoop. At the right moment it releases its tail from its mouth and the tail jabs the victim. In one version of this yarn the snake also possesses the ability to whistle, which it does with amazingly human characteristics and thereby attracts its victims to it. In another story a Hoop Snake rolls vigorously along pursuing a young lad. Just when it is about to sting him, the boy ducks behind an apple tree and the snake jabs its stinger into the tree. Immediately the tree wilts and dies, dropping all its apples and leaves. The Hoop Snake story appears to be entirely American, although the erroneous notion that snakes carry a sting in their tails is a very old belief, going back at least to the Bible (Rev. 9:19). No snake has a stinger or venom gland of any sort in its tail. In the southern United States, the Mud Snake

(*Farancia*) and the Rainbow Snake (*Abastor*) both have sharp terminal scales on the tail. When handled they make exploratory probing movements with the tip of the tail, but are unable to inflict even a minor scratch with this scale. Of course, no snake can take its tail in its mouth and roll along like a hoop.

One of the most widespread fictions about snakes, and one of the most difficult to correct, is the belief that in some species the mother snake swallows her young for protection. This is another old yarn that goes well back in history. In Spenser's "Faerie Queene" we find this belief associated with a mythical dragon. Despite its age and the efforts of scientists to dispel it, the fallacy persists today firmly entrenched in the minds of many people.

The scientist is interested in ferreting out facts and must rely on all the accurate information available when he seeks the truth. He has no desire to cast aspersion on any supposed demonstrations of a mother's love, even in a snake. Among other animals, such parental care is not unknown and there are several forms in which the developing eggs and the young are carried in the mouth of one of the parents. Among the fishes, for example, many of the African and a few of the South American Cichlids have adopted this method of parental care. The chore is usually undertaken by the mother, in whose mouth the young remain for a while after hatching. Later the young fish may be seen swimming about in the water, but they remain close to their mother and promptly are taken into her mouth if danger threatens. In certain sea catfishes the developing eggs and the newly hatched young are carried in the mouth of the male for as long as two months, during which the parent does not eat. In one species of frog from South America, the male carries the developing eggs and the tadpoles. In all the animals where such care is known to take place, the floor of the mouth or some other structure shows modification to form a more or less definite pouch. In snakes, however, it is difficult to see where the young could be protected without going into the digestive tract, where they would be injured by the strong digestive juices. No special structures that could serve as brood pouches have ever been observed in snakes. If the phenomenon of swallowing the young is actually as common as the number of accounts by "eye witnesses" would indicate, then surely some qualified herpetologist should have been fortunate enough to view the proceedings. Thousands of baby snakes have seen the world for the first time in our large zoological gardens, and many have been reared there. Yet this strange performance has never been witnessed in any zoo or by any trained student of reptiles in nature.

There are several possible misinterpretations that might provide the basis for this story. As pointed out in Chapter 11, the developing eggs in many snakes are retained in the body of the female until the embryonic development is complete and the young are ready to leave the egg. Such young are fully capable of fending for themselves as soon as they leave the eggs. If a female of this type, carrying young about to hatch, is vigorously belabored with a club, her swollen body may easily burst, releasing the young. The observation of such an event could be interpreted as lending support to the snake-swallowing yarn by the uncritical and by those unaware that not all snakes lay eggs. Another possible contributing feature that might be misinterpreted is that many snakes feed on other snakes, usually much smaller. Some different species look superficially alike to the layman. When he sees a large snake eating a smaller one he might assume that he is actually looking at the unusual performance of a snake swallowing its young for protection. In the hundreds of thouasnds of snakes preserved in the collections of our large natural history museums there are many that contain young in all stages of development. There are also many that contain other snakes that have been eaten. None has ever been seen with the young of its own species in the mouth or the anterior part of the digestive tract.

Even today the majority of people fear snakes. Fear often produces hallucinations. Under the emotional strain that comes to many people as the result of an encounter with a snake, it is difficult to separate actual observation from hallucination. Significantly enough, nearly all the eye-witness accounts of this story about snakes swallowing their young are based on memory of an event that took place some time in the past, frequently in childhood.

Another snake yarn of ancient vintage that is widespread concerns Milk Snakes. The belief is that certain snakes obtain their nourishment by sucking milk from cows. As a result of these habits, the farmer is deprived of a large share of his milk. In the language of the punster, this is udder nonsense! First of all, it would be an anatomical impossibility for a snake to extract milk from a cow. Secondly, the sharp teeth in the mouth of the snake would be enough to cause any self-respecting cow to revolt vigorously against such an outrage. Even if it were possible for a snake to get milk from a cow, it has been shown experimentally that the snake most often associated with this myth in the United States could hold only about one-third of a glass of milk. The loss of such a small amount certainly would not be noticed by the farmer.

The only plausible basis for this story is that some snakes frequent barns, granaries, and other farm buildings. These snakes are in search of the mice and young rats usually abundant in these places.

It is a common occurrence for some variation to occur in a cow's milk supply. When his cow gives less milk than usual and he sees a snake nearby, the farmer may try to relate the two events and assume that the snake is the cause for the small amount of milk obtained. The belief is so widespread, however, that a snake need not even be anywhere nearby to be blamed for deviations from a large milk supply. In the eastern United States one of the King Snakes is frequently referred to as the "Milk Snake" because of its association with this story. In other parts of the country and in other parts of the world, other species are involved.

Snakes are sometimes thought to have the power to charm their prey. According to this myth, animals (usually small birds) are charmed or hypnotized by the evil eye of the snake. Under the spell the hapless victim slowly approaches the snake and is quickly swallowed. The effectiveness of this yarn is greatly enhanced by the unblinking eye of the serpent; but despite this constant stare, snakes cannot charm their prey. Most wild animals exhibit exploratory behavior to such a high degree that we refer to them as being very curious. This behavior is shown both to animate and inanimate objects. Some of the animate objects, whether dangerous or harmless, may be approached and investigated as long as the object remains motionless. I have watched a bird approach and investigate a coiled snake in this fashion. As soon as the snake moved part of the body, the bird would fly away but would return soon. This bird was not charmed; it was merely curious.

It is possible that an occasional bird or small mammal may be so frightened as to be incapable of escape. However, this seems to be an unlikely reaction to judge from the behavior of mice, rats, and birds when placed in a cage with live snakes.

Snakes in turn are reported to be charmed by some supposedly gifted human beings. The best known and most colorful of these so-called snake charmers are those of India, who, to the tune of the flute, demonstrate their wiles on the highly venomous Cobra. This snake is an excellent performer. It spreads its broad hood and raises the anterior part of the body into a vertical position, swaying from side to side, apparently in time with the music. The result seems to be a rather spectacular demonstration that music does charm the most dangerous and savage beast! But does it? All evidence indicates that snakes do not hear airborne sounds and hence are deaf to the notes of any flute. Careful observation shows that the snake charmer is swaying from side to side as he plays his instrument. The alert Cobra, which spreads its hood only when it is excited, is following the movements of the swaying flutist.

How does the snake charmer avoid being bitten by the Cobra? There are several ways in which he can prevent such a danger. A simple method of obtaining partial protection is to pull out the enlarged fangs in the front of the upper jaw. This will not give complete protection, since the snake can still bite. The smaller teeth in the mouth could break the skin and allow the venom to enter the blood. However, these defanged snakes are usually reluctant to bite.

Since the missing fangs will be replaced by new ones in a short time, another method is to pull the fangs and then crush or remove the bone to which the fangs are attached. This procedure prevents any replacement of the fangs, but still does not entirely remove the danger of receiving a venomous bite, as indicated above. A safer way to avoid the possibility of a bite is to sew the snake's mouth shut. This can be done in such a way as to be completely unnoticeable. When this operation is properly performed, the snake is entirely harmless and can be handled without danger. But it will not live long without being able to eat.

Occasionally a snake charmer will handle venomous snakes that are in full possession of their fangs and do not have their mouths sewed shut. These persons may handle sluggish species or forms that are slow to bite. Or they may feel that they have acquired an immunity to the bite of a particular species through repeated bites in the past. Or they may believe that they know their snakes well enough to avoid exciting them to the point of biting. Regardless of the basis for this false sense of security, it is an extremely dangerous way to earn a living or to obtain a thrill. Most persons who engage in such activities carry scars of their past follies and seldom live out their allotted span of time.

One of the most notorious and widely feared of all American snakes is the "Puffing Adder," "Blowing Adder," "Spreading Adder," or Hog-nosed Snake (*Heterodon*). When encountered, this snake puts on a fearful display of ferocity. It flattens its head and the anterior part of the body, somewhat in the fashion of a Cobra, spreads the head and anterior part of the body, opens its mouth, hisses loudly, and makes spasmodic thrusts with its head and the fore part of its body. The breath expelled with each hiss is supposedly filled with venomous fumes.

This performance is one of the most amazing acts of any snake in North America. It is sheer bluff! Despite its fearsome appearance, this snake is entirely harmless and rarely bites even if a hand is put directly in front of its mouth. On several occasions I have put my hand down by one of these snakes when it was performing; and although it would hit my hand with its head, it would not bite even then.

If the Hog-nosed Snake is still molested after this bluffing performance, it will go into the final stage of the act. Now the snake opens its mouth wide, sticks out its tongue, and rolls over on its back. It usually gives a few feeble twitches and then remains motionless, apparently dead. At this point, if the snake is turned over on its belly, it will quickly roll over on its back again. Apparently this is the only position in which a dead snake should lie!

If the snake is left undisturbed for several minutes, it will raise its head and, no further danger being in sight, roll over on its belly and crawl away. A number of snakes in various parts of the world "play possum" in order to avoid danger from an antagonist, but none in North America puts on a performance to compare with that of the Hog-nosed Snake. When these snakes are taken into captivity, they quickly lose their inclination to perform in this fashion. It is virtually impossible to stimulate captive individuals to go through the act.

The belief that the long, slender Coachwhip Snakes will attack and viciously whip people is more prevalent in the southern United States than in any other part of the country. According to one version of this yarn, the snake wraps the fore part of its body around the legs of its victim and, thus holding the unfortunate person, whips him soundly with its tail. These snakes, as their name implies, do look something like a braided whip. The anterior one-third of the body is darker in color than the posterior two-thirds, and the scales of the long tail give the appearance of braid. Despite the superficial similarity to a whip that this snake shows, the snake does not use the tail as a lash either for offense or defense.

What factual basis there may be for this yarn besides the similarity in appearance is hard to determine. Coachwhip Snakes, like many other snakes, vibrate their tails rapidly when disturbed. Because of the long, slender tail and its similarity to a whip, someone may have interpreted the tail movement as a warning that the snake was about to whip the intruder. Another possibility is that a Coachwhip may have been encountered suddenly; and, in the snake's efforts to escape, its long tail may have struck the leg of the intruder accidentally. Coachwhips are among the fastest of our snakes and usually dash off at first sight of a human being.

A Southern minister recently told me a story that he heard as a child. He believed that it might be the origin of the whip snake story. A slightly inebriated mule-skinner was seen going home at dusk with the handle of his long whip stuck through his belt in the back and the lash dragging behind him. He had temporarily forgotten about the whip and looking back was frightened to see what he believed to be a large snake about to bite him in the leg. He immediately took flight as fast as he could. This action caused the lash of the whip to fly back and forth, giving him a thrashing. He was convinced that the snake was whipping him and ran all the harder. After about half a mile or more the whip worked loose from his belt. However, the painful welts on the man's back were ample proof for him of the viciousness of the whip snake's attack!

Rattlesnakes, which are confined to the Americas, have excited the imaginations of American settlers since the days of the first travelers on the mainland. Many of the tales and beliefs about the rattlesnake have been reviewed in a scholarly work which was published in 1929 by Rheua Vaughn Medden. This author reminds us of the esteem in which this serpent was held in the early days of American history, and we find that the rattlesnake has been a part of the emblem on several of the flags of this country. Even today there are many who believe that the rattler is an honorable character who will always give warning before he strikes. Unfortunately, all rattlesnakes do not seem to have been informed of this code of ethics, for some of them show no hesitation in biting first and rattling later or not at all.

In the southwestern United States the belief is fairly widespread that rattlers will not cross a horsehair rope. Thus a cowboy sleeping on the ground can avoid acquiring a rattlesnake bedmate simply by coiling his horsehair lariat around his sleeping roll. Unfortunately rattlers are not discouraged so easily. The placing of the rope around a bedroll at night serves only to put the sleeper's mind at rest.

A colorful yarn that is often encountered tells the story of a man who was out hunting game. He was bitten by a large rattlesnake. The snake bit the man on the leg, piercing a pair of high-top leather boots. The man died despite treatment. Years later his son, finding the boots in a closet, put them on to go hunting and mysteriously died with the symptoms of snakebite. Some years later a grandson found the boots, wore them, and he, too, died from some strange cause but with the symptoms of snakebite. Examination of the boots revealed the fang of a rattlesnake embedded in the leather of one of the boots in such a fashion that any wearer would be pricked by the point of the fang. This story has been retold from coast to coast with variations on details and the number of generations killed. It is pure fantasy, because the amount of venom that would remain in such a fang is too small to produce fatal results. Moreover, venom dries very quickly outside the venom glands and soon loses its potency when exposed to air.

Many of the truly venomous snakes are thought to bite and kill themselves to avoid capture. This is not true. In fact, snakes are largely resistant to their own venom. If they accidentally bite their own bodies, they appear to suffer chiefly from the mechanical injury resulting from the penetration of the fangs. Snakes do not bite themselves intentionally, but in their frenzied attempts to bite a molester they occasionally inflict an accidental bite on themselves.

Another myth relating to the biting reactions of snakes is that venomous snakes cannot bite under water, or, if they do, that the venom will not be injected. This is a dangerous and erroneous belief. Snakes can and do bite under water. The bite of a venomous species is just as dangerous under water as it is out of the water. This notion is probably based on an experience with one of the harmless Water Snakes, which bite viciously both in and out of the water and are frequently mistaken for venomous species. The bites of these snakes, while nonvenomous, may still be painful as a result of the numerous sharp teeth. A few of the Water Snake species are slow to bite, either in or out of the water.

There are many other dangerous myths relating to the bites of snakes. Most of these concern the treatment of snakebite. Treatment varies from the use of whiskey taken internally to eating some of the snake that bit you. The remedies recommended vary in wide variety between these two examples and are just as detrimental or useless. Correct first aid and proper treatment should be thoroughly known to anyone going into the country where venomous snakes may be found and to everyone who is around live venomous snakes. The correct treatment can be found in a number of popular books on snakes.

Perhaps even more disturbing than the bite of a venomous snake is the thought of harboring a live one in one's intestines. A fairly widespread story relates the sad plight of a beautiful girl who as a child swallowed the egg of a rattlesnake while drinking from a woodland spring. The egg hatched, the snake grew large over the years, and doctors were at a loss as to how the snake could be removed without exciting it and causing it to bite the girl. The details vary and other species of snakes are involved, but essentially the same story recurs. It is, of course, purely fictional. Snake eggs and the young of our snakes are too large to be swallowed accidentally. Even if they were swallowed, the digestive fluids would kill them in a short time.

There are many tall tales relating to the maximum size of amphibians and reptiles, especially snakes. The reported size of an animal is subject to a variety of personal biases and to several physical factors. Authentic maximum sizes are much smaller than those reported by many uncritical laymen who accept length records based on measurements of skins, which are known to stretch considerably, or who are willing to accept a "careful estimate" without measuring. The subject of maximum size is presented in Chapter 12.

A frequently encountered belief is that wherever one snake occurs its mate will also be found or will soon appear. This belief, in one form or another, applies equally to dead or live snakes. The fable can be illustrated from Mark Twain's *Huckleberry Finn.* We find Jim bitten by a rattlesnake. Huck assumes the blame because he had placed a dead rattler on Jim's blanket to frighten him. Huck remorsefully says, "That all comes of my being such a fool as to not remember that wherever you leave a dead snake its mate always comes there and curls around it."

One basis for this belief is that in the spring and, rarely, in the fall, at which times snakes are mating, they naturally may be encountered in pairs. It is true that during the breeding season, in some species, the sexes locate one another by scent. It is possible that a male might trail a female and thus appear on the scene. This exaggerated notion also receives support from the common human tendency to romanticize about animals. Many of the supposed mates occasionally encountered might prove to be of the same sex if carefully checked. As mentioned in Chapter 11, some herpetologists have been guilty of making similar assumptions in the case of the male "combat dance" reported for some snakes. Without verifying the sex of the two individuals so engaged, this phenomenon has been reported as a "courtship dance." In all cases where the sex of the two snakes has been checked, both have been found to be males. People are inclined to remember the occasions when a coincidence supports folklore rather than the vast number of times when there is no evidence in accord with the legend.

CHAPTER 2

Economic Values

THE AUTHORS OF A RECENT POPULAR book on American amphibians and reptiles stated that these animals were of little value. In concluding their discussion of the value of reptiles, they said, "As a group they are neither 'good' nor 'bad,' but are interesting and unusual, although of minor importance. If they should all disappear, it would not make much difference one way or the other." This statement indicates a common tendency to base generalizations on incomplete information and, from the standpoint of economics, to evaluate importance on the basis of *direct* commercial or dollar value.

In considering the beneficial, or credit, side of these animals, both their direct and indirect values must be included. Direct benefits are obtained through their use as food and as sources of clothing or ornamental objects, and through special uses. Indirect benefits accrue when the activities of these animals favorably influence other plants or animals that are of direct help to us, or when they prey upon or otherwise harm other creatures that we consider undesirable.

A Source of Food

In this country no salamanders are used for food on a commercial basis, although some of the large, eel-like aquatic species are regularly caught for food in the southern United States. Frogs, however, are a different story. Frog legs are highly esteemed as a table delicacy and bring a good price in the markets of the country.

For the purpose of supplying part of this market demand, many attempts have been made to raise frogs in confinement on "frog farms," but none has proved sufficiently successful to support a business devoted solely to the production of frog legs. Enticing advertisements may be seen in outdoor magazines calling attention to the large sums awaiting industrious persons who undertake to raise frogs. The advertisements offer instruction in frog farming, or a limited number of "super-giant, fast-breeding, tasty-thighed breeding stock." As pointed out by Karl P. Schmidt, the only one who makes any money from such an enterprise is the man selling the lessons or the breeding stock.

These remarks apply to the raising of frogs in confinement as a profitable, self-supporting commercial enterprise. However, the cropping of frogs from small ponds on a controlled basis does afford a regular means of augmenting our food supply. The control of ponds can be carried out simply and yet in a way that materially increases the number of frogs produced. The Japanese have practiced such methods for many years. Recently a farmer in Alabama reported harvesting 250 frogs per year over a three-year period, from a farm pond of one and a half acres. At the prevailing price of frog legs, the annual yield from this pond would be valued between $100 and $125. In this instance the pond had been stocked several years earlier by a natural movement of frogs into it from a stream an eighth of a mile distant. The only care provided by the farmer was partial control of predators. Usually, where artificial ponds are used, it is advisable to introduce the larger local species of frogs in order to get production started as soon as possible. Active control of predators, an abundant food supply, and ample shelter are essentials for a good yield of frogs. These essentials can usually be provided with little trouble or extra work.

The majority of frogs that reach the market, however, have been caught in the wild by professional frog hunters working at night with a light. The amount of their income varies, of course, with the abundance of frogs and the market demand. In the United States most of the frogs brought to market are collected in the Gulf States, the northern Middle West, and the northeastern states. Formerly the American demand for frogs was filled entirely by domestic sources, but today large numbers of frog legs are imported, principally from Japan and Cuba.

The Cuban exporting trade is a relatively new enterprise. It was started by the introduction of the American Bullfrog (*Rana catesbeiana*) into that country and has shown remarkable growth. In 1941 we imported 381,457 pounds of frog legs, but by 1948 the imports had reached 766,262 pounds. The Cuban production of frog legs bears an interesting relation to the local price of tobacco. When the tobacco price is low, many tobacco workers take up frog hunting to augment their income. When tobacco goes up, these workers are too busy to bother with frogs, and the number collected drops perceptibly. If you're fond of frog legs, don't smoke too many Cuban cigars!

In the United States the Bullfrog (*Rana catesbeiana*), the Southern Bullfrog (*Rana grylio*), the Green Frog (*Rana clamitans*), and the Leopard Frog (*Rana pipiens*) are the species that make up the bulk of the commercial frog trade. There is considerable difference in size among these species. Formerly only the larger adults were used, but now virtually all sizes may be sold. The Bullfrog is by far the most famous of the frog leg species and has been introduced beyond its natural range in the United States and into many foreign countries. Conversely, with the increased demand for frogs and the development of more efficient collecting methods, populations of the commercially important species have been greatly reduced in some areas. Many states have found it necessary to institute laws regulating the hunting of frogs.

Among the reptiles, turtles are most widely used for food. Commercially only a few species are sold, but many others are relished by local inhabitants. Three Marine Turtles—the Green (*Chelonia mydas*), the Loggerhead (*Caretta caretta*), and the Ridley (*Lepidochelys olivacea*)—are marketed, but only the last two are sufficiently abundant in waters of the southern United States to be caught locally. A large processing house in New York City handles approximately 3,000 Green Turtles a year, chiefly for Green Turtle soup. All the turtles used in this enterprise, however, are caught off the coast of Central America.

Almost any fresh-water turtle has been or can be eaten, but only a few species are really considered desirable. In 1920 the U. S. Commissioner of Fisheries published a 20-page report on "Fresh-water Turtles: a Source of Meat Supply," by H. Walton Clark and John B. Southall. This bulletin detailed the relative merits of our native turtles as a table delicacy. The Diamondback Terrapin (*Malaclemys terrapin*), particularly the northern race, was the real aristocrat among the species. It sold for as high as $120 a dozen back in the Gay Nineties and the early part of the present century.

This turtle was in such demand that the Federal Government experimented to see if it could be raised commercially. The project did not prove successful because of the turtle's slow reproductive and growth rate, and because of a decrease in demand for it. It is sold and served in restaurants along the eastern seaboard and is still an epicurean's treat, although its high cost prevents most people from ever trying it.

Far from being aristocratic in appearance or manner is the Snapping Turtle (*Chelydra serpentina*). Yet this turtle is sold and consumed today in larger quantity than any other native species in North America. It is the primary species caught by the commercial fresh-water turtle trapper and appears in fairly good supply in markets in many of our larger cities east of the Rocky Mountains. In 1952 a turtle trapper in Ohio was receiving 40 cents a pound live weight and 80 cents a pound dressed weight for snappers. In 1936-37 the state of Connecticut conducted a campaign to reduce the number of Snapping Turtles in its fresh waters. More than 51,000 pounds of turtles were collected and given to the poor for food.

Inhabitants of various regions have their local favorites. The Suwannee Turtle (*Pseudemys floridana suwannensis*) is locally referred to as "Suwannee Chicken," and Archie Carr, whose lifelong study of turtles includes their relative merits as gastronomic delights, considers the designation to be well justified. The Gopher Turtle (*Gopherus polyphemus*) is also consumed by meat-hungry inhabitants of the southeastern states, but most people that I have talked to prefer fresh-water turtles to this land species.

The Soft-shelled Turtles (*Trionyx*) are widely acclaimed and have apparently had their range extended westward by those who found their flesh desirable. In the state of Florida in one recent year some 146,600 pounds of Soft-shelled Turtles were sold for food.

The lizards and snakes of North America are used as food in negligible quantities. As a novelty Ross Allen cans Eastern Diamondback Rattlesnakes (*Crotalus adamanteus*) and sells the canned product in an "à la king" type of preparation. In 1953 a small can sold for $1.50, or for $12 per dozen. Alligators were formerly eaten in large numbers by the Seminole Indians and the natives of the southern states. In recent years, laws have regulated the hunting of 'gators in most states, and hence the eating of this species is now much reduced.

A Source of Materials

Amphibians are of insignificant importance in furnishing materials for clothing or ornamentation. In earlier days the Alligator (*Alligator mississippiensis*) was hunted in large numbers for the leather industry. This industry started around 1800, reached a peak during the Civil War, has since had its ups and downs, and has declined sharply in this country in recent years. The majority of crocodilian hides being processed in the United States at the present time are imported. Accurate records are not available for the earlier years of this industry, but one estimate for Florida alone from 1800 to 1891 places the number of Alligators killed at 2,500,000. Another estimate places the number of skins processed annually around 1902 at 280,000 skins; about half of these were believed to have come from Central America, however. Recent figures are probably more reliable than estimates of the earlier kill. Ross Allen and Wilfred T. Neill have given figures for Florida alone, which are shown in Table 1.

TABLE 1

Alligator Skins Collected in Florida

Year	*Number of Skins*	*Maximum Price per Green Skin*
1929	190,000	$ 1.50
1930	188,000	2.50
1931	150,000	2.75
1932	145,000	2.75
1933	130,000	2.75
1934	120,000	3.00
1935	162,000	3.00
1936	150,000	3.00
1937	130,000	4.00
1938	110,000	4.00
1939	80,000	5.25
1940	75,000	7.00
1941	60,000	8.75
1942	18,000	15.75
1943*	6,800	19.25
1944	7,000	21.00
1945	12,000	22.75
1946	10,000	15.75
1947	25,000	13.30

* (Law passed in Florida in 1944 to protect the species, permitting large individuals only to be collected during a limited open season.)

PLATE I. Here's a Rattlesnake that hasn't heard about the legend that he's not supposed to crawl over a horsehair rope. Unfortunately, none of the snakes know of this and readily cross such ropes. (New York Zoological Society photograph)

Plate II. A Red-spotted Newt (*Diemictylus v. viridescens*) descending vertically in water after gulping air at the surface. The salamander can move straight up or down in the water by regulating the position of the air in the body. (Photograph by Dr. Charles Stine, Jr.)

These figures on the number of hides collected in Florida are of interest in indicating the scope of the hide-hunting industry in that state. They also show the fluctuations in number of animals taken annually. These fluctuations result partly from changes in the abundance of the animals, the effectiveness of protective laws, and the fluctuating economic state of the country.

Another heavy drain on the alligators of Florida was the sale of small individuals as souvenirs, either alive or mounted. The numbers sold annually between 1929 and 1945 was undoubtedly in the thousands. When the law prohibiting the sale of young 'gators went into effect, the trade was so well established that it continued, deriving its specimens from other states that had not yet passed laws prohibiting such traffic. Today the Alligator is partially protected in virtually every state in which it occurs. The pet trade has therefore shifted to selling young Caimans (*Caiman c. crocodilus*) imported from South America, which are passed off as Alligators. A card received from a Florida dealer in 1952 stated: "Once again it's legal to ship Alligators out of Florida." To this announcement the following footnote was added: "The Game and Fresh Water Commission has given us authorization to ship baby Caiman (the South American Alligator) from our Sunshine State." The price was $15 a dozen, f.o.b. Florida. It will be only a matter of time before our Latin American neighbors will find it necessary to pass laws to protect their crocodilians if they wish to save them from the fate of our Alligator.

The collecting of tortoise shell from Hawksbill Turtles (*Eretmochelys imbricata*) was never of great commercial importance in this country, but tortoise shell was a familiar item of commerce before the age of plastics. Native snakes have been used in the ornamental and leather industry on a small, almost novelty-souvenir basis. Rattlesnake skins are often tanned for belts, pocketbooks, wallets, ties, shoes, and many other small items. Several efforts have been made to establish a profitable but small leather industry utilizing the skins of several species of southern Water Snakes (*Natrix*). During one such effort a small group of collectors in south Florida took more than 500 snakes in a single night. Except for the Alligator hide industry, none of these has been of more than local importance.

Laboratory Uses

Among the special uses that are made of our amphibians and reptiles, one of the most important, from the standpoint of numbers and financial importance, is the use of these animals in biological laboratories. Because of their small size, hardiness, relative cheapness, and particular attributes, several species are widely used both alive and preserved. High school, college, and medical school laboratories include one or more representative amphibians and reptiles in anatomy and physiology studies. Many species are used in research work of various types. No figures are available to indicate the scope of this important industry, but it runs into hundreds of thousands of dollars. For instance, one large supply house advertised in 1953 that it had just received a new shipment of 10,000 "giant bullfrogs" for laboratory use.

The most widely used and versatile of all our species for the biology laboratory is the widespread, hardy Leopard Frog (*Rana pipiens*). Preserved specimens of this frog are dissected by every embryonic biologist who goes to college, and each budding medical student makes his first inquisitive probes on the twitching muscles of this frog's legs. The beating of its heart, the circulation of its nucleated red blood cells, the impulses of its nerves, and the ovulation and development of its eggs have all taught man much about himself as well as about amphibians. Today interest in the physiology of this frog has moved beyond the confines of the biologist's laboratory and is presently important to millions of human homes where the early recognition of pregnancy is deemed desirable. The male Leopard Frog (*Rana pipiens*) is rapidly replacing the female rabbit in the primary test for pregnancy. In this test the injection into the frog of hormones present in the urine of pregnant women causes the male frog to extrude spermatozoa within two hours. This new test has the advantage of being highly accurate, yielding definite results in a very short time and costing very little. Most local species of frogs and toads can be used in the test, but the Leopard Frog, because of the ease of obtaining and keeping this species, is the most widely used.

We tend to think of snake venoms as a curse on all nonserpentine animal life. However, man's ingenuity has turned these complex mixtures of chemicals to his profitable use. First of all, venoms are employed to manufacture a counteragent to be used in the treatment of snakebite. At first small doses of venom, and then increasingly larger doses, are injected into a laboratory animal, such as a horse or rabbit. The animal builds up an immunity to the venom, and when it can tolerate without harm a dose several times the lethal amount, some of its blood is drawn off. The antibodies produced in the immunization process are separated out and purified. If this immune blood serum is injected into a victim suffering from a dose of the same type of venom, it assists in neutralizing the toxic elements. Because the venom of snakes varies from species to species, immunity is built up most effectively against the type for which the animal was conditioned.

In order to produce an agent for use against a number of different kinds of venoms, a mixture of the several venoms must be used. The immunity factor will then give wider protection, although it may not be so effective against some kinds of venom as that made solely for one type.

Agents that are produced for use against snake venoms are called antivenins. When antivenin is used, care must be employed to test the victim for sensitivity to horse serum *before* it is used. A single antivenin is produced in North America; it is designed to give protection against the bite of any Pit Viper occurring in North, Central, or South America. It is made by Wyeth, Inc., of Philadelphia, through the use of a mixture of venoms from several species of Rattlesnakes (*Crotalus*) and South American Pit Vipers (*Bothrops*).

In addition to their use in the manufacture of antivenin, snake venoms have been used in medicine for other purposes. For many years a coagulating factor from Cottonmouth venom was used widely in the treatment of hemophilia. However, most of the other venoms that have been used medically on a large scale are from Old World snakes.

Believe it or not, turtle and snake oils are still used in sufficient amounts to warrant their being processed on an economical basis. In 1953 a New York newspaper carried an advertisement for a "Turtle Oil Blend" skin cream, which was allegedly "highly concentrated with extra potency." A 1953 dealer's price list advertised Rattlesnake Oil at $1 per ounce, $10.40 per pint, $16 per quart, and $51.20 per gallon. The list does not state whether this oil has "extra potency" or not.

Amusement and Pet Trades

Amphibians and reptiles play a definite role in many small enterprises concerned with entertainment and amusement and with the pet trade. The latter involves the greatest number of individual animals and the largest financial investment. This matter is treated in Chapter 13. Here it is sufficient to point out that the amphibian and reptile pet trade has become a very lucrative business involving millions of individual animals each year. Because of the heavy drain on local amphibian and reptile populations to meet the demands of this industry, some states have belatedly passed laws prohibiting the taking of specimens except for scientific purposes. It is unfortunate that the collecting of animals for pets has not been regulated on a common-sense basis rather than operated on undesirable extremes. However, the general abuses to date have justified the extreme protective legislation. It is hoped that the future will enable us to operate in a more enlightened fashion allowing limited numbers of pets to be taken and properly kept, to the benefit of both pet and owner.

The use of amphibians and reptiles in amusement and entertainment covers a wide variety of human activities—from roadside and carnival reptile shows to turtle races, "Frog Olympics," and as bait for fishing. Most reptile or snake "shows" have an ephemeral existence and are barely able to provide attractions for the public. On the other hand, there have been a few notable successes that have been shrewdly built up into permanent establishments with a countrywide reputation. These exceptions may operate with a $50,000 to $100,000 gross income per year, but for each successful one there have been scores of failures. In connection with reptile shows, it is of interest to look into their source of supply. One report states that in Florida there are more than 120 professional reptile collectors who devote full time to this occupation. In one recent year more than 20,000 rattlesnakes alone were collected by these hunters and sold for six or seven dollars each. The "turtle derbies," "horned toad jamborees," and "rattler roundups" are all small-scale operations put on for the sake of novelty. Most are one-time affairs that are of little economic importance, but they do increase the uses of the animals.

The term "Frog Olympics" was originated by Walter Rose, of South Africa, for the frog-jumping contests originated in California and later introduced into southern Africa. The origin of such contests goes back to Mark Twain's tale of the famed jumping frog of Calaveras County, California. In memory of this classic yarn an annual jumping contest is held at the Calaveras County Fair. The owner of the winning frog is awarded $200 plus a $1,000 bonus if the frog exceeds the contest record for 16 feet 4 inches for three consecutive jumps. Thousands of people gather each year to cheer on the amphibian contestants, which are usually Bullfrogs (*Rana catesbeiana*), bearing such names as "Zip In" and "Heliotrope." The contest record was set in 1944 by a jumper named "Maggie." Mr. Rose, hearing about this feat and realizing that several South African frogs were capable of better performances, stirred up provincial pride and inspired the holding of the first worldwide "Frog Olympics." A long-legged African species exceeded the record of the heavier Bullfrogs, winning the world's championship. The success of Mr. Rose's efforts to put frog jumping on an international basis is indicated by an item from the May 14, 1953 issue of the *New York World-Telegram and Sun:*

Alien Frogs Fly to Jumping Duel

Four jumping frogs from England and South Africa took off from La Guardia Field today on their final jump to California where they will compete in a frog-jumping contest.

They'll compete with entries from six other countries in attempts to break the 16 foot 4 inch record for three successive jumps. The contest will take place in the Calaveras County Fair Friday.

Now that the contests have assumed an international flavor, it only remains for some enterprising frog fancier to import one of the so-called "Flying Frogs" from the Indo-Australian area to shatter all local records.

The use of animals as bait in fishing may seem like an incidental matter, but the sport of fishing is now a billion-dollar business in this country. In some regions, frogs and live "spring lizards" or salamanders are considered excellent lures to attract fish. One southern dealer did a "spring lizards" business of $20,000 in 1953. Add them all together and the total begins to assume substantial proportions.

Pest Control

Probably the greatest economic value of amphibians and reptiles is the great but indirect service they perform in pest control through their feeding habits. All groups contribute to this beneficial service, but some frogs, some lizards, and some snakes are of greater importance than others, because of their occurrence and habits. It is known that the Red-spotted Newt (*Diemictylus v. viridescens*) and the Painted Turtle (*Chrysemys picta*) may consume large numbers of mosquito larvae during the summer, and that Alligators (*Alligator mississippiensis*) sometimes include large numbers of undesirable garfish in their diet. These are helpful aids to man's interests, but they are not comparable with the service performed by toads (*Bufo*), many lizards, and many snakes.

Virtually all species of frogs contribute to man's welfare through their feeding habits. As pointed out in Chapter 10, these creatures are carnivorous—primarily insectivorous. The kinds of insect they eat vary with the habitat in which they live and also with the season. Frogs are not notable for their dietary fastidiousness, but appear to consume the most easily obtainable and palatable food. The quantity consumed depends to a large extent on size, although it is also influenced somewhat by temperature.

The most easily assessed benefit that man derives from these food habits is the consumption, by amphibians and reptiles, of various insect pests of cultivated plants. It is impossible to estimate accurately the value of this activity in terms of dollars, although various attempts have been made to do this. Our agriculture largely involves plants grown on dry land. The frogs that are most abundant and active on dry land at some distance from the water are the species called toads (*Bufo*). Hence it is not surprising to find that toads have established something of a reputation as desirable pest-controllers. Numerous books and articles, including Government pamphlets, have recounted the great benefit that we derive from the toad's insect diet. In most communities the local species of toad is welcomed in the garden and field, despite the prevalence of folklore myths depicting the toad as the source of human warts.

Probably the most interesting story relating to man's use of these amphibian allies in combating insect pests have to do with the

Marine Toad (*Bufo marinus*), which man has transported around the world. This is one of the largest living species of toads in the world. It is a native of extreme southern Texas and Central and South America, but it has been distributed by man over a greater geographical area than any other amphibian, with the possible exception of the American Bullfrog. It has been unsuccessfully brought into southern Florida.

The detailed value of the feeding habits of our native species of toads, lizards, and snakes, is pointed out in Chapter 10. Here it is sufficient to state again that the Government has published a special bulletin on the economic importance of the toad. The studies of George F. Knowlton have demonstrated the value of lizards in the control of insect pests. His studies particularly have shown how effective lizards are in the control of the beet leafhopper in Utah. Raymond B. Cowles has pointed out the value of the Alligator Lizards (*Gerrhonotus*) in feeding on Black Widow Spiders.

Gopher Snakes (*Pituophis*), Rat Snakes (*Elaphe*), King Snakes (*Lampropeltis*), and Racers (*Coluber*) have been lauded for their service in the control of rodents, since they consume large numbers of these injurious mammals. Although Rattlesnakes (*Crotalus* and *Sistrurus*) and Copperheads (*Ancistrodon*) also serve in this capacity, their service is seldom acknowledged because of their harmful potentialities.

Fresh-water turtles as a group are generally condemned by fishermen who are eager to find an excuse for their failure to catch fish. Actually, the scientific studies of turtle food habits that have been made by Karl F. Lagler have indicated that few species are directly harmful and that some may be beneficial. He found, for example, that the Common Musk Turtle (*Sternotherus odoratus*) is an important scavenger, with more than 40 per cent of its food being made up of carrion. Species such as the Painted Turtle (*Chrysemys picta*) appear to be more or less neutral in their food habits, consuming large quantities of plant food. Other species may be of some importance in competing with fish for food, and a few may be harmful in feeding on game fish and other economically important species. From his extensive studies on turtles in Michigan, Lagler concluded that, "with the possible exception of the Snapping Turtle, the aquatic turtles of Michigan are probably of greater significance as competitors with fish for food than as predators upon fish. Pending further investigation and with the knowledge that aquatic turtles are beneficial to man because of their scavenger-habits, their suggested role in the control of insect-and-parasite-pests, and their potential food value to humans (probably excepting the Musk Turtle), the conservation of these species is recommended and means for accomplishing this are given."

Some of the forms that have been mentioned as being beneficial to man occasionally eat species that are also beneficial. For example, the toads (*Bufo*), which render yeoman service through the eating of large numbers of harmful insect pests, occasionally provoke man's ire by feeding on beneficial insects, such as honeybees. The largely beneficial Black Racer (*Coluber c. constrictor*), which feeds mostly on rodents and other snakes, occasionally takes a bird in its diet. The Bull Snake (*Pituophis catenifer sayi*), a veritable paragon among rodent-eaters in most places, may be condemned in a duck refuge for feeding on large quantities of duck eggs and young ducklings. However, before we rise up in wrath against these transgressions, let us remember that the robin is a large-scale consumer of beneficial earthworms, that the thrush sometimes takes beneficial insects along with injurious ones, and that most of our wildlife species must be evaluated in the sum total of their relationships and not just in part.

Certain species, particularly when occurring in close proximity to or competing with man's interests, are harmful beyond doubt. Venomous snakes should certainly be controlled near human habitations. Venomous species do cause direct harm through their bites, both to human beings and to domestic animals. No accurate figures are available to indicate the exact scope of this damage, but from all evidence available it is a minor factor—less in importance, for example, than the damage caused by lightning. Fish-eating species should be eliminated in and around fish hatcheries. Snapping Turtles (*Chelydra serpentina*) should be removed from wildfowl refuges and around duck ponds. On the other hand, in large sanctuary areas predatory species may serve to keep populations in balance. For instance, where concerted drives have been carried on to wipe out all snakes, rodent populations have usually increased markedly.

The mere presence of amphibians and reptiles may have an effect on the human occupants of the area—usually a disturbing one. The presence of snakes, harmless or venomous, may even prove a deterrent to human occupancy. On the other hand, the presence of lizards may serve as a source of encouragement because of their insectivorous diet and interesting ways. The presence of a frog breeding area, particularly where large and loud choruses are present, may also prove disturbing to human inhabitants of the vicinity. Snake-proof fences have been developed and sold to bring peace of mind to the residents. Frog breeding pools have been fenced off to keep the frogs out for the same reason. However, in one case the disturbing frogs were welcomed. In 1951 the Blue Ridge Mountain Festival was held at Washington, Virginia. When the site of the concert was surveyed by the musical director, he feared, at first, that Bullfrogs (*Rana catesbeiana*) in a nearby river would be a distraction and would therefore have to be cleared out. However, he was pleased to find that their musical quality was just right for the festival. He said, "I noticed that every time their leader or leaders, croaked, he or they hit C-sharp right on the nose. The result was so pleasing, we're going to make it part of the program." Actually, for everyone disturbed by the calling of frogs, there must be hundreds who find it pleasing music, to judge by all that's been written on the subject.

In summary, the beneficial aspects of amphibians and reptiles seem to outweigh by far their harmful features. The direct economic value of the groups is small by comparison with that of other groups of vertebrates, yet the sum total of all income-producing activities wholly or partially dependent on them is substantial. The greatest value of amphibians and reptiles to man is indirect, through the control of harmful animal populations. The desirability of several species has been recognized sufficiently to merit legal protection. Species protected by law in some states, either for economic or conservation reasons, include the Bullfrog (*Rana catesbeiana*), the Southern Bullfrog (*Rana grylio*), the Green Frog (*Rana clamitans*), the Leopard Frog (*Rana pipiens*), the Wood Turtle (*Clemmys insculpta*), the Box Turtle (*Terrapene c. carolina*), the Desert Tortoise (*Gopherus agassizi*), the Alligator (*Alligator mississippiensis*), the American Crocodile (*Crocodylus a. acutus*), the Green Anolis (*Anolis c. carolinensis*), and the Gila Monster (*Heloderma suspectum*).

CHAPTER 3

Classification

WHAT ARE THESE ANIMALS WE CALL amphibians and reptiles? Where do they fit into the Animal Kingdom? To answer this we must examine briefly the biologists' system of classifying the animals of the world. In order to comprehend any great mass of facts, we must arrange them in smaller categories that possess certain similarities that make the groups easily recognizable and that are not found in other groups. These categories, in turn, can be subdivided into smaller and smaller units, as desired. The features or attributes on which we base our classification grouping can be any character or feature of the objects we are studying. For example, early man may have classed all animals into categories depending on whether they were edible or not, or whether they ate plant or animal food. When the ancient Greeks started to group the animals they knew, they placed all that lived in water in one group, all that lived on land in another group, and all that lived in air in still another category. Such groupings are based on a characteristic shared by all members of each group, but the animals placed together in this fashion may have little else in common and are not always closely related.

Today our system of classification endeavors to use features or characters that give us groups of related animals. By dividing and subdividing our major categories, a system of ranked groups can be set up in which the degree of relationship differs from the highest to the lowest bracket, and in which members of similar ranks exhibit somewhat similar degrees of similarity and relationship. This system of classification is based largely on structural or morphological characters that are inherited from generation to generation. Because the system was developed years ago when the language of science was Latin, the names used for the various groups are Latin or latinized terms. The science of biological classification is called taxonomy or systematics.

Let us consider the classification of the Tiger Salamander in order to see how the system works. The salamander is obviously a member of the Kingdom Animalia (Animal Kingdom). This large group is further divided into major divisions called phyla (singular, phylum). One of these phyla contains all the animals that possess an internal skeleton and two other common structural features. This is the Phylum Chordata; in addition to some small marine organisms it includes the great group of backboned animals that we call the Vertebrata (vertebrates). Seven large classes make up the group of vertebrates. These are Mammals, Birds, Reptiles, Amphibians, Bony Fish, Cartilaginous Fish, and the Jawless Vertebrates. In popular terms the last three of these classes are referred to collectively as fish or fishlike vertebrates. Our salamander has characters that place it among the amphibians. Thus, so far it is a member of the Animal Kingdom, the Phylum Chordata, and the Class Amphibia. The classes are divided into subgroups that are termed orders, and these into families. The class Amphibia contains three living Orders: Salientia (Frogs and Toads), Caudata (Salamanders), and Apoda (Caecilians). In the Order to which the Salamanders belong there are eight living Families, with the Tiger Salamander a member of the Family Ambystomidae. All members of this Family look a good deal alike but differ in a number of characters. On the basis of the differences, several groups or genera (singular, genus) are recognizable. The genera are composed of one or more species. The species is the basic unit of biological classification. Thus the Tiger Salamander is a species of Salamander belonging to a genus in the Family Ambystomidae of the Order Caudata in the Class Amphibia of the Phylum Chordata in the Animal Kingdom.

In the biological system of classification there are seven basic categories that make up the classification hierarchy, as shown in Figure 1. In this figure the classification and relationships of the Tiger Salamander are shown diagrammatically. Now let us see how this system of classification indicates relationships. Members placed in the same group have more attributes in common, and hence are more closely related to one another than they are to members of any other group. Units in the same vertical columns have more attributes in common and are more closely related to one another than they are to units in another vertical column. Starting at the bottom of the diagram with a single species unit and moving toward the top of the diagram, we find increasingly inclusive groups of more remote relationship. Thus all Tiger Salamanders are members of the same species and are all very much alike, exhibiting

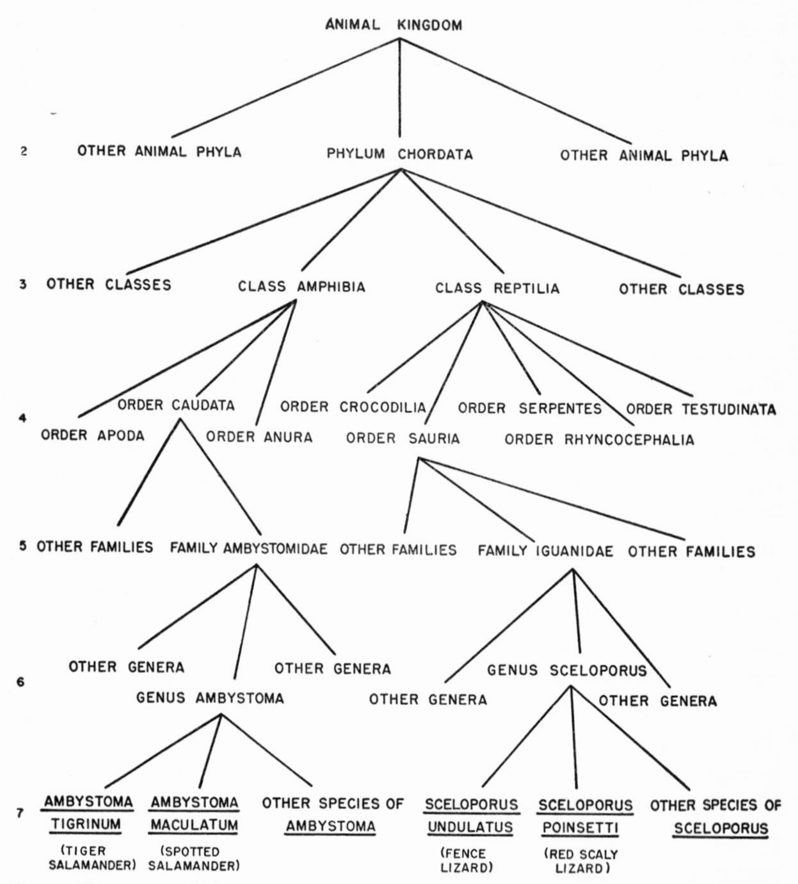

FIG. 1. Diagram of the seven primary units of classification and the lines of relationships within the units.

only minor individual differences. This species is closely related to the Spotted Salamander, and members of the two species have a sufficient number of characters in common to be classified in the same genus. However, members of the two species never interbreed; and constant minor differences, such as the arrangement of the yellow pigment on the back and other features, enables us always to distinguish between the two, identifying them as separate species.

Every species in the genus *Ambystoma* is more closely related and has more in common with every other species in that genus than it does with any species in another genus in the Family Ambystomidae. The same is true for the members of different groups on the same horizontal level of the diagram. In the Class Reptilia, the Fence Lizard is a species in the genus *Sceloporus*, and therefore it is closely related to the Red Scaly Lizard that belongs to the same genus. Both species have their differences, and reproduction does not take place between the two.

Any of the seven categories may be further divided for increased refinement of the system, or additional groupings may be added where needed. For our purposes we usually need refer only to the seven basic divisions. In this system the species is the primary unit of classification. A species can be defined as a group of similar individuals, alike in most characters and forming actual or potentially interbreeding natural populations, but incapable of breeding with other such groups. One of the most important attributes of a species is the fact that members of the same species are capable of interbreeding freely with other members of the species, but *not* with members of a different species. This reproductive isolation from other related species is of utmost importance in maintaining the distinctive characters of the species. If species could interbreed freely with other species, there would be a mixing of attributes and the distinctions would disappear.

Every species that is known has a name. The classification of the Tiger Salamander provides an example. The name "Tiger Salamander" is a common or vernacular name that is used for this animal in the eastern United States. In the Great Plains area the same species might be called the "Yellow-barred Salamander." Thus common names vary from region to region, and much confusion may develop from their use unless they are standardized. Our system of classification was developed in Europe, where the diversity of languages made the matter of names even more confusing. Thus a system of international names was necessary to provide accuracy. A system of naming all animals and plants was proposed by Carolus Linnaeus in the eighteenth century. This is our present system of scientific names, a two-name, or binominal, system in which each species has a name consisting of two Latin or latinized words. The first word is the name of the genus to which it belongs. This word is always spelled with a capital letter. The second word is the trivial name, which in combination with the generic name, indicates a particular species. The trivial name in zoology is *always* spelled with a lower case letter, and both names should be italicized (or underlined in handwritten or typewritten matter) to clearly set them off as the scientific name.

By means of this precise system of names, anyone anywhere in the world can refer to the same species without ambiguity. Various vernacular or common names can still be applied to the animals, but only the scientific name has the universal sanction of scientists. The scientific name of the Tiger Salamander is *Ambystoma tigrinum.* Thus we see that it belongs to the genus *Ambystoma* and is the species *Ambystoma tigrinum.*

Species that are distributed over a wide geographic area frequently exhibit localized variations that are sufficiently constant to enable one to recognize a high percentage of the population from that area. Where this occurs it enables us to recognize geographic divisions of the species, and to give the local populations a distinguishing name. The subdivisions of a species are termed subspecies or races. They are named by adding a third word to the binominal species name to make it a trinominal (three-word) name. The Tiger Salamander, for example, occurs in North America from coast to coast, and the population in different parts of the country are sufficiently different to warrant recognition and separate names. In the eastern part of the country the subspecies is named *Ambystoma tigrinum tigrinum* and is referred to as the typical or nominate subspecies, since it includes the population that was first named when the species was described. On the west coast the subspecies is named *Ambystoma tigrinum californiense.* Here the third word indicates the geographic area where the subspecies is found. This is not always the case. The word making up the name may be a geographic term, a descriptive term, or a modified proper name or noun. For example, the Clouded Tiger Salamander is *Ambystoma tigrinum nebulosum,* referring to the indistinct yellow markings in this race. In writing the name, it is common practice merely to abbreviate the generic name after the full combination has once appeared in the paper. Also, the trivial name for the species may be abbreviated in referring to the typical subspecies. Thus *A. t. tigrinum* may be used if the full combination has just appeared. It is not always good practice to abbreviate the species name if the race is other than the typical one. Therefore, it would be preferable to write *A. tigrinum nebulosum* rather than *A. t. nebulosum*. The subspecies of the Tiger Salamander are classified as subdivisions of a species rather than as different species because they represent actual (or potentially) interbreeding natural populations and are not reproductively isolated from one another.

We habitually refer to the various taxonomic categories as units that are recognizable by the use of certain characters or combinations of characters. This suggests that the taxonomic hierarchy consists of a series of artificial groups arbitrarily recognized. This is an erroneous impression. Actually the taxonomist strives to recognize natural units and groups in nature. He does not always succeed completely, and sometimes the groups have little reality in nature. In order to approximate more closely the natural groups, he includes all types of information and characters that may help him recognize the true lines of affinity and the fundamental differences. It is a great tribute to the skill of workers in this field that, with few exceptions, the data from widely different fields of investigation fit into the framework of the classifications recognized.

There are many perplexing problems that face the taxonomist in his efforts to classify the life of the world. In some cases it is difficult to decide whether a group is of ordinal status, whether it should be kept as a smaller subdivision, or whether several species are sufficiently similar to be included in a single genus. The most frequent problem that faces the taxonomist of living animals is whether a differentiated local population represents a new species or a subspecies of an already recognized species. It is beyond the scope of this account to review the criteria that are used in reaching a solution to such problems. But it is necessary to call attention to these problems because they result in differences of opinion regarding the classification of the animals. In a healthy, growing science new information and fresh evaluation of old data frequently result in changes in the system. Thus the classifications listed in various books often exhibit minor differences that are confusing to the beginning student or lay reader. These minor differences are a necessary part of the growth in scientific knowledge. It is perhaps small comfort to realize that the professional worker is also plagued by these changes and disagreements, but they are necessary for the achievement of ultimate stability.

From time to time there appear in each field of biology certain recognized works that serve as a standard point of reference for the classification and nomenclature of the particular group of animals treated. In American herpetology, *A Check List of North American Amphibians and Reptiles* has appeared in six editions. This work has served as an important stabilizing factor in the study of herpetology in this country. The first five editions were prepared by Leonhard Stejneger and Thomas Barbour. Following the death of these eminent workers, the task of preparing this important book was taken up by the renowned and experienced herpetologist Karl P. Schmidt, of the Chicago Natural History Museum. His first edition, the sixth for the work, appeared in 1953. While it is impossible at this stage of our development in the field to reach complete accord on the treatment of each form, this work represents a remarkably high achievement in the system of names used. An innovation in this volume is the assignment of common names to all named forms. For simplification of reference in the present book, I will use without modification the names, scientific and common, and the classification of the sixth edition of *A Check List of North American Amphibians and Reptiles,* by Karl P. Schmidt.

Relation to Other Vertebrates

Amphibians and reptiles belong to the larger group of animals called the vertebrates, including the fish, the birds, and the mammals. All the fishlike vertebrates are aquatic, living their entire lives in water except for brief forays on land by a few species. They exhibit many adaptations for their life in water and so are ill-fitted for the land. This is such a truism that we all accept the usefulness of the expression "like a fish out of water." The body is more or less streamlined, elongate, and devoid of supporting limbs; oxygen is acquired from the water by means of gills; fertilization of the eggs is usually external; and the eggs, which must be laid in the water, lack a hard protective shell. Exceptions can be found to each of these statements, but they indicate the general completeness of the fish adaptation to its watery existence.

At the other extreme of vertebrate adaptation, the mammals and birds are well modified for life on land, in the air, underground, or even in water. Limbs are usually present to support the body, which is not streamlined except for the forms that have taken to the water or the air; oxygen is obtained by taking air into the lungs in all forms; fertilization is internal; and a hard-shelled egg is laid on land or the young are retained in the female's body until development is complete. The body characteristically is covered with a thick insulating coat of hair or feathers.

Amphibians and reptiles stand in an intermediate position between the aquatic fish on the one hand and the terrestrial birds and mammals on the other. The amphibians began to invade the land long ago, but as a group they still lie with most of the body in the water and only a small part on land. They are poorly adapted for living on dry land and typically are still tied to the water for reproduction. Their moist, bare skin exposes them to the constant danger of drying out if they get too far from moisture.

Reptiles show a further advance toward living on land. They breathe by means of lungs throughout life; the body is covered with scales or horny plates, which give added protection from moisture loss; but the greatest advance for land life was the appearance of the shelled egg which can develop only on land. These are the primary structures involved in the improved conditions for living on the land. Neither the amphibians nor the reptiles have achieved an internal source of heat; nor have they achieved a thick insulating coat outside the body. These are but a few of the salient features involved in comparing the amphibians and reptiles with the other classes of vertebrate animals. In the sum total of their attributes they stand in an intermediate position between the morphological and physiological development exhibited by the two extremes.

Fossil History

The intermediate condition of the amphibians and reptiles just mentioned is readily explained by an examination of the fossil history of the groups (Figure 2). The interrelations of the groups can also be better understood by an examination of the past story of their development. This story is based on the examination and careful study of the fossilized remains of animals that lived long ago. The fossil record of life extends back more than a billion years, but the first indication of any vertebrate was about 400 million years

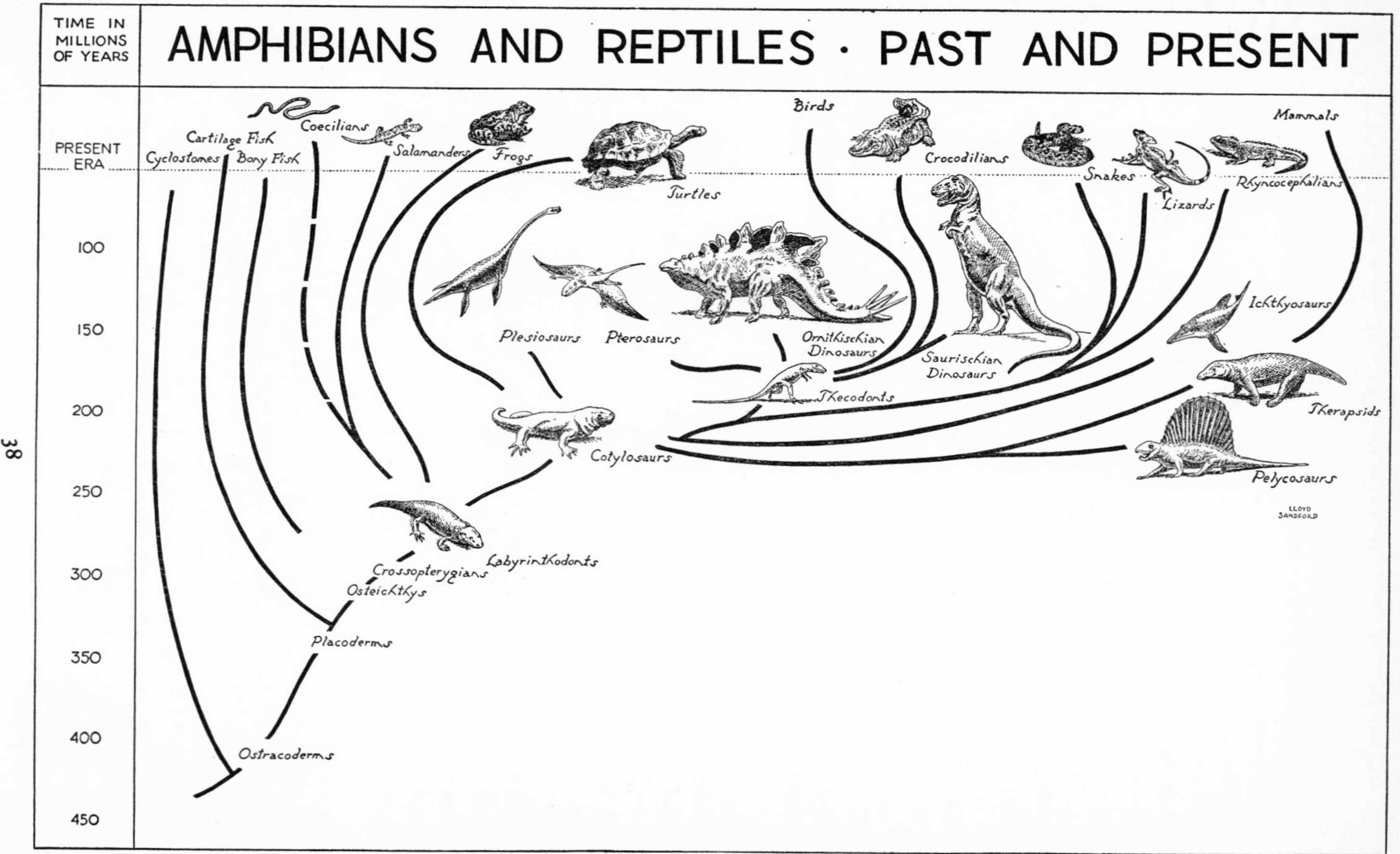

FIG. 2. Diagram of relationships of living amphibians and reptiles to those of the past, as well as to other vertebrate animals.

ago. This was a primitive, fishlike, backboned form, which ultimately gave rise to several different types of fish around 350 million years ago. One of these fish groups, the Lobe-finned Fish or Crossopterygians, produced the ancestor of the Amphibia, the first land vertebrate. This took place about 300 million years ago. The earliest amphibians possessed legs for moving about on land, but they showed many resemblances to their Lobe-finned ancestors.

The first amphibians, called Labyrinthodonts, gave rise to the other lines of amphibian development from which our modern salamanders, caecilians, and frogs descended. Along another path of modification the Labyrinthodont produced the ancestral reptile, the Cotylosaurs. While the amphibians have been on the earth for approximately 300 million years, they have never been a spectacularly flourishing group. Rather quietly they have lived their modest lives, achieving fossil fame chiefly as the first vertebrates to invade the land and in providing an ancestral role for the remaining vertebrate classes.

Unlike the amphibians, the reptiles came into their own and were the most abundant and diversified vertebrate life for more than 100 million years, during what is known as the "Age of Reptiles." This started about 200 million years ago and lasted until about 65 million years ago. During this time there lived marine Ichthyosaurs, Mosasaurs, and Plesiosaurs, flying Pterosaurs, a host of small and large Dinosaurs, and numerous lesser groups. A total of seventeen orders of reptiles existed at that time, compared with the five orders today. The Dinosaurs were of considerable interest. Some walked on two legs, some on four; some were carnivorous, others vegetarians; some were plated, some had spikes; some were the size of a chicken, some were the largest animals that have ever walked on the earth—reaching a length of 90 feet and a weight of 50 tons. In comparison with these forms our living reptiles are indeed small remnants. At the end of the Age of Reptiles, around 65 million years ago, virtually all the reptiles disappeared except for the five groups that survived down to the present time. Of these five, the Rhyncocephalians, the Crocodilians, and the turtles seem to be waning groups on the way out as far as number and diversity of species is concerned. Only the lizards and snakes appear to be flourishing. Prior to the disappearance of the host of reptile types, one line of reptile development gave rise to the mammals and another to the birds.

From this brief review of the past history of the two groups, it is easy to understand the relationships of the groups. If we look only at modern amphibians, reptiles, and mammals, it is difficult to imagine that they ever had much in common. Yet when we go back through the fossil record we find the transition from amphibian to reptile so gradual that there are some fossils that are almost impossible to identify definitely as an amphibian or a reptile because they have characters in common with both. Similarly, the transition from reptile to mammal is one of the best known stories in the fossil record. Several fossils represent virtually every conceivable intermediate stage between the reptile condition and that of the early mammal.

Our modern amphibians and reptiles are not specific survivors of the Age of Reptiles. They, too, have descended from ancestral forms that existed or came into being during that ancient time. Our modern orders are recognizable among the fossils from about 100 million years ago, but our present species are all much younger, many being survivors from an age of less than a million years ago.

CHAPTER 4

North American Amphibians

THE TERM "AMPHIBIAN" IS DERIVED from the Greek *amphi*, meaning both, and *bios*, meaning life. We use it to mean "an animal living both on land and in water." The amphibians, in a very real sense, characteristically live double lives. A water-living larval form emerges from the typical amphibian egg and lives out its larval life in the water, breathing by means of gills. At the end of this life, or period, the larva undergoes a transition, or metamorphosis, losing its gills and undergoing several other changes in its bodily structure. It then crawls out of its watery abode and takes up its second life on land. This is the common life cycle of these animals and the basis for calling them amphibians. There are exceptions to this traditional life pattern, but it remains one of the outstanding features of most amphibians. This alone is not sufficient to distinguish the amphibians readily from the other vertebrates.

The Class Amphibia consists of backboned animals with bare, soft or warty skin, which is richly supplied with mucous glands. There are no scales present, except those hidden in the small body folds of the caecilians. External legs are usually present; the front legs with four fingers, the hind legs characteristically with five toes. Gills are always present during the larval stage but are usually lost at metamorphosis. Lungs are generally present in adults but are absent in some forms. Eggs, without protective shells, are typically deposited in water. Amphibians are found on land, underground, in trees, and in fresh water, but not in salt water seas. Members of the group possess no means of regulating the body temperature from within and are dependent on outside sources of heat for this purpose.

The class is divided into five orders, three of which are living today. These are the Caudata or salamanders; the Salientia or frogs

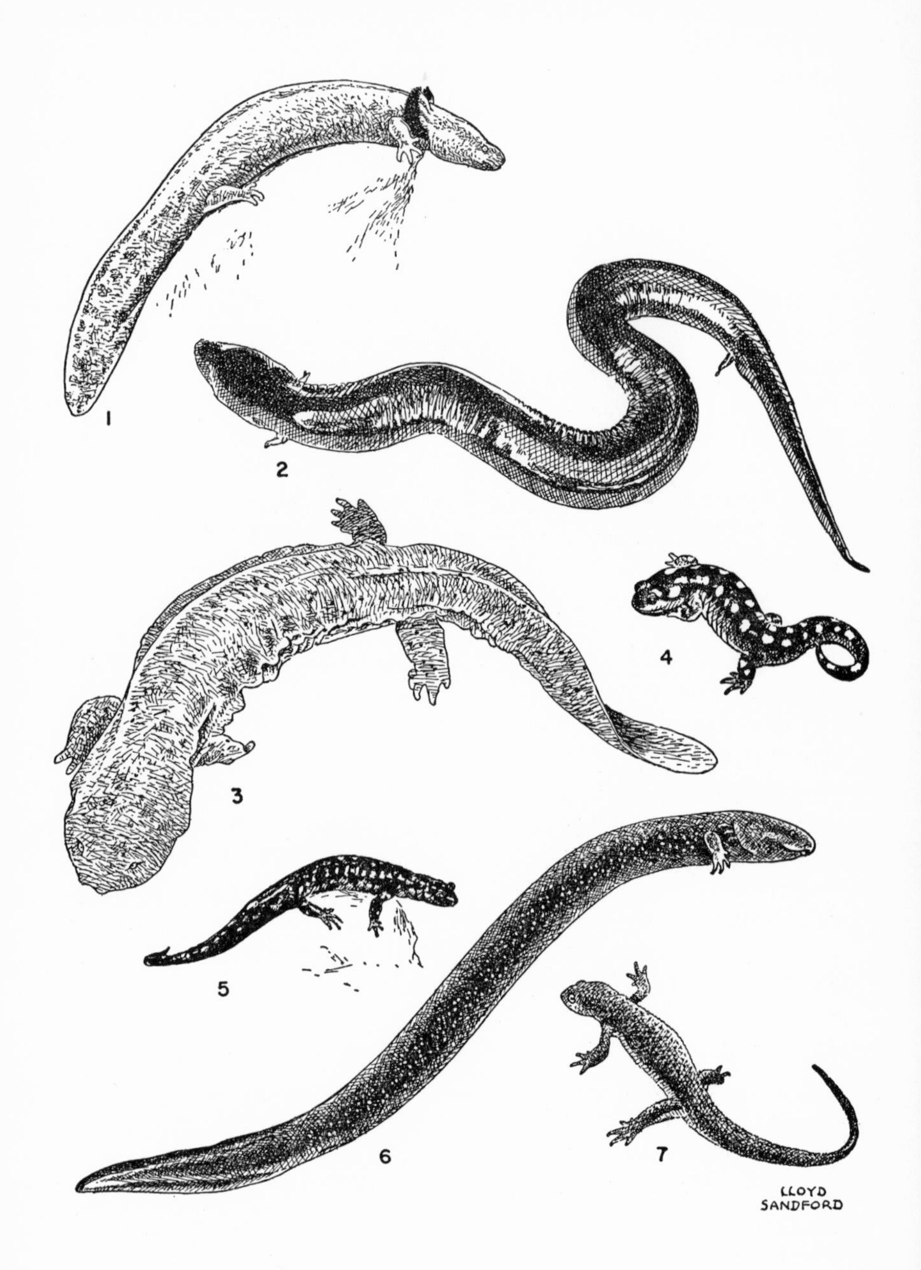
1
2
3
4
5
6
7
LLOYD
SANDFORD

and Toads; and the Apoda or caecilians. The caecilians are greatly elongate, legless, burrowing or aquatic forms that inhabit the tropical regions of the Old and New World. Externally they look like large earthworms. The order contains a single family. There are no caecilians in North America as herein defined.

Salamanders

Members of the order Caudata, or salamanders, characteristically have an external appearance similar to that of the more familiar lizards, for which they are sometimes mistaken (Figure 3). A few specialized forms lack external limbs or have the legs reduced to small flaps. The tail is always present in both larvae and adults. The legs, when present, are not greatly elongated for jumping, as they are in the frogs. The larval stage is very similar to the adult and not of the tadpole type. True teeth are present in both jaws of larvae and adults. Adults of some species may possess gills. Salamanders are primarily inhabitants of the humid areas of the Northern Hemisphere, occurring as far north as Alaska in North America. A few species are found in Africa and South America, but the group is entirely absent in Australia.

Eight living families make up the order; and North America, which is endowed with a relatively rich salamander fauna, has representatives of seven of these, with only the Asiatic family Hynobiidae being absent. Two of the families, Amphiumidae and Sirenidae, are confined to the southeastern United States, while a third family, the Ambystomidae, occurs only in North America and Mexico.

Of the seven families that comprise our salamander fauna, the first family is the Cryptobranchidae, which includes but two living genera—one in eastern Asia and one in the eastern United States. One of the Asiatic species is the largest living amphibian, the

---

Fig. 3. Representatives of the seven families of salamanders occurring in North America. 1. Proteidae—Mudpuppy (*Necturus maculosus*). 2. Amphiumidae—Amphiuma (*Amphiuma means*). 3. Cryptobranchidae—Hellbender (*Cryptobranchus alleganiensis*). 4. Ambystomidae—Spotted Salamander (*Ambystoma maculatum*). 5. Plethodontidae—Slimy Salamander (*Plethodon glutinosus*). 6. Sirenidae—Great Siren (*Siren lacertina*). 7. Salamandridae—Rough-skinned Newt (*Taricha granulosa*)

Japanese Giant Salamander (*Megalobatrachus japonicus*), which is known to reach a length of five feet. In the United States the family is represented by a single species, the Hellbender (*Cryptobranchus alleganiensis*), with two races. While our species does not attain so large a size as its Asiatic relative, it is one of our largest salamanders, reaching 27 inches in length. The Hellbenders are inhabitants of cold streams and are aquatic throughout life.

The Mudpuppies of the genus *Necturus* represent the second family, the Family Proteidae. This family also has but two living genera, being represented in Europe by a small, pale, eel-like cave dweller. The Mudpuppies occur in the eastern United States, where there are three species and five races. They are permanent larvae that do not undergo metamorphosis. They have three pairs of reddish, filamentlike gills throughout life, and are entirely aquatic, being found in streams, ponds, and lakes.

The Family Sirenidae is confined to the southeastern United States. Two genera, three species, and six subspecies make up the family. All are completely aquatic with an elongate, eel-like body. Like the Mudpuppies, they are permanent larvae and possess three pairs of gills throughout life. Only the forelimbs are present, and these are proportionately small in size. The Sirens are inhabitants of sluggish streams, ponds, and ditches of the southeastern states. One species ranges northward in the Mississippi Valley to lower Lake Michigan.

The Family Ambystomidae, with 3 genera, 13 species, and 12 subspecies in the United States, is one that contains some of our best known salamanders. The family is also represented in Canada and Mexico. Two of the genera in the United States have but a single species each, and both are restricted to the northwestern region. Members of the third genus occur from coast to coast, from southern Canada to the Gulf, and include such well-known forms as the Eastern Tiger Salamander (*Ambystoma tigrinum tigrinum*), the California Tiger Salamander (*Ambystoma tigrinum californiense*), the Spotted Salamander (*Ambystoma maculatum*), and the Marbled Salamander (*Ambystoma opacum*). The species are stout and mainly land dwellers as adults, normally without gills. They return to the water to breed. In some localities the larvae do not undergo metamorphosis and remain aquatic, gill-breathing forms throughout their lives, but this is exceptional.

The aquatic and terrestrial newts of our ponds, lakes, and larger streams belong to the Family Salamandridae. This family is found in North America, Europe, Asia, and northern Africa. In North America it is represented by two genera, five species, and ten subspecies. One genus is found throughout the area east of the Rocky Mountains, and the other west of the Great Divide. Members of the family always possess four limbs, have no gills in the adult stage, and breathe primarily by means of lungs. The eggs are always laid in water. In some localities the eastern species may pass through a postlarval land stage, called the Eft, which differs in appearance from both larval and adult stages.

The next to the last family, the Amphiumidae, occurs only in the southeastern United States. It is a small family with but a single genus and species; the latter contains two races. This salamander is greatly elongated, eel-like, with four limbs present, but reduced to minute flaps. Gills are absent in the adult, which breathes by means of lungs. This is primarily an aquatic species, but the female lays her eggs on land in a damp situation near the water, usually remaining with the eggs. It is an inhabitant of swamps, muddy lakes, drainage ditches, and sluggish streams.

The Family Plethodontidae is the largest family of living salamanders. Representatives occur in Europe. Central and South America, and North America from the southern border to and including Alaska. The family is predominantly North American, with 16 genera, 56 species, and 72 subspecies known from that continent. These are small to medium-sized salamanders, with the adults usually lacking gills. All are lungless, breathing by means of a vascularized throat area and the skin. Limbs are always present. Species of this large and diverse family are aquatic, semiaquatic, terrestrial, and arboreal. Some lay their eggs in water and pass through a typical larval period, but a few lay their eggs on land and have no aquatic larval stage. Here the larval development takes place inside the egg and the hatchling has the body form of the adult.

Frogs and Toads

Members of the order of frogs and toads are easily recognized in the adult stage by the short body, the elongate legs for jumping or hopping, and the absence of a tail (Figure 4). The adults never possess gills, but breathe by means of lungs. The larval stage has an

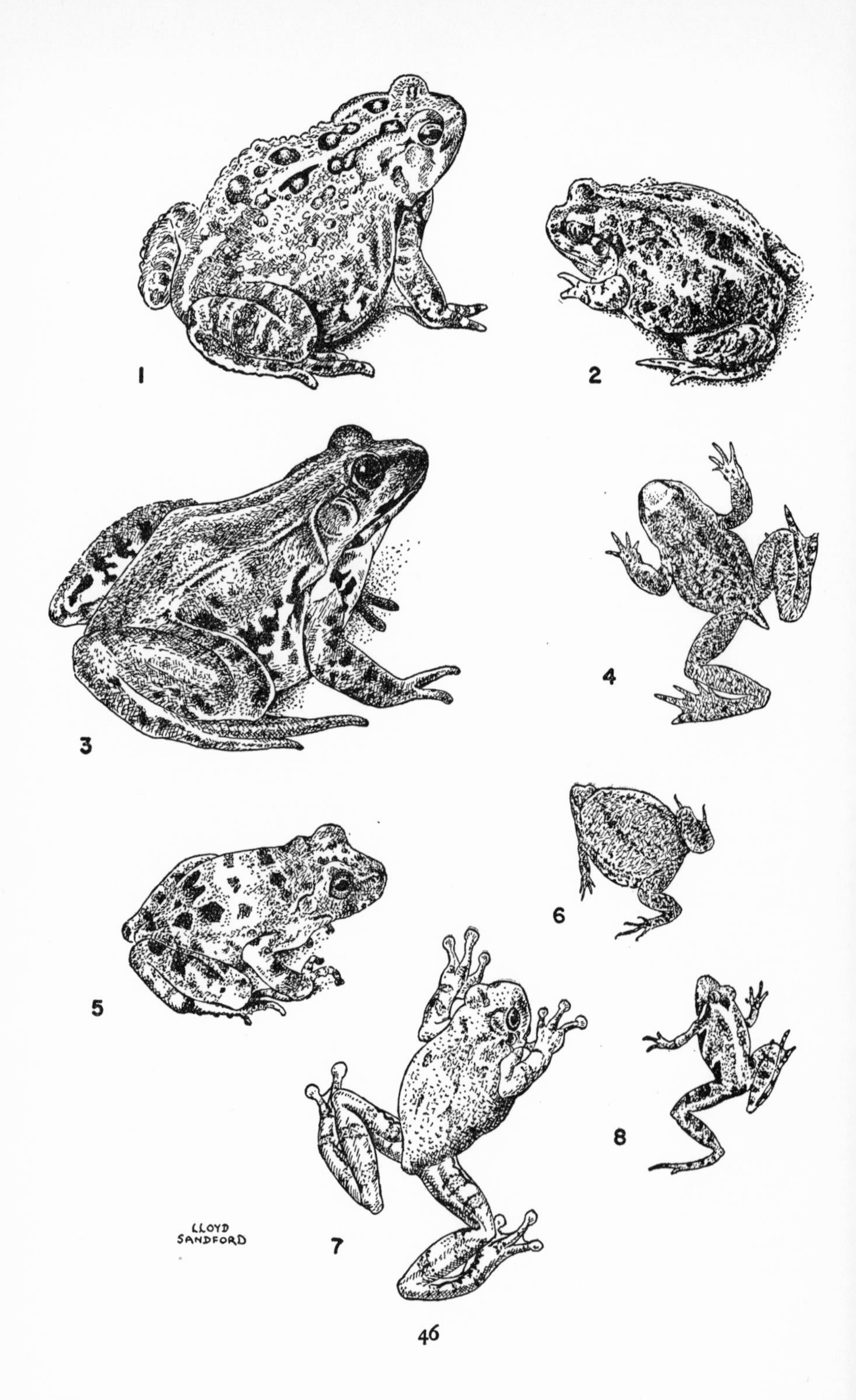
1
2
3
4
5
6
7
8
LLOYD
SANDFORD

appearance completely unlike the adult, having a plump rounded or oval body, a long muscular tail, and no limbs until near the end of the larval period. This is the familiar tadpole, or pollywog. The larvae lack true teeth and have the jaws covered with a horny beak-like structure. Adults may possess true teeth but only in the upper jaw. Frogs and toads are virtually cosmopolitan on the land areas of the world, being absent only from the perpetually frozen polar areas, the drier deserts, the salt-water seas, and some oceanic islands. They may dwell on the land, underground, in trees, or in fresh water.

The term "toad" is frequently used in several different ways: as part of the common name for members of one family or one genus of frogs; and sometimes to indicate an amphibian supposedly quite different from the frogs. "Frog" is the vernacular name for all the tailless amphibians, and the term "toad" is restricted to use in the common name of several more or less dry-skinned frogs belonging to unrelated genera.

About a dozen living families of frogs are recognized in most recent classifications. The number is increased by one or two by some workers, who feel that additional families should be recognized. Seven families are listed for North America in Schmidt's *Check List*. The first of these families is the Ascaphidae, which in North America includes a single genus and species with three subspecies. This species, the Tailed Frog (*Ascaphus truei*), is the most primitive of American frogs. It is found only in the northwestern United States and southwestern Canada. It is a small animal inhabiting mountain streams; it is one of the most aquatic frogs in this country. The males have a tail-like extension of the cloaca that is used at mating as an intromittent organ for the transfer of sperm to the female. This is the only species of frog in which fertilization of the eggs is internal. The only other living representative of this family is a genus of mountain-stream-inhabiting frogs from New Zealand.

FIG. 4. Representatives of the seven families of frogs found in North America. 1. Bufonidae—American Toad (*Bufo americanus*). 2. Pelobatidae—Eastern Spadefoot Toad (*Scaphiopus holbrooki*). 3. Ranidae—Green Frog (*Rana clamitans*). 4. Ascaphidae—Tailed Frog (*Ascaphus truei*). 5. Leptodactylidae—Robber Frog (*Eleutherodactylus latrans*). 6. Microhylidae—Narrow-mouthed Toad (*Microhyla carolinensis*). 7. Hylidae—Gray Tree Frog (*Hyla versicolor*). 8. Hylidae—Cricket Frog (*Acris gryllus*).

The Spadefoot Toads, consisting of one genus with four species and five subspecies in the United States, are the North American representatives of the Family Pelobatidae. Members of this family also occur in Europe and Asia. All are nocturnal, burrowing, terrestrial frogs, with vertically elliptical pupils. The Spadefoots, as their name suggests, have a prominent, sharp-edged tubercle on the inner side of the foot. This is used in digging in loose earth or sand. These frogs occur from coast to coast, being found principally on loamy or sandy soils.

The next family, the Leptodactylidae, is often classified together with the family that includes the True Toads (Bufonidae). The primary differences are internal skeletal characters difficult to see. The Leptodactylids are largely tropical forms found mainly in Australia and South America, but with a number of genera and species in Central America and the West Indies. A small representation is found in southern Texas and southern Arizona, where three genera and five species have been reported. A sixth species, the Greenhouse Frog (*Eleutherodactylus ricordi planirostris*), has been introduced and is now well established in Florida. All are small, secretive species, with interesting but poorly known breeding habits, including development of eggs on land.

The Family Bufonidae and its primary genus, *Bufo*, are nearly cosmopolitan in distribution, unrepresented by native species only in Australia. This family consists of the Toads of the genus *Bufo* and its close relatives. Only this one genus occurs in North America, where it contains 13 species and 17 subspecies. One (or more) species is found in every state of the United States and the provinces of southern Canada. The greatest number of species in this continent occur in the southwestern states. Members of this family range in adult size from about one to seven inches in snout-to-vent length. All are characterized by a more or less warty skin, a pair of prominent glands above and behind the eyes, usually a stout body, and only a fringe of web on the hind foot.

The Family Hylidae is the largest family of frogs in North America. Members of this family are the Tree Frogs (*Hyla*) and their allies. This family is worldwide in distribution, occurring on all continents. In North America there are three genera containing 20 species and 22 subspecies. In size our species vary from the tiny Least Tree Frog (*Hyla ocularis*), which is only ⅝ of an inch in snout-to-vent length to a maximum length of 5⅛ inches, in the case of the Cuban Tree Frog (*Hyla septentrionalis*). Like the preceding family, members of this family occur virtually throughout North America except for the more arid portions of the desert and perpetually frozen Far North. Most species are easily recognized by the dilated adhesive pads at the tips of the fingers and toes. Some species, such as the Cricket Frogs (*Acris*), are entirely terrestrial, while other species—for example, the Squirrel Tree Frog (*Hyla squirella*) —are largely arboreal.

One of the least known groups of our native frogs is that of the Narrow-mouthed Toads (*Microhyla* and *Hypopachus*). These small, burrowing frogs belong to the Family Microhylidae, inhabiting mainly tropical and subtropical lands around the world. In the United States there are only two genera, with a single species each but with a total of four named races found only in the southern and southwestern parts of the country. These forms are easily identified, since they possess a distinctly narrowed head with a prominent fold of skin across the back of the head behind the eyes, and a very small mouth. They are seldom seen above ground except when breeding, and even they are so small and secretive that they are difficult to locate.

The True Frogs (*Rana*) include many of the most familiar species of amphibians. With their allies they make up the Family Ranidae, which, like the Family Bufonidae, is cosmopolitan except for Australia. There is but a single species in South America. The family reaches its greatest diversity in the Old World. The large worldwide genus *Rana* is the sole member of the family in the Western Hemisphere. In North America it has 15 species and 19 subspecies, more than in any other frog genus in this area. Some member of the genus is found in every state of the United States and in all the southern provinces of Canada, with one species, the Wood Frog (*Rana sylvatica*), occurring within the Arctic Circle in Northwestern Canada. The greatest diversity of native species is in the southern half of the United States. This genus includes the largest frogs in the world; our largest frog, the Bullfrog (*Rana catesbeiana*), attains a maximum snout-to-vent length of about 7¼ inches. Most species occur in close proximity to water and have well-developed webs on the hind feet.

In summary, two orders of amphibians, the salamanders and the frogs, are found in the United States and Canada where they are represented by a total of 14 families, with seven in each order.

These families have a total of 38 genera, 142 species, and 179 subspecies. The North American salamanders are a more diverse group than our frogs; there are 26 genera, 82 species, and 109 subspecies of salamanders. The largest and most diverse family of amphibians in the world is the family Plethodontidae, which in North America alone has 16 genera, 56 species, and 72 subspecies. The largest single genus of American amphibians is the type genus of the same family, *Plethodon*, with 18 species. The largest genus of frogs in this country is *Rana*, with 15 North American species. The amphibian species with the greatest number of subspecies is Jordan's Salamander (*Plethodon jordoni*), with eight races. Salamanders are predominantly temperate or subtropical animals and reach their greatest diversity in the Northern Hemisphere. Thus it is not surprising that our salamander fauna is the most varied and largest in number of named forms found anywhere, with the possible exception of Middle America. In contrast, frogs exhibit the greatest number of species and genera in the warmer tropics and subtropics, and our frog fauna is exceeded in number by the frog fauna of several warmer lands.

CHAPTER 5

North American Reptiles

THE WORD "REPTILE" COMES FROM the Latin *repere* (to creep) and means "a creeping thing." Thus reptiles are commonly considered to be animals that creep. This notion is incorrect and is based on a historical misconception. Numerous reptiles do not creep, and many animals other than reptiles do creep. Like the amphibians, the reptiles are a class of backboned or vertebrate animals that must depend on external sources for their body warmth. Here the likeness stops, for the reptiles exhibit a number of differences from the amphibians. They have an outer body covering of scales or horny plates, nearly devoid of skin glands. External legs with five fingers and five toes are usually present. The adults all breathe by means of lungs, and gills are not present except during embryonic development. Reptiles lay shelled eggs that develop on land, or they bring forth their young alive. The shelled egg possesses a set of embryonic enveloping membranes called the allantois and amnion, which are found only in reptiles, birds, and mammals, and make it possible for the embryo to develop out of water. The land-developing egg is an amazing improvement over that of the fishlike vertebrates and the amphibians. It has enabled the reptiles to occupy many more areas than would otherwise be the case. Development from the egg is direct, without any intermediate larval stage. Reptiles occur on land, underground, in trees, in fresh water, and in the oceans. They occur in nearly all parts of the world except the areas of perpetual ice toward the poles, but the greatest concentration of species and the largest body sizes are found in warm tropical regions.

The Class Reptilia is divided into a total of 17 orders, five of which survive at present. The living orders are the Chelonia or turtles, the Crocodilia or crocodilians, the Rhyncocephalia or beakheads, the Sauria or lizards, and the Serpentes or snakes. In many

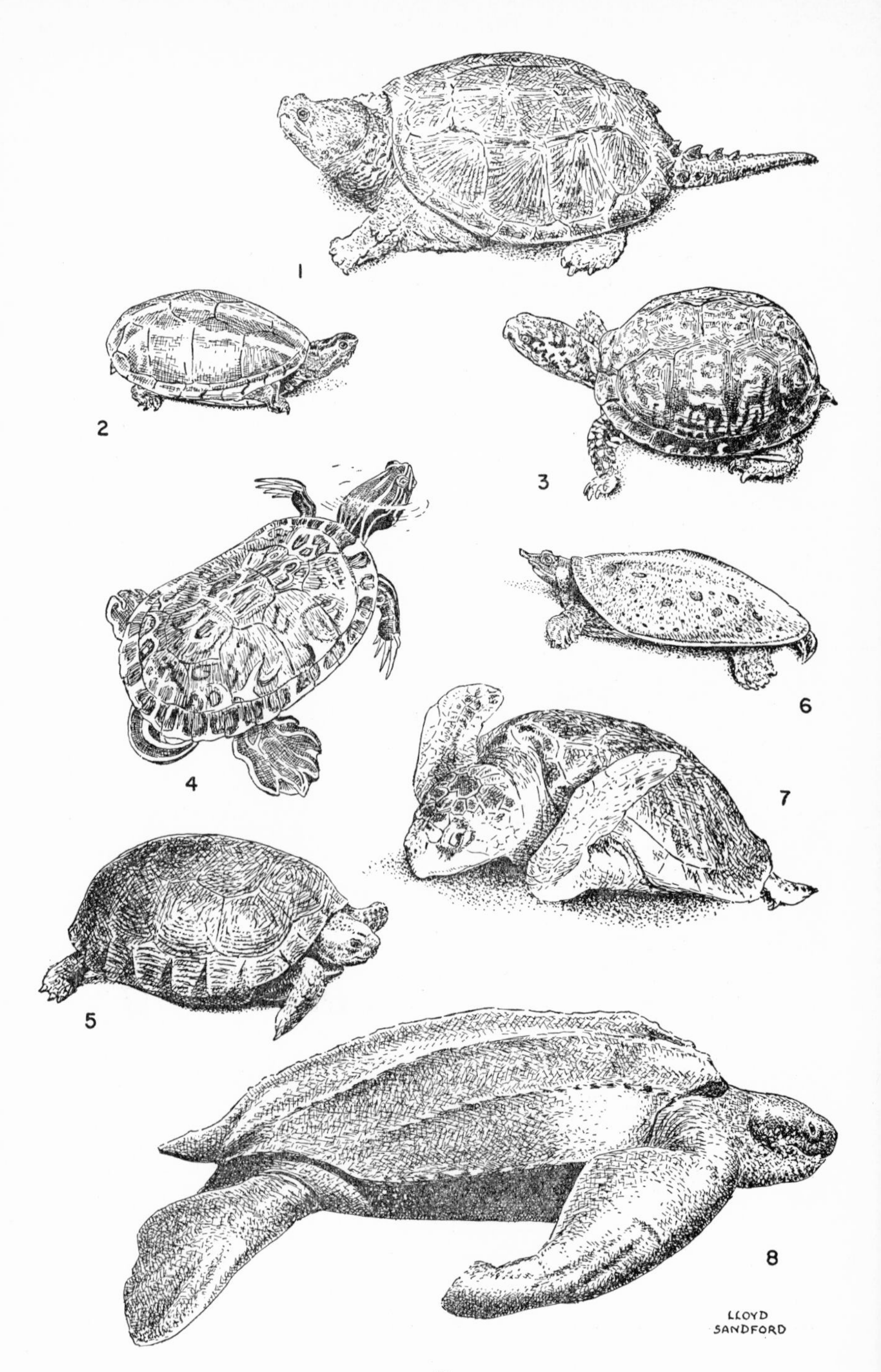
1
2
3
4
5
6
7
8
LLOYD
SANDFORD

PLATE III. A Texas Alligator Lizard (*Gerrhonotus liocephalus infernalis*) climbing down a small tree. Note the use of the tail in gripping the trunk. (New York Zoological Society photograph)

PLATE IV. A Green Frog (*Rana clamitans*) floating at the surface of the water in a characteristic position exposing only the top and front of the head. Note the position of the eyes enabling the animal to see above and below the water. (New York Zoological Society photograph)

classifications the lizards and snakes are grouped together in a single order, the Squamata, but, since the living species of each group are so diverse, there is much merit in separating the two. The beakheads are represented today by a single genus and species, the Tuatara (*Sphenodon punctatus*), which occurs only on a few remote, rocky islets off the main islands of New Zealand. It is the last remnant of an ancient and once flourishing group of superficially lizard-like reptiles. All the other living orders occur around the warmer regions of the world, with some extending through the temperate areas, even to the Arctic Circle.

Turtles

Turtles are an ancient group of leisurely and long-lived reptiles. They are one of the easiest of reptiles to recognize (Figure 5). All have a short and broad body that is encased in a protective shell, usually of solid bone overlaid with horny plates. The head, neck, limbs, and tail can be drawn into the shell with varying degrees of success, providing slight to virtually complete protection. Turtles are the only vertebrates in which the limb attachments are *inside* the ribs. This unique structural condition enhances the protection provided by the shell. All living turtles completely lack teeth, the jaws being covered with a sharp horny beak. All members of the order have two pairs of legs, usually with five fingers and toes bearing claws. Some of the completely aquatic species have the front limbs modified in the form of paddles or flippers. All turtles lay eggs, depositing them on land. Turtles live on land, in fresh water, and in the oceans. They occur on all continents and in the warm seas.

The turtles are often subdivided into major groups. The most frequent of these divisions is based in part on the method of withdrawing the neck under the shell. For example, if you suddenly

---

Fig. 5. Representatives of the seven families of turtles occurring in North America. 1. Chelydridae—Snapping Turtle (*Chelydra serpentina*). 2. Kinosternidae—Striped Mud Turtle (*Kinosternon bauri*). 3. Emydidae—Box Turtle (*Terrapene carolina*). 4. Emydidae—Southern Terrapin (*Pseudemys floridana*). 5. Testudinidae—Gopher Turtle (*Gopherus polyphemus*). 6. Trionychidae—Soft-shelled Turtle (*Trionyx ferox*). 7. Chelonidae—Green Turtle (*Chelonia mydas*). 8. Dermochelidae—Leatherback Turtle (*Dermochelys coriacea*).

pick up a Box Turtle (*Terrapene*), it may quickly draw the head and neck into the body under the shell. It does so by bending the neck in a vertical S-shape; the neck passes completely out of sight. Another group of turtles—found in Africa, Australia, and South America—withdraw their head and neck by drawing the neck horizontally across the front of the shell, leaving a good portion of it and the head exposed. These turtles are called the "sideneck turtles." In addition to the manner of withdrawing the neck, there are several pronounced skeletal differences that distinguish these two groups of turtles. No living sideneck turtles occur in the Northern Hemisphere, so they will not be considered further. Two other groups of turtles are sometimes accorded separate treatment from the other "vertical neck turtles." These are the soft-shelled turtles living in the fresh waters of North America, Africa, Asia, and the East Indies, and the Leatherback Turtles (*Dermochelys*) of the warm oceans. Both of these have a number of attributes that set them apart from the other turtles, but most classifications do not accord them more than family rank. We will group all of these together in the one Order Chelonia, in which twelve living families are recognized. Seven of the living families are included among our North American Turtles.

The first family is the Chelydridae, including the familiar Snapping Turtles (*Chelydra* and *Macrochelys*). The genus *Macrochelys* contains but a single species, which occurs in the lower Mississippi Valley and the Gulf States. The genus *Chelydra*, with one species and two subspecies, occurs over a wide portion of the United States east of the Rockies, continuing south to northern South America. These two genera are the sole members of the family. They are characterized by their large heads, small, flattened shell, and long tail with its rounded knobs on top. The lower shell is much smaller than the upper. The Alligator Snapping Turtle (*Macrochelys temmincki*) is the largest fresh-water turtle in the world, attaining a maximum shell length of 26 inches and a weight of more than 200 pounds. It inhabits swamps and sluggish streams. The Common Snapping Turtle (*Chelydra s. serpentina*) lives in ponds, lakes, and larger streams. It has the remarkable capacity to exist in large numbers in regions of thickly settled human habitation, despite persecution by man and heavy predation on its eggs by a number of animals. Because of its habits of remaining in and under water most of its life, it may occur abundantly in an area without being discovered by many of its human neighbors. For example, it is a species that is still common in many of the park ponds in New York City and other large metropolitan areas. It is truly a hardy survivor.

The Family Kinosternidae is also restricted to the Western Hemisphere. In North America it is represented by two genera, the Musk Turtles (*Sternotherus*) and the Mud Turtles (*Kinosternon*), with a total of 7 species and 11 subspecies. These are small, relatively secretive, aquatic turtles, with large heads and short tails. The shells are low rounded ovals that are never more than six inches long. Our smallest turtle, the Striped Mud Turtle (*Kinosternon b. bauri*), with a maximum shell length of three and three-quarters inches, is a member of this family. The species are partly scavengers, feeding on carrion. When disturbed they emit an acrid, pungent odor that gives the Musk Turtle its common name.

Half of our North American turtle species belong to the Family Emydidae, which in this continent contains 8 genera, 19 species, and 35 subspecies. This is a large family, occurring in Asia and Europe as well as North, Middle, and South America. Many of our best known species belong to this group: the Box Turtles (*Terrapene*), the Painted Turtles (*Chrysemys*), the Pond Terrapins (*Pseudemys*), the Map Turtle (*Graptemys*), and others. All have the feet modified for walking, but usually with a web between the toes; the skin and the shell are frequently marked with bright colors. Members of the family are aquatic, semiaquatic, or terrestrial. Virtually all species frequently bask in the sun. They range in size from the small Muhlenberg's Turtle (*Clemmy's muhlenbergi*), with a maximum shell length of about 4 inches, to the large Suwannee Turtle (*Pseudemys floridana suwannensis*), which is known to attain a shell length of 16 inches. Representatives of the family occur throughout the United States and in the southern provinces of Canada, but species are most abundant in the southeastern and Gulf States.

One genus and three species constitute our sole representation of the Family Testudinidae. These are our land turtles, or tortoises that rarely or never go near the water. They live in burrows in the ground and are well adapted for living on dry land. The shell is high and rounded, the feet are short and trunklike with short claws, and the tail is short. The family includes the land tortoises of Africa, Asia, Europe, and the Americas. The giant land turtles of the Galápagos Islands and the islands of the Indian Ocean, reaching a maximum weight of more than 500 pounds, belong to this family. None of our species attains such a large size. The largest of our species is the Desert Turtle (*Gopherus agassizi*), which has a maximum shell length of 14⅛ inches. The three species inhabiting the United States occur in the warmer southern and southwestern parts of the country.

The Family Chelonidae includes all our marine turtles except the Leatherback Turtle. The species all have low, hard, streamlined shells, and front legs modified to form large paddles. The shell is small in relation to the size of the body and does not provide a protective cover for the limbs in time of danger. The skin of the head is divided into large, distinct plates or scales. All members of this family are strictly aquatic, rarely coming to land except when the female comes ashore to lay her eggs. A total of 4 genera, 4 species and 8 subspecies are occasionally recorded along our shores, but they occur with regularity only along the southern coasts. The Green Turtle (*Chelonia mydas*) and the Hawksbill (*Eretmochelys imbricata*) are probably the best known members of the family, chiefly because of their economic value.

The Family Trionychidae includes the unusual Soft-shelled or "Pancake" Turtles (*Trionyx*) with their long, fleshy nose and the flattened, flabby shells that are covered only with leathery skin. The family also occurs in Africa and Asia, where it is more abundantly represented. In North America 1 genus, 2 species, and 6 subspecies occur east of the Rocky Mountains; one of the species has been introduced and is now established in the lower tributaries of the Colorado River in Arizona and California. Soft-shells are inhabitants of large slow-moving rivers, clear ponds, and lakes. They occasionally come out on the bank or a log to bask in secluded spots, or make short overland journeys, but more commonly remain in the water.

The last turtle family, the Dermochelidae, contains only the unusual Leatherback Turtle (*Dermochelys coriacea*), with a single species divided into an Atlantic and Pacific subspecies. This is the largest of living turtles, with a maximum shell length of up to eight feet and a weight of up to three-quarters of a ton. Size is not the only unique feature of this turtle, for it has a structure so unique that it is sometimes classified separately from all other turtles. Unlike any other living turtle, its shell is composed of separate, small bony plates imbedded in the skin and not fused with the rest of the

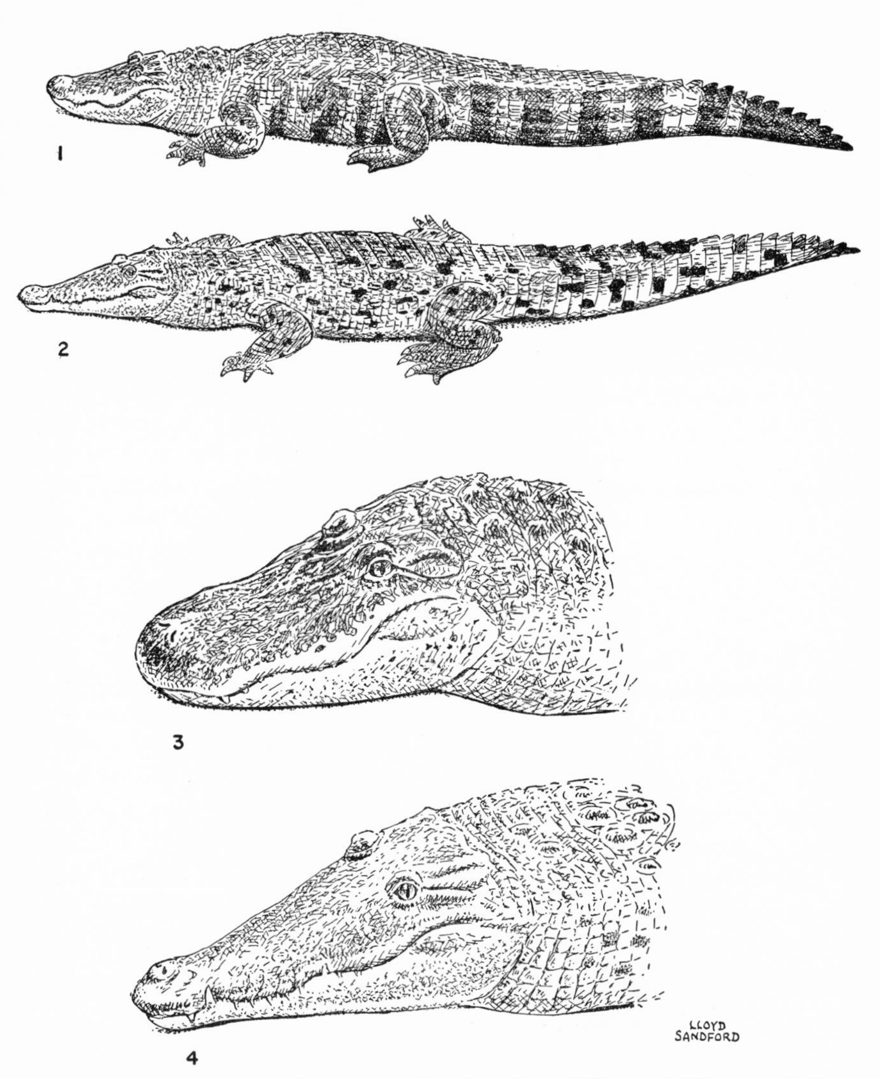

FIG. 6. Our native crocodilians: 1 and 3. American Alligator (*Alligator mississippiensis*) and 2 and 4. American Crocodile (*Crocodylus acutus*). The enlarged drawings of the heads show the most easily recognized differences between the two. Note the enlarged lower tooth near the front of the jaw in the crocodile and the fact that this tooth cannot be seen in the alligator when its mouth is shut.

skeleton. The ribs and backbone are not joined to this covering, as they are in the shells of other turtles. Some of the bony plates are arranged in rows forming raised keels that extend the length of the shell; there are seven such keels on the upper shell and five on the lower. This turtle is usually found in the warmer tropical seas.

Crocodilians

The members of the order of crocodilians occur in and around water throughout the tropical and subtropical regions of the world. Most species are large in size, with some attaining a length of more than twenty feet, although a few reach their maximum size at a length of six feet. All have four legs, a long muscular tail, the body covered with horny platelike scales, a long bony snout, and numerous conical teeth set in bony sockets. All reproduce by eggs, and some construct large nest mounds which they guard, whereas other species merely bury the eggs and abandon them. The group includes the crocodiles, alligators, caimans, and gavials. These are sometimes grouped in several families or combined in a single family. The single-family treatment is utilized by Schmidt, and therefore we include only the Family Crocodilidae. In North America it is represented by two genera and two species (Figure 6): the American Alligator (*Alligator mississippiensis*) and the American Crocodile (*Crocodylus acutus*). The American Alligator inhabits the southern areas from central Texas east to the Atlantic, while the American Crocodile is found today in the United States only in extreme southern Florida. Both were in danger of extinction as a result of the great numbers collected and shot for economic reasons. Under Federal and State protection they are both making a good comeback, but still require careful study to insure their future existence in this country. The crocodile occurs in such a small area in this country that it was in greater danger of being exterminated than the alligator. The same species of crocodile occurs in parts of the West Indies, Middle America, and the northern part of South America, whereas the American Alligator is found only in the southern United States.

Lizards

The lizards are the most diverse group of reptiles from the standpoint of the number of living families, of which there are twenty-one. In North America we find representatives of nine of the families (Figure 7). Lizards usually have four legs, a long tail, movable eyelids, external ear openings, and a more or less firm skull. A number of different families contain members that have greatly reduced or entirely lost the external limbs. In this respect they superficially resemble snakes. Some lizards lay eggs, whereas others bring forth living young. In size they range from tiny geckos little more than two inches in total length to the large Komodo Monitor (*Varanus komodoensis*), with a total length of more than ten feet. In North America our longest, the Eastern Glass Lizard (*Ophisaurus ventralis*), is little more than three feet in total length. Lizards are cosmopolitan, occurring on all continents; they are found on many oceanic islands where no other reptile life exists. At least one species of European lizard occurs as far north as the Arctic Circle, but in North America only four species occur in Canada, and these are found in the southernmost portions. One genus of lizard, *Heloderma*, with two species, has developed a crude venom apparatus. These are the only venomous lizards in the world.

One of the most interesting of all groups of lizards is the Family Gekkonidae. Members of this family are chiefly nocturnal, with large eyes that usually have vertically elliptical pupils and usually lack movable eyelids. The digits are frequently dilated to form adhesive organs that aid the lizards in climbing smooth surfaces. This is a large, predominantly Old World family, with numerous species in Africa and Asia, but occurring on all continents. With the exception of a few species in New Zealand, all species lay eggs, usually two in number and with hard, brittle shells. In the United States 2 genera, 2 species, and 5 subspecies, occurring in the southwestern states, are considered to represent our sole native members of the family. Along the Gulf Coast and in southern Florida an additional three genera and four species are recorded as introduced forms. There may be some question whether one of these, the Reef Gecko (*Sphaerodactylus notatus*), was "introduced" in the sense that it

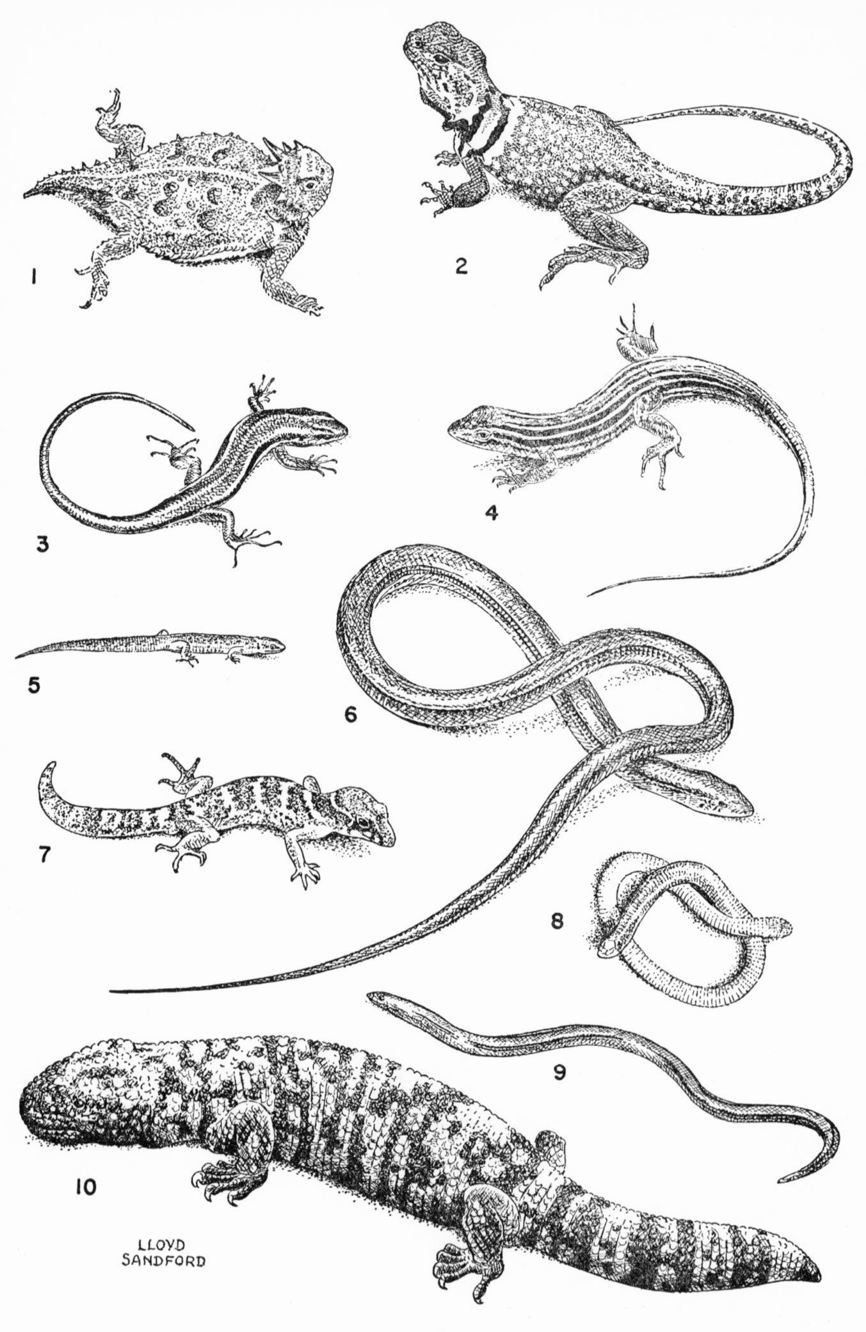
1
2
3
4
5
6
7
8
9
10
LLOYD
SANDFORD

was brought into this country intentionally or unintentionally by human agency. It may have reached this country without man's assistance.

By far the largest of our families of lizards is the Family Iguanidae. This is primarily a family of the Western Hemisphere, ranging from southern Canada to southern Argentina, including the West Indies. In the Old World it occurs in Madagascar. It also occurs in the Fiji and Friendly Islands. In North America, 10 genera, 40 species, and 64 subspecies are recognized. All are more or less typically lizardlike animals with four well-developed legs, a long tail, and prominent eyes with movable lids; the tongue is short and fleshy; and there are usually large distinct plates on the head. Most species lay eggs, but a few bring forth living young. The group occurs over most of the United States, but the greatest concentration of genera and species is in the southwest. A single species is definitely reported in British Columbia. These lizards are active, diurnal, basking forms, usually found on rocks, trees, and bushes or scurrying about on the ground. The family does not include our largest or smallest lizard, but it does exhibit a considerable range in size, from a total length of about 4½ inches to 16½ inches.

The Family Anguidae contains an interesting assemblage of elongate or snakelike lizards that, in North America, are characterized by being covered with squarish, overlapping scales, with bony platelets underlying each scale, and with a more or less prominent fold along the side of the body. With the exception of a few species in South America, this is a family of the Northern Hemisphere, occurring in southern Asia, Europe, and North and Middle America. The greatest number of species occur in North and Middle America. In North America there are 2 genera, 8 species, and 11 subspecies. The Alligator Lizards (*Gerrhonotus*) are western species, being found from Texas west to the Pacific and from British Columbia

---

FIG. 7. Representatives of the nine families of lizards found in North America. 1. Iguanidae—Texas Horned Lizard (*Phrynosoma cornutum*). 2. Iguanidae—Collared Lizard (*Crotaphytus collaris*). 3. Scincidae—Five-lined Skink (*Eumeces fasciatus*). 4. Teidae—Eastern Race Runner (*Cnemidophorus sexlineatus*). 5. Xantusidae—Yucca Night Lizard (*Xantusia vigilis*). 6. Anguidae—Slender Glass Lizard (*Ophisaurus attenuatus*). 7. Gekkonidae—Banded Gecko (*Coleonyx variegatus*). 8. Amphisbaenidae—Florida Worm Lizard (*Rhineura floridana*). 9. Anniellidae—Footless Lizard (*Anniella pulchra*). 10. Helodermatidae Gila Monster (*Heloderma suspectum*).

southward into Mexico. All are elongate lizards with small legs and long tails. All are relatively slow-moving and secretive. Some species are live-bearing, whereas others lay eggs. The genus *Ophisaurus* contains the three species and two subspecies of Glass Lizards or "Glass Snakes." They lack external limbs completely, but, like most lizards, have external ear openings and movable eyelids. This genus occurs from Texas northward through the Great Plains to Wisconsin and eastward along the Gulf Coast to the Atlantic. The greatest abundance of species is in the southeastern states. All lay eggs. Our longest lizard is the Eastern Glass Lizard (*Ophisaurus ventralis*), which is reported to attain a maximum length of slightly more than three feet.

The Family Helodermatidae includes but a single genus and in the United States only one species, the Gila Monster (*Heloderma suspectum*). This is the only venomous lizard occurring in North America and, with is relative the Mexican Beaded Lizard (*Heloderma horridum*), the only venomous lizard in the world. It possesses grooved teeth and large bony plates, or osteoderms, under the scales. The Gila Monster is confined to southwestern Utah, southern Nevada, Arizona, southwestern New Mexico, and northwestern Mexico. This lizard is rather lethargic by nature and, despite its venom, has been sold frequently in the pet and curio trades. It is now protected by law in Arizona.

The Footless Lizards (*Anniella pulchra*) are the sole living members of the Family Anniellidae, which is found only in southwestern California and in the northwestern portion of the adjacent Mexican state of Baja California. This is a small, snakelike lizard that completely lacks external limbs. The maximum total length attained is about nine inches. There is no external ear opening, and the eye is somewhat concealed but does have movable lids. This lizard is a burrowing species, inhabiting sandy soil and rarely being found above ground. It is live-bearing. Two races are recognized.

The Xantusidae is another strictly American family of lizards, inhabiting southwestern North America, Middle America, and Cuba. All species are small, not exceeding eight inches in total length. One genus, the Night Lizard (*Xantusia*), and four species are found in Arizona and California. The largest of the four species, the Island Night Lizard (*Xantusia riversiana*), is restricted to three islands off the California coast. These lizards, as their common name indicates, are primarily nocturnal in habits. They are quite secretive by day. All are live-bearing.

The Family Teiidae is primarily a South American family, but it also has representatives in North and Middle America and in the West Indies. Only a single genus, the Racerunners (*Cnemidophorus*), has reached North America, where it has seven species and eleven subspecies. This genus contains numerous species and ranges from this area to South America. These species are moderate-sized, elongate, sleek, very active, and fast. They occur from coast to coast and are inhabitants of hot, dry, usually sandy areas; one wide-ranging species, the Eastern Racerunner (*Cnemidophorus sexlineatus*), occurs from Texas north to South Dakota and Minnesota, east to Indiana, southward in the Mississippi Valley, and east along the coast to Maryland. All members of the genus lay eggs.

The skinks form a large and diverse cosmopolitan family, Scincidae, of smooth, shiny lizards. The group has its greatest diversity and number of forms in the Indo-Australian area. In North America we have 3 genera, 17 species, and 11 subspecies. Representatives are found from coast to coast but are rare or absent in the most arid deserts; three species occur in Canada. The scales have platelets of bone under them, but frequently have an iridescent luster. They range from a very small size to more than a foot in total length in this country and even larger on other continents. The legs are usually small in relation to the body, and in one form, the Sand Skink (*Neoseps reynoldsi*), are reduced to tiny flaplike structures with one toe in front and two in back. Some lay eggs, others have live young.

One of the most peculiar and least known of our lizards belongs to the Family Amphisbaenidae. Members of this family constitute an unusual group of wormlike, usually legless, burrowing lizards found around the Mediterranean, throughout most of Africa and Middle and South America. One species, the Florida Worm Lizard (*Rhineura floridana*), found only in north and central Florida, is the only member of the family definitely known to occur in the United States. Overenthusiastic herpetologists who wish to increase our fauna beyond its known limits have made unsupported claims or suggestions that another species of the family occurs in Arizona or Florida, but no specimens have yet been collected. The Florida Worm Lizard looks superficially very much like an earthworm.

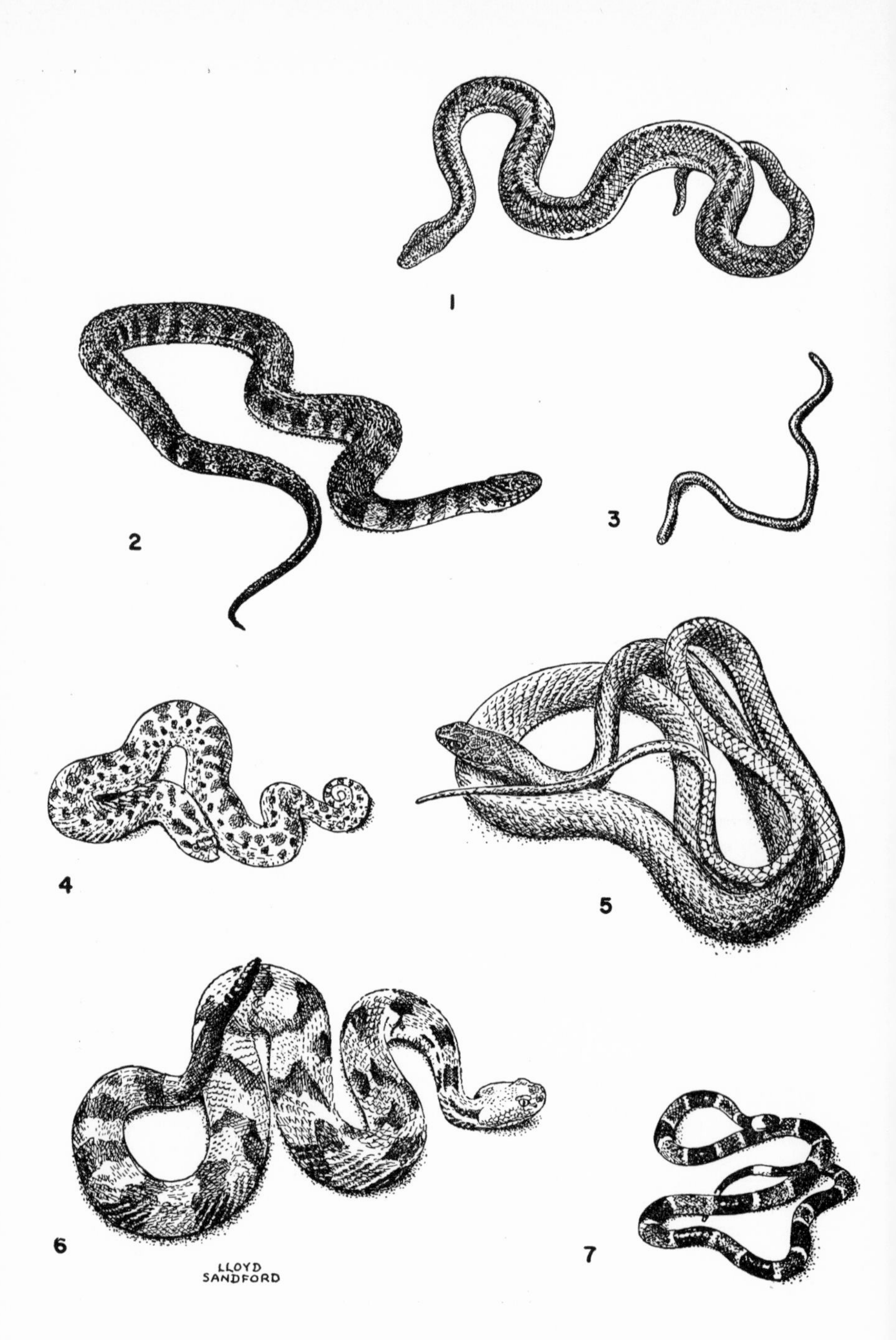
1
2
3
4
5
6
LLOYD
SANDFORD
7

The head is small, slightly pointed, without external ear openings, with the eyes concealed; the body is elongate, without external limbs, with transverse rings or grooves, and with a short tail. Like other members of the family, this is a burrowing form rarely found above ground. It lays eggs and attains a maximum total length of about eleven inches.

Snakes

From the standpoint of number of genera, species, and subspecies, the snakes are our most diverse and numerous reptiles. In North America the 1953 *Check List* includes 46 genera, 115 species, and 234 subspecies of snakes—more genera and subspecies than all other groups of reptiles of this continent combined, and nearly as many species as are found in this combined total. All snakes have greatly elongated bodies and tails, with no (very minute remnants in two families) external limbs, no movable eyelids and no external ear openings. Several bones of the skull are loosely joined, giving the skull considerable flexibility and movement. Snakes occur on all continents; the greatest abundance of forms is in the warm tropical and subtropical regions. One European species occurs up to and barely within the Arctic Circle. Snakes range in size from small eight-inch species to giants of over thirty feet in length. Our largest North American species get nowhere near so large, attaining a maximum length of a little more than eight feet. Nine or ten living families are usually recognized, with five of these occurring in North America (Figure 8). Four families of snakes, including two found within our boundaries, contain species that possess enlarged front fangs and a powerful venom, making them dangerous to man.

The first of our native families is the Leptotyphlopidae. These are small, roundheaded, blunt-tailed, secretive or burrowing species often mistaken for worms. They possess internal remnants of hind

---

FIG. 8. Representatives of the five families of snakes occurring in North America. 1. Boidae—California Boa (*Lichanura roseofusca*). 2. Leptotyphlopidae—Blind Snake (*Leptotyphlops dulcis*). 3. Colubridae—Common Water Snake (*Natrix sipedon*). 4. Colubridae—Western Hog-nosed Snake (*Heterodon nasicus*). 5. Colubridae—Racer (*Coluber constrictor*). 6. Crotalidae—Timber Rattlesnake (*Crotalus horridus*). 7. Elapidae—Coral Snake (*Micrurus fulvius*).

legs and the hind limb girdle. The eyes are hidden beneath scales of the head. The species are primarily inhabitants of the warm parts of Africa, southern Asia, and Middle and South America, including the West Indies. The only genus in the family, *Leptotyphlops*, has two species and six subspecies in the southwestern United States from California to Texas. The maximum total length attained by any of our species is a little more than fifteen inches. All species lay eggs.

Two genera, two species, and five subspecies represent the Family Boidae. This is essentially a family of tropical snakes inhabiting Middle and South America and the West Indies, with a few species in Africa, Asia, Madagascar, and the East Indies. The family includes some extremely large constrictors, as well as some small, sand-dwelling burrowers. All boas produce living young. They are usually muscular snakes with relatively stout bodies. All possess remnants of hind legs, which are visible externally as minute "spurs" on either side of the vent. The Rubber Boa (*Charina bottae*), attaining a maximum total length of about two feet, is found over a wide area in the montane forested section of western North America as far north as southwestern British Columbia. The California Boa (*Lichanura roseofusca*) occurs in the deserts and dry hills of Arizona and southern California, and southward into Baja California and Sonora, Mexico.

The third family, the Colubridae, includes the vast majority of our snakes and most of the snakes of the world. It is a diverse assemblage of forms occurring throughout the parts of the world inhabited by reptiles. Actually, the family contains several more or less discrete aggregations of genera and species that are difficult to define clearly enough to designate them as families. All lack any remnant of hind legs, and none possesses enlarged, tubular, front fangs. Some species are small and some are large, none approaches the great length of the big constrictors; some lay eggs, some have living young; some have enlarged, grooved teeth in the rear of the upper jaw and possess a venom that can immobilize small prey; some are burrowers, some are tree dwellers, some live in fresh water, most live on the surface of the land. In North America there are 38 genera, 92 species, and 188 subspecies. They occur in every state and in most habitats except the areas of perpetual ice or snow; only a few races of Water Snakes (*Natrix*) have invaded the brackish waters at the edge of the sea. The family includes such well-known forms as the Garter Snakes (*Thamnophis*), the Water Snakes (*Natrix*), the Racers (*Coluber*), the Rat Snakes (*Elaphe*), the King Snakes (*Lampropeltis*), and the Gopher Snakes (*Pituophis*).

The Coral Snakes (*Micrurus* and *Micruroides*), with 2 genera, 2 species, and 3 subspecies, comprise our sole representatives of a large, predominantly Old World family of venomous snakes, the Elapidae. This family includes some of the world's most deadly snakes—for example, the African Mambas (*Dendroaspis*), the Cobras (*Naja* and *Ophiophagus*) the Australian Taipan (*Oxyuranus scutellatus*), the Death Adder (*Acanthophis antarcticus*), and the South American Coral Snakes (*Micrurus*). All members of the family possess enlarged fangs that are more or less immovably fixed in the front of the upper jaw. The two species that occur in the United States are limited to the southern and southwestern sections of the country. Both are relatively small, secretive species. Their bite can easily be avoided by not handling the snakes; virtually all records of bites by Coral Snakes in the United States resulted when the snakes were actually handled. The Coral Snake (*Micrurus fulvius fulvius*) of the southeastern states occasionally reaches a length of more than three feet; it is more dangerous than the other members of this family found in the United States. The Arizona Coral Snake (*Micruroides euryxanthus*) attains a total length of not more than 19½ inches. Both species lay eggs.

The Family Crotalidae includes the Pit Vipers—venomous species with movable fangs in the front of the upper jaw and a prominent facial pit. Our most important venomous snakes belong to this family. It is primarily a New World family, with many species in North, Middle, and South America, but representatives also occur in eastern Europe, Asia, and the East Indies. Three genera, 17 species, and 32 subspecies represent the family in North America. This list includes the Copperhead (*Ancistrodon contortrix*) of the eastern United States, the Water Moccasin (*Ancistrodon piscivorous*) of the southeastern United States, and the Rattlesnakes (*Crotalus* and *Sistrurus*), with some representatives in almost every part of the United States and in southern Canada. North American members of the family vary in maximum size from a total length of just under two feet to slightly more than eight feet. The Eastern Diamondback Rattlesnake (*Crotalus adamanteus*), the Western Diamondback Rattlesnake (*Crotalus atrox*), the Timber Rattlesnake (*Crotalus horridus*), and the Prairie Rattlesnake (*Crotalus viridis*) are our most dangerous venomous snakes, sometimes inflicting fatal bites. All members of the family produce living young.

In summary, four orders of living reptiles, turtles, crocodilians, lizards, and snakes are found in the United States and Canada. A total of 22 families contains 89 genera, 236 species, and 400 subspecies. The largest and most diverse of the orders, in number of different forms on this continent, is the order of the snakes, with 46 genera, 115 species, and 234 subspecies. The largest single family is also one of snakes, the Family Colubridae, which in North America has 38 genera, 92 species, and 188 subspecies. The genera with the largest number of species are the Scaly Lizards (*Sceloporus*) and the Skinks (*Eumeces*) with 15 species each. The species with the greatest number of recognized races is the Western Garter Snake (*Thamnophis elegans*) with 11 subspecies.

Most of the reptile orders reach their greatest diversity and maximum number of different forms in the tropics and subtropics. Thus the number of species in North America is exceeded in other continents, with the possible exception of the turtles. This group of reptiles has a greater number of genera and species in the temperate and subtropical regions than in the warmer countries. Therefore our turtle fauna is one of the largest and most diverse in the world.

CHAPTER 6

Occurrence of Amphibians and Reptiles

THE QUESTION "WHERE DOES IT live?" may be answered by the biologist in several ways. It can be answered in terms of geographic distribution, the habitat occupied, and the specific portion or niche of the habitat in which the animal lives. For example, the Spotted Salamander (*Ambystoma maculatum*) occurs in the eastern United States and southeastern Canada. Its habitat is the hardwood and mixed hardwood evergreen forests of this area, where it is found in or under rotting logs, in old stumps, under stones, among the leaves on the ground, or in shallow underground retreats. The Eastern Four-toed Salamander (*Hemidactylium scutatum*) occurs in parts of the same geographic area, but is absent in the southern third of this region. Its habitat is in wooded or sparse areas around or adjoining bogs, coniferous swamps, or larch meadows, where it is found on land in sphagnum moss, under logs or bark.

Every species and subspecies has its own particular distribution in relation to its geographic range, its habitat, and its particular niche. These are important characteristics of the animal and are as distinct as its coloration, shape, or size. Each animal is adapted or adjusted to living under the specific conditions of its particular environment and is unable to live in other environments. We recognize this fact in some better-known animals by such expressions as "like a chicken in water" or "like a hog on ice."

The study of where animals occur and why they occur where they do is very complex and involves the consideration of a great many factors. It is actually a part of two different fields of zoology —zoogeography and ecology. Zoogeography is defined as the scientific study of animal life in relation to its distribution on the earth and the mutual influence of environment and animals upon each other. In order to interpret and understand the distribution of animals today, we must know something about the conditions in past ages concerning both the animals and the earth. It is important to recognize the mutual relationship between animal and environment. The environment, effective within the inherited capabilities of the animals, is influential in molding the characters of a population occurring in a given locality. As a rule, members of a widely distributed species differ from locality to locality in one or more discernible attributes. This is termed geographic variation and frequently occurs in a gradient pattern. The animal as part of the environment completes the mutuality of the relationship and contributes to the character of the environment. The details of this relationship are properly within the province of the science of ecology.

Ecology can be defined as the study of life in relation to its environment. It can be seen from this definition that ecology and zoogeography are closely related and overlapping studies. They are sometimes combined into the single approach of ecological zoogeography. Ecology is very broad in scope, including virtually every phase of natural history studies. In fact, ecology is sometimes referred to as scientific natural history or quantitative natural history. Zoogeography is concerned primarily with distribution of animals in relation to major world features, whereas ecology is more concerned with the details of the environment and the animals' occurrence in it. The present chapter describes the general conditions of the occurrence of amphibians and reptiles in North America.

Geographic Range

The geographic range of species and subspecies is customarily expressed in terms of political boundaries. This provides a more or less precise indication of the area in which the form occurs and, depending on the extent of one's geographical knowledge, something of the type of habitat in which it lives. The geographic range of an animal is really the distribution of the habitat or habitats in which it occurs. To understand clearly what is meant by the term "habitat," it can be defined as the physical situation in which the animal lives, including the soil, plants, and climate. A habitat may extend over a large geographical area—for example, the northern coniferous forests—or it may be limited to a very small area, as in the case of an underground well or stream.

Karl P. Schmidt has summarized the varying characteristics of the geographic ranges of animals, pointing out that few have a continuous distribution throughout the area occupied. This is because the habitats are generally not continuous but discontinuous, forming islands or a mosaic pattern of suitable sections that can be lived in. This may be understood easily if we think of a form living in fresh water, such as the Snapping Turtle (*Chelydra serpentina*). It does not occur continuously throughout its geographical range, but only where there are suitable bodies of fresh water. Schmidt also emphasizes the important point that geographic ranges of land, fresh-water, and marine species may be delimited in quite different terms.

The geographical distribution of the habitats is influenced by the major physiographic or land features of the continent. These are reflected in the climate, soils, plants, and animals of the habitats. Each habitat contains one to several species of plants and animals that are characteristic of it and occur only in that habitat. Such forms are called "indicator species." By mapping the major habitats and their indicator species, a series of life zones or biotic provinces can be designated. Such areas may include one to a number of distinct habitats; they are useful in discussing the distribution of animals. However, it should be realized that the boundaries of these provinces are not sharply delimited as are those of a state. Rather, they usually grade gradually from one to another. Some boundaries are clearly defined, as in passing from the land to the sea. It must also be realized that some species may be restricted to a single biotic province, whereas others may occur in several. In *The Biotic Provinces of North America*, Lee R. Dice has analyzed and mapped the boundaries of these provinces as indicated in Figure 9.

Amphibians are represented in all the provinces except the Aleutian and the Sitkan. From the southernmost provinces to the northern there is a gradual decrease in the number of species represented, as illustrated in Table 2. In North America a single species of amphibian, the Northern Wood Frog (*Rana sylvatica cantabrigensis*), occurs within the Arctic Circle and barely gets into the Eskimoan biotic province in northwestern Canada. Colin Mills cites a record for the Red-sided Garter Snake (*Thamnophis sirtalis parie-*

talis) from the Northwest Territories of Canada almost up to, but not within, the Eskimoan Province. Mills says, "This snake has the most northerly range of any snake in North America." This is the northernmost record of any reptile on this continent and is exceeded only by the European Common Lizard (*Lacerta vivipara*) and the Common European Adder (*Vipera berus*), both of which occur within the Arctic Circle in the Scandinavian Peninsula.

To illustrate the general principle that amphibians and reptiles are represented by more species in the southern than in the northern part of the continent, a tally of native species (exclusive of marine forms) listed in Schmidt's *Check List* is presented in Table 2 for

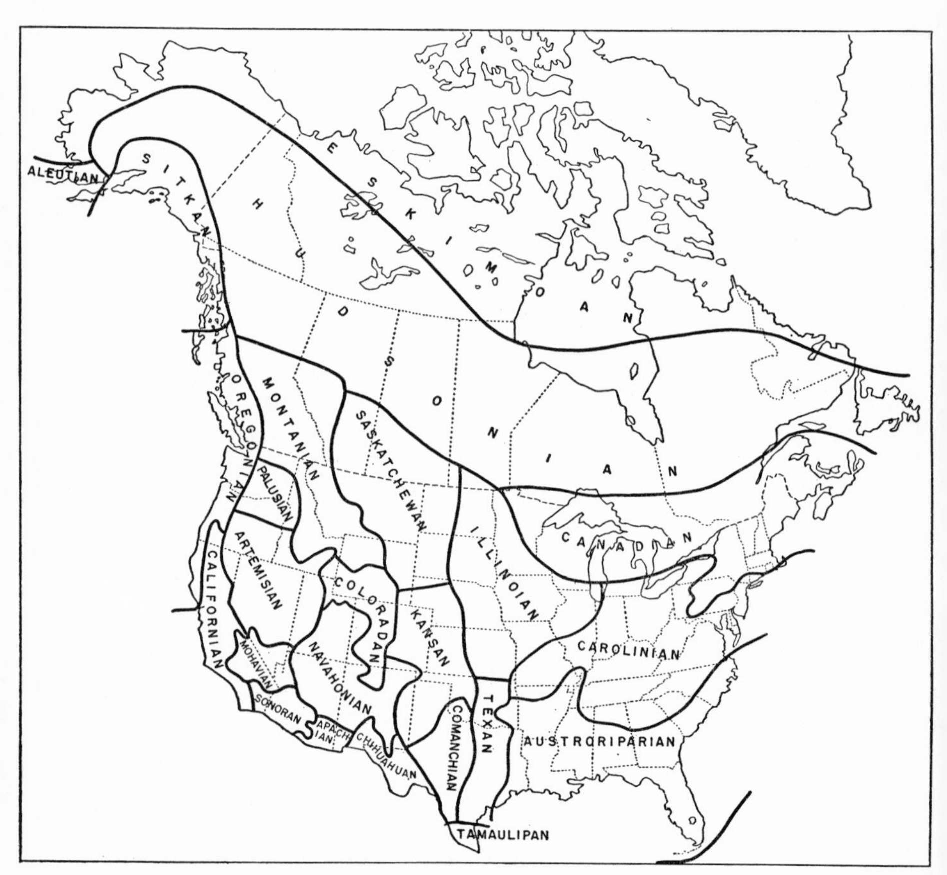

Fig. 9. The biotic provinces of North America (as mapped by Lee R. Dice).

four states. It affords a comparison between New York and Florida; and between Washington and California.

TABLE 2

COMPARISON OF NUMBER OF SPECIES REPRESENTED

	New York		Florida		Washington		California	
Amphibians								
Salamanders	18		18		12		15	
Frogs	13		20		7		13	
Total		31		38		19		28
Reptiles								
Turtles	13		17		1		3	
Crocodilians	0		2		0		0	
Lizards	3		15		6		32	
Snakes	20		39		10		32	
Total		36		73		17		67
Total Amphibians and Reptiles		67		111		36		95

Examination of the figures in the table shows the differences in total number of species. It also shows that the north-south difference in species is more pronounced in the reptiles than in the amphibians; and within the amphibians it is greater for the frogs than the salamanders. The latter difference reflects the Northern Hemisphere abundance of salamanders as a group and the more tropical character of the frogs and most reptiles. Another interesting difference is apparent from the figures in this table—namely, the greater abundance of species in the eastern, as compared with the western, section of the country. The only exception to this is found in the lizards, many species of which are inhabitants of hot, dry habitats. Texas, the largest state in the United States, has the largest number of species of lizards for any state. This is partly owing to its being a meeting place for many eastern and western species, and a few Mexican forms that barely cross the border.

Viewed in terms of the biotic provinces, the Austroriparian (see Figure 9) is the richest in total number of species of amphibians and reptiles. It has the greatest number of species of frogs, turtles, crocodilians, and snakes. The Carolinian Province (see Figure 9) has the greatest concentration of species of salamanders. Several of the southwestern provinces combined exhibit the greatest diversity of lizards. It was mentioned earlier that indicator species are restricted in distribution to a single province, whereas other species occurred in several different provinces. A small number of species are so adaptable to, or so tolerant of, a wide variety of habitat conditions that their geographic range extends virtually from coast to coast. These include the Tiger Salamander (*Ambystoma tigrinum*), the Wood Frog (*Rana sylvatica*), the Painted Turtle (*Chrysemys picta*), the Garter Snake (*Thamnophis sirtalis*), the Racer (*Coluber constrictor*), and the King Snake (*Lampropeltis getulus*). Two or three others can be added to this list with minor qualifications.

Factors Influencing Geographic Distribution

What are the primary factors that determine the geographic range of a species or subspecies? First is the inherited physiological constitution which can operate efficiently only within particular physical limits. This determines the ecological toleration of the animals. Second is the geographical distribution of the environments that possess the ecological requirements of the animal in question. The third factor is really a phase of the second but is sufficiently important to list separately. This is the presence of harmonious biological elements in the habitats. The fourth factor is the location of the geographical area in which the species originated and the opportunities for movement away from this region of origin. This factor takes into consideration the animal's habits and abilities to move about and get from one place to another. Also, it includes a consideration of the pathways along which the animal could travel and the barriers that might handicap or completely prevent its movement in a given direction. Obviously, a small burrowing species like the Dwarf Blind Snake (*Leptotyphlops humilis*) cannot move about as readily under its own powers as the Whip Snake (*Masticophis flagellum*), and the barriers for the two would be quite different. However, the Blind Snake might actually occupy a larger area because it was more successful in surmounting the barriers to its dispersal or had more time to occupy its range. Being smaller in size, it might be assisted occasionally by some other unintentional but still effective agent, such as a bird that might have seized it only to drop it later some distance away but still alive, or a log that might carry it for miles during a flood.

Finally, there are the historical factors reflected in the changes that have taken place in time. All the factors listed are not static conditions, fixed for all time, but are changing constantly. By the same token, the geographic range of virtually all species is undergoing constant change. As a result of population pressure the animals tend to extend their ranges in all directions around the outer boundaries. In one direction there may exist an insurmountable barrier, such as the sea in the case of a land-dwelling amphibian; but in the opposite direction there may be a suitable environment unoccupied by the species, and it may be able to spread a short distance, gradually moving farther and farther over the years. On the other hand, adverse environmental changes may occur in one part of the range, so that the species can no longer live there. More often such a change occurs on the edge of the geographic range, where the environmental conditions barely meet the requirements of the species; but it may occur anywhere, even in the middle of the range. The latter change results in a discontinuity in the animal's range. The present geographic range of a species is the result of the operation of all the foregoing factors during the whole existence of the species.

From the study of fossil remains of formerly living species a great deal of information has been amassed that aids us in understanding the geographic distribution of our present animals. Many times there is the story of animals with a wider geographic distribution than they have today. For example, Alligators of several species formerly occurred over many parts of the United States and even southern Canada. Today our only Alligator occurs in the southeastern United States. Most recently, since the arrival of Europeans in North America, the geographic ranges of some species have been curtailed. The best-known cases are those that are attributable to direct local extermination by man. Thus the Timber Rattlesnake (*Crotalus h. horridus*) formerly occurred in Maine. No specimen has been reported from that state since 1860, however. A similar condition appears to have come about on Long Island, New York, and in north central New Hampshire, where the species also occurred but has not been found in many years. Direct campaigns have been conducted to bring about the extermination of venomous snakes in restricted areas, with varying degrees of success.

Indirectly man's activities have also affected the geographical distribution of species, mostly in a detrimental way. The burning of natural areas, the clearing of woodlands for agriculture, the draining of swamps and wet prairies, the introduction of domestic animals that have destroyed both the wild animals and their habitats, and the increase in building activities—all these have a marked effect on many species. There are a few instances where man's disturbance of the environment has had a beneficial effect—at least the effect of increasing the local reptile population while not enlarging the geographic range.

Man has materially increased the geographic range of a number of species, either intentionally or unintentionally. Intentionally this has been done when he has introduced a species into a new region for some specific purpose, usually as a source of food. Thus the Bullfrog (*Rana catesbeiana*), which formerly occurred naturally east of the Rocky Mountains, has been introduced and is established in virtually every part of the United States. Other species of frogs have been moved about locally for similar reasons. Toads (*Bufo*) have been transported to assist in the control of insect pests. Several turtles have had their range extended to provide food for human beings. For example, Emory's Soft-shelled Turtle (*Trionyx ferox emoryi*) had its range extended westward to Arizona and California.

Any amphibian and reptile that is commonly kept as a pet has frequent opportunity to extend its range. Many pet owners keep their pets in poorly built cages, with the result that the animals escape; or, tiring of the pet, the owner unwisely lets it go in the nearest vacant lot or park. This deplorable habit has resulted in the death of many a pet as a result of being liberated in a completely unsuitable environment. Occasionally animals have been able to hold their own, survive for a few years, or in rare instances become established. Common Newts (*Diemictylus v. viridescens*), Alligators, and Red-eared Turtles (*Pseudemys scripta elegans*) are probably the most frequent victims of this treatment. Because of their size and distinct appearance, Alligators are reported more frequently outside their natural range than the others. Scarcely a year passes without one or two small specimens being found in a lake or stream in New York City. The same thing happens in many other localities. Near the limits of the natural range the individuals may survive, extending the range slightly. Richard A. Edgren, Jr., has called attention to a colony of Red-eared Turtles established in Michigan north of the natural range of the species. The Texas Horned Lizard has been carried to various parts of the country by enthusiastic pet owners, and escaped or released individuals have turned up in some surprising places. The species now appears to be established in Florida.

One of the most interesting unintentional range extensions made by man was the introduction of the Western Diamondback Rattlesnake (*Crotalus atrox*) into Wisconsin. This apparently occurred when specimens escaped or were released from a carnival touring the region. The species persisted in the area for a number of years, but it is now reported to have disappeared from the state. Bernard Martof has reported the role of the "spring lizard" bait industry in the unintentional distribution of several species of salamanders, including the Dusky Salamander (*Desmognathus fuscus*), the Black-bellied Salamander (*D. quadramaculatus*), and the Red Salamander (*Pseudotriton ruber*).

In many cases of unintentional range extension by man, the human agent is not aware that he has any contact with the animal. Many individuals of different species are transported from one area to another hidden in some material—for example, in lumber, cork, potted plants, and bales of vegetable matter. It is known that a number of foreign species are brought into this country every year in this manner, and the establishment in the southern United States of several tropical species is believed to have resulted from this type of transportation. Walter Auffenberg has brought the method up to date by reporting the unintentional introduction of Scarlet Snakes (*Cemophora coccinea*) from Florida to Texas by airplanes, being carried in packing material.

The introduction of a form into a new area, by whatever means, does not necessarily result in its establishment in the region. From the history of most introductions it apparently requires several individuals or repeated introductions to insure establishment. At least, most of the known introductions of single or few individuals have failed. Often the animals are placed in environments to which they are not adapted and in which they are consequently not able to meet their requirements. Sometimes the environment is such that adults can survive but cannot reproduce. Establishment of the species, and hence the extension of its geographic range, is accomplished only when the species reproduces itself in the new area.

In foregoing paragraphs the extension of the geographic range by means of a human agency has been considered. These are the best-known cases of range extension within a relatively short period. However, there are apparently some cases of recent natural extension of the range without man's aid. Leonhard Stejneger has suggested that the Red-eared Turtle extended its range eastward in the Ohio River Valley within human history. In Missouri within the past twenty-five years the Western Cottonmouth (*Ancistrodon piscivorous leucostoma*) seems to have extended its range northward more than fifty miles. As the distribution records for our amphibians and reptiles become more complete, it appears certain that we will be able to record cyclical fluctuations in the expansion and contraction of a species range in a marginal habitat. Thus in favorable years we will perceive slight outward expansion; and in unfavorable years, contraction. Karl P. Schmidt postulates such a condition—for example, for the Five-lined Skink (*Eumeces fasciatus*) at the northern extremity of its range. To judge from what scattered data we have on this in herpetology and from observations on other animals, it appears to be the rule rather than the exception where the range limit is a climatic factor rather than a physical barrier.

Habitats

In North America amphibians and reptiles occur in every major habitat except the perpetually cold northern regions. And no amphibian occurs in any of the marine habitats. On the land, amphibians and reptiles occur from sea level up to an altitude of more than 10,000 feet. In California the Pacific Rattlesnake (*Crotalus viridis oreganus*) has been recorded from an elevation of 11,000 feet, and the Mount Lyell Salamander (*Hydromantes platycephalus*) has been taken at 10,800 feet. In Colorado, Albert P. Blair found no amphibians or reptiles above 10,000 feet, but at that elevation he did find one snake, the Wandering Garter Snake (*Thamnophis ordinoides vagrans*); three frogs, the Boreal Toad (*Bufo b. boreas*), the

Western Chorus Frog (*Pseudacris nigrita triseriata*), and the Leopard Frog (*Rana pipiens*); and one salamander, the Clouded Tiger Salamander (*Ambystoma tigrinum nebulosum*). The Sacramento Mountain Salamander (*Aneides hardyi*) is found at an elevation of 9,000 feet in New Mexico. The Yosemite Fence Lizard (*Sceloporus occidentalis taylori*) occurs up to an elevation of 8,200 feet in Yosemite National Park; and the Southern Mountain Lizard (*Sceloporus graciosus vandenburgianus*) has been reported up to 9,000 feet in southern California. The Sierra Alligator Lizard (*Gerrhonotus coeruleus palmeri*) also occurs up to 9,000 feet in California; and the Common Western Skink (*Eumeces skiltonianus*) has been reported from 8,000 feet in elevation. Virtually all turtles are found below 5,000 feet in elevation.

Within the major habitats on the land, the amphibians and reptiles occur in a variety of ecological niches. These range from a complete subterranean existence, such as we find in the Florida Worm Lizard (*Rhineura floridana*), through various intermediate stages to the surface dwellers, the rock inhabitants and semiarboreal forms, and the largely arboreal forms, such as the Common Tree Frog (*Hyla v. versicolor*) and the Squirrel Tree Frog (*Hyla squirella*). Few species or subspecies are confined to a single niche, but move from one to another. Often one function, such as resting or sleeping, is performed in one niche, whereas foraging for food or reproduction may be performed in quite a different part of the habitat.

The Eastern Spadefoot Toad (*Scaphiopus h. holbrooki*) may remain underground during the day, coming to the surface to forage for food on humid nights throughout the warmer part of the year. In the colder months it remains underground both day and night. It breeds on the surface in water. Similarly the Prairie Rattlesnake (*Crotalus v. viridis*) remains underground during the colder months of the year. It forages for food in the daytime on the surface of the ground, occasionally prowling into a promising rodent burrow. When its stomach is filled and it is not in a reproductive mood, it may rest in a rodent burrow, under a clump of sagebrush, or in a rocky crevice. The Arboreal Salamander (*Aneides l. lugubris*) may forage for food beneath or in a rotting log on the surface of the ground, it may lay its eggs in a similar situation, or it may forage and lay its eggs 60 feet above the ground in a tree.

Home Range

The habit of animals to move about from one niche to another and from one habitat to another, to perform their various life functions in different situations, is a general, almost universal characteristic. It reaches its culmination in the long seasonal migrations of many birds, fish, and butterflies. The activities of amphibians and reptiles are more circumscribed and usually take place within a small area—from a few yards to a mile or two. The area within which the individual lives is termed its "home range." In many species there is no basis nor need for further subdivision into breeding range, foraging range, and activity range or territory. Many animals perform all their life functions and live their entire lives within the small area that makes up the home range. Other species, such as some salamanders and most of our frogs, have an activity or feeding range quite separate from their breeding range. The American Toad (*Bufo terrestris americanus*) may carry on its non-reproductive activities within an area 100′ x 100′, but for the short annual breeding period it may move several thousand feet away. Thus the total individual range must include the two areas, but for complete understanding it is sometimes desirable to separate the two.

Where the individual range is large, the movements over the area may be seasonal in nature and totally unrelated to reproductive activities. Snakes that hibernate during the winter in large groups in "dens" occupy an area around the den site in spring and fall, but move out into other regions during the summer. Angus M. Woodbury and Ross Hardy have demonstrated a similar seasonal movement in the Desert Tortoise (*Gopherus agassizi*). Aquatic turtles and alligators sometimes exhibit seasonal movements associated with changes in water levels. All of the area traversed during the annual cycle of activities is part of the home range.

Some species have a definite "home site," a more or less permanent point of seclusion to which the animal regularly returns when not foraging for food, carrying on reproductive functions, or basking. A hollow log, a stump, a rotten tree, a cavity beneath a stone, a rocky crevice, an abandoned mammal burrow, a crayfish hole, and occasionally a burrow made by the amphibian or reptile itself may form such a retreat. The animal's activities radiate out from this "home site," and it forms the focal point of the home range. The Spadefoot Toads (*Scaphiopus*), the Narrow-mouthed Toads (*Hypopachus* and *Microhyla*), the Gopher Frog (*Rana capito*), the Mole Salamander (*Ambystoma talpoideum*), and the Eastern Tiger Salamander (*Ambystoma t. tigrinum*) are frequently known to occupy definite underground burrows that serve as such home areas. While these amphibians are capable of digging in soft soil, they sometimes occupy burrows dug by other animals. The burrows of the land tortoises (*Gopherus*) and the dens of the Alligator (*Alligator mississippiensis*) are excavated by the reptiles themselves. Many snakes and lizards that dwell in burrows generally inhabit excavations made by other animals. There are, of course, exceptions that dig their own. Such appears to be true of most species of Racerunners (*Cnemidophorus*) and the Crowned Snakes (*Tantilla*). There are a number of species that burrow in sand and sandy soil, but these seldom occupy discrete burrows and hence are not comparable to the foregoing.

Amphibians and reptiles may occur as lone individuals throughout their lives, having only brief contact with other members of their species at the time of mating. In such individuals, mating may occur when two members of the opposite sex meet in isolation, or when they come together in breeding aggregations. In most amphibian species that breed in water, the latter is the common condition. Most reptiles also fit into this category, but a few, such as the Box Turtles (*Terrapene*) and the Chain King Snake (*Lampropeltis g. getulus*) in Florida, seem to belong to the former group.

Other species live pretty much as separate individuals, but occur in well-marked colonies. This is true of many True Frogs (*Rana*), many land-dwelling salamanders (*Plethodon, Aneides, Batrachoseps*), small semiburrowing snakes (*Diadophis, Sonora, Tropidoclonion*, and *Tantilla*), and a number of lizards (*Cnemidophorus, Eumeces*). A few species live in closely associated groups to the extent that they can be considered gregarious. Fresh-water turtles and some lizards, such as most geckos and Iguanids, and some species of Water Snakes (*Natrix*), are the best examples of such forms on a year-round basis. Gregarious aggregations occur in many other species during the breeding period, at the time of hibernation or estivation, and in some instances when an unusually abundant food supply is available.

The term "territory" is used where animals occupy a definite area and defend it against intruders of the same species. Such animals are usually gregarious, and the males establish territories in which several females live. This is the generalized territorial condition, and all stages of development can be found between this and the absence of territories. The territory may include all of the area in which an individual is active, or there may be a small home area surrounded by a narrow no-man's land. The arrangement and size of the territories depends in part on the nature of the species, the abundance of the individuals, and the type of terrain. Where several females occur within the territory of one male, they in turn may have small territories that they defend against intrusion by one another. The territories may be maintained throughout the entire activity period or may be held only during the breeding season.

No strictly maintained territories have been reported in North American amphibians, although a territorial type of distribution has been observed among individuals of some species. Among reptiles, the Alligator (*Alligator mississippiensis*) maintains a fairly definite territory in both sexes. The bellowing of the males serves to keep away intruding males and possibly attract females. If this does not prove effective, the males may resort to fighting to keep out trespassers. Females will fight to drive other females and small males out of the territory being maintained.

A number of species of lizards exhibit a well-developed system of territories. Bernard Greenberg has reported on the territorial conditions in the Banded Ground Gecko (*Coleonyx variegatus*). A high-pitched squeak and body contact is utilized to maintain the small territorial area guarded by the males of this species. Several Iguanid lizards and some skinks are known to have territories. The most studied territorial development in North American reptiles is that found in the Green Anolis (*Anolis c. carolinensis*). The lizard is voiceless, and vision is the primary stimulus involved in the maintenance of the territory. The males possess a brightly colored dewlap under the throat that can be expanded or contracted, giving a bright flash of color when flared. When an intruder enters the territory of another male, the defending male flares his dewlap and bobs the forepart of his body in a series of push-ups. The intruder, if a male, may flash his dewlap and bob back, or he may flee. If he persists, the threatening movements are continued until the two come in contact and fight. The loser is banished from the area. If the intruder is a female, she merely bobs several times or does nothing.

In the mating season she is then courted; at other times, ignored. The territories are maintained more vigorously during the mating season.

Turtles and snakes may have an incipient or crude territorial development, but at present there is no evidence to support such a theory. Land Tortoise (*Gopherus*) and Box Turtle (*Terrapene*) males have been observed fighting in the wild, usually during the mating season. Captive individuals have been observed to drive others out of specific parts of outdoor enclosures. Male snakes have been observed in "combat," both in nature and in captivity. This is described in the chapter on reproduction, but the significance of these observations is not clearly understood at the present. Far more detailed information is needed on the activities of the animals in the wild.

CHAPTER 7

Locomotion and Movements

An important characteristic of animal life is the power of locomotion—the ability to move from one place to another. Different kinds of animals differ greatly in their powers and capabilities of locomotion, but all animals are able to move in one fashion or another. In all forms, movement involves propelling the body through or over a medium in equilibrium with gravitational and frictional forces. These forces vary considerably with the medium, the bulk and form of the animal, and the type of locomotor structures used. What are the different types of locomotion exhibited by amphibians and reptiles? How are these used and how effective are they?

Amphibians

Among the amphibians we find forms that walk, run, hop, crawl, swim, climb, and parachute. The first four methods are used to move over the surface of the ground. The walk is the basic method of locomotion on land for all four-legged animals. It is the typical type of movement of most terrestrial salamanders. Here the body is lifted off the ground so that friction is reduced to the points of contact of the four feet and sometimes the tail. The legs propel the body forward, each leg being moved in a definite rhythm and order, so that only one leg is off the ground at any one time. Thus the weight of the body is supported firmly at all times by the other three limbs. The rhythm of leg movements can be diagramed simply by the accompanying sketch, in which the open circle indicates the foot that is not in contact with the ground.

This is a leisurely pace that provides the animal with excellent equilibrium at all times when it is moving. When emergencies arise and greater speed is demanded, the walk can be converted into a run by supporting the body on only two limbs at any one moment. Thus greater speed is gained at the sacrifice of body stability. Here the limbs that support the body are on alternate sides—right front and left hind, or left front and right hind. In a salamander that is walking or running, the muscular power that propels the body by means

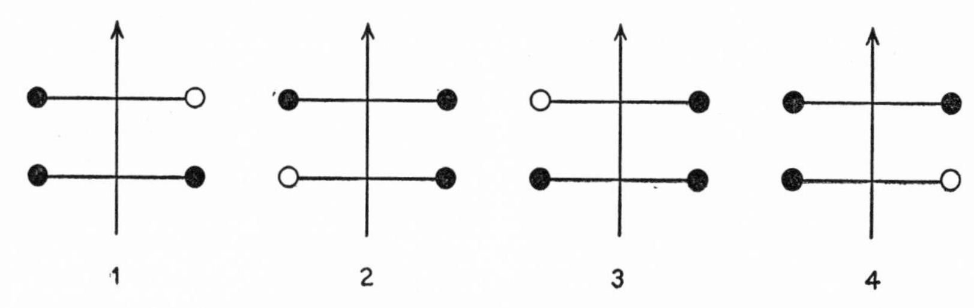

of the limbs comes partly from the limbs alone. The body undulates from side to side as the limbs are moved, thus adding the force of the body muscles to that of the legs (see Figure 10, no. 1).

When the length of the limbs is short in relation to the total length of the body and tail, as it is in the Worm Salamander (*Batrachoseps a. attenuatus*), the body is not completely lifted from the ground. The undulations of the body propel the animal forward by exerting pressure on the hind side of the undulation. When the limbs are still further reduced, the animal crawls by a series of lateral undulations. In crawling, the body muscles alternately contract on one side to form the inner loop of the undulations, and pressure against irregularities of the surface on the back side of the undulations moves the body forward. A virtually legless salamander, such as Amphiuma (*Amphiuma*), moves entirely by such lateral undulations when out of the water.

Hopping or jumping is the characteristic method of locomotion of frogs on land. Here the propulsive force comes solely from the enlarged hind legs moved simultaneously and suddenly to propel the body through the air for short distances. Here the front legs serve to orient the forepart of the body in a position suitable for hopping and are used at the end of the hop in landing. In this type of locomotion the movement of the legs used for propulsion must be simultaneous, or nearly so, in order for the animal to move in balance (see Figure 11, no. 1). Amphibians that characteristically hope can also walk and may do so for short distances. Similarly, the

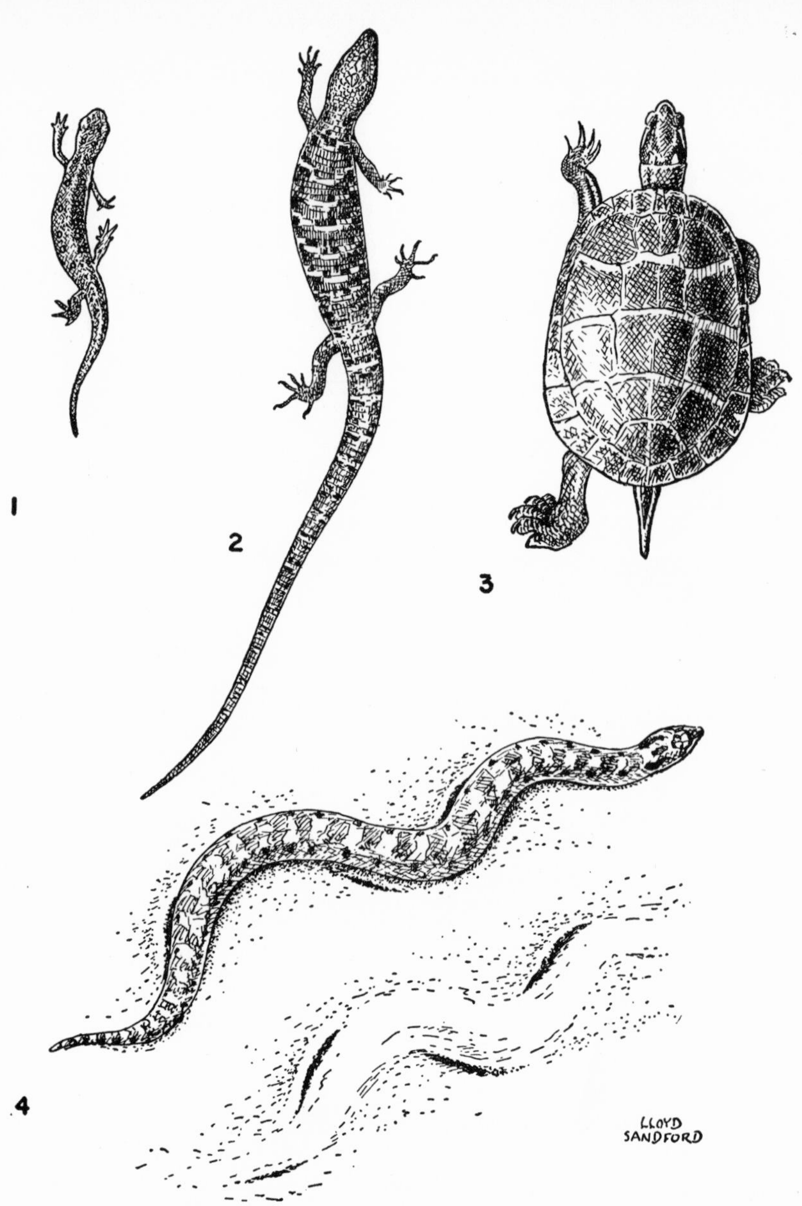

FIG. 10. Body position and leg movement in walking for (1) the Red-spotted Newt (*Diemictylus viridescens*), (2) the Alligator Lizard (*Gerrhonotus liocephalus*), and (3) the Painted Turtle (*Chrysemys picta*). Drawing 4 shows the position of the body of the Hog-nosed Snake (*Heterodon platyrhinos*) in serpentine or lateral undulatory locomotion and the track left on sandy soil. Note the small piles of dirt on the *back sides* of the loop, providing an easy method of indicating the direction in which the snake was moving—toward the right of the page.

species that habitually walk can hop or jump after a fashion when the occasion demands. The Black Salamander (*Aneides flavipunctatus*) can jump for a distance equal to, or slightly greater than, its total length. It does this by lifting the tail, hitting it sharply against the ground, and at the same time jumping with the hind legs.

In climbing, the amphibians employ the characteristic locomotion used on the ground. Thus in the salamanders the movement is the same as in walking; and in frogs climbing is usually done by means

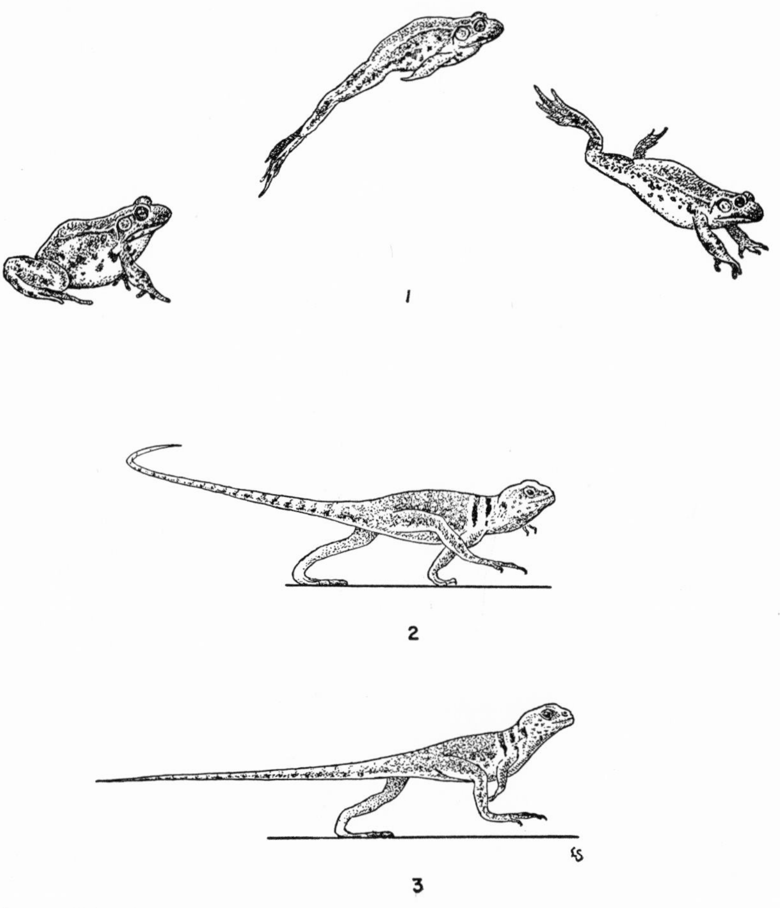

FIG. 11. Hopping positions of body and legs of the Green Frog (*Rana clamitans*) at start, middle and near the end of hop (drawing 1), and body and limb positions of Collared Lizard (*Crotaphytus collaris*) in quadrupedal (drawing 2) and bipedal (drawing 3) running.

of hopping, although they walk when on a smooth steep surface. Robert C. Stebbins has reported a most interesting pair of adaptations in the Mount Lyell Salamander (*Hydromantes platycephalus*), an inhabitant of granitic rocky areas in the Sierra Nevada. This salamander possesses a short blunt-tipped tail and partially webbed, fleshy soled feet. When walking on an incline, the salamander habitually moves at right angles to the slope and uses its tail as a prop on the downhill side. Stebbins said that individuals could not readily be induced to walk directly up a slope, but tended to veer to one side. When they did go directly up a slope, the tail was used as a prop, swinging in pendulum fashion. The fleshy soled feet, kept moist by glandular secretion and the damp substratum, provide effective adherence to the smooth rock. The frogs that climb most frequently are members of the Tree Frog Family, the Hylidae. The Tree Frogs possess enlarged, rounded disks on the

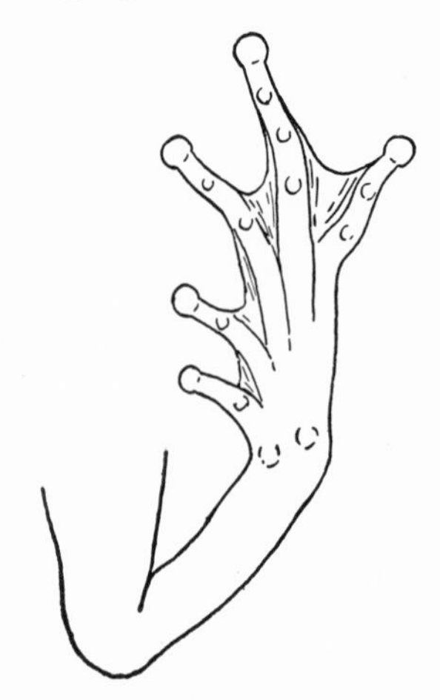

Fig. 12. Hind foot of Tree Frog (*Hyla*) showing expanded adhesive disks on ends of toes.

ends of the toes (Figure 12). The lower surface of the disks consists of minute short, wedge-shaped projections that fit into minute irregularities of the surface, acting as friction grips. The pad of the disk is provided with glands that secrete a sticky mucus. The result is a very effective adhesive structure that enables the frog to climb straight up a smooth-barked tree or even a glass windowpane.

Some of the climbing species have the ability to descend through the air from fair heights by retarding the rate of fall sufficiently so that they do not come down in a straight line and can descend without injury. This is termed "parachuting" and is quite different from gliding as seen, for example, in the Flying Squirrel. Parachuting involves the presence of structures that increase the body surface and a behavior pattern in which the animal assumes, while in the air, a constant position exposing the greatest amount of surface area perpendicular to the direction of the fall. This locomotor ability is known for only a few arboreal species but is probably present in a number of the tree-dwelling Hylids, such as the Squirrel Tree Frog (*Hyla squirella*).

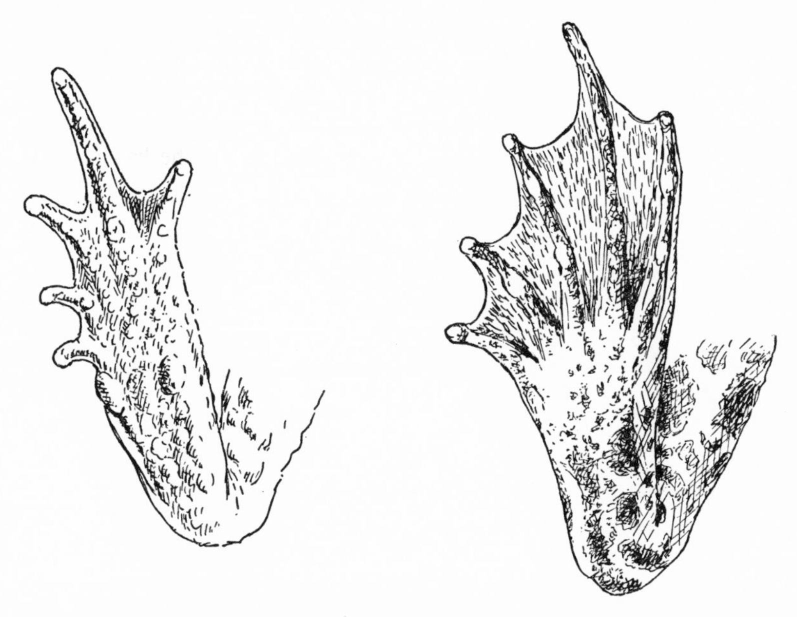

Fig. 13. Hind foot of toad (*Bufo*), on left, and of true frog (*Rana*), on right; note the extensive web between the toes of the frog.

Swimming is well developed in all amphibians. Salamanders swim by lateral undulations of the body and tail, with the main propulsive force coming from the tail. In larval frogs—the tadpoles—the tail is the sole organ of propulsion. In the elongate, eel-like salamanders, such as Amphiuma (*Amphiuma*) and Siren (*Siren*), swimming is accomplished through lateral undulations of the entire body and tail. Frogs swim with simultaneous kicking movements of the hind legs; the front legs are held motionless along the side of the body.

Reptiles

Reptiles move about by all of the methods noted in the amphibians, with several modifications. The basic form of locomotion in all forms with legs is walking. The sequence and rhythm of leg movements is the same as that diagramed for the salamanders. In crocodilians and turtles this is the method normally used for moving over the ground. In the turtle, with its large shell, the walking pace is slow and deliberate, so that the shell is always balanced steadily on the legs that are in contact with the ground at any one time (Figure 10, no. 3). In long-tailed turtles, like the Snapping Turtle (*Chelydra* and *Macrochelys*), and in the crocodilians the tail is too long to be lifted from the ground. It is therefore dragged along, leaving a characteristic track. The legs are not well suited for locomotion on land, and at frequent intervals there is a pause in which the body is lowered to the ground. After a rest the body is again raised and the journey continued. If haste is needed, the walk can be speeded up to a laboriously uncertain gait that most nearly approximates running in the sequence of leg movements, but suggests an uncoordinated flinging of the body in the general direction of the movement.

Lizards with well-developed limbs walk and run with ease and agility. Here the running on four legs is a well-coordinated, smoothly executed gait that attains good speed (Figure 11, no. 2). Lizards can hop, but do so only under special circumstances. Some species of lizards have developed a means of running on the hind legs only (Figure 11, no. 3). When speed is needed, the lizard starts running and rears up, with the front feet and tail clear off the ground, supported only by the hind legs. This method of running is used in North America only by a few fast Iguanid Lizards, such as the Collared Lizards (*Crotaphytus*) and the Desert Iguanas (*Dipsosaurus*). In the Old World some members of the superficially iguanidlike family, the Agamidae, also use this method of locomotion, but the most famous bipedal lizards are doubtless the Central and South American Basilisks (*Basiliscus*). Members of this genus not only run on land reared up on their hind legs, but also cross short stretches of water in the same fashion.

Long-bodied lizards with short legs walk with considerable lateral movement of the body, like the salamanders (Figure 10, no.

2). With increased shortening of the limbs and lengthening of the body, the method of locomotion becomes one of crawling rather than walking. The final stage is the serpentine movement, accomplished without legs by a series of lateral undulations. The Glass Lizard (*Ophisaurus*) and the Silvery Footless Lizard (*Anniella*) exemplify this end stage among the lizards. It is of course, as the word serpentine suggests, the most common type of locomotion seen in snakes (Figure 10, no. 4).

Legless lizards crawl only by means of the serpentine locomotion of lateral undulations. While this is the commonest means of crawling seen in snakes—and all snakes may employ this means—some species have developed other types of crawling. Heavy-bodied snakes, such as the Boids and Crotalids, are able to move in a straight line by what is termed rectilinear locomotion. In these forms the skin is loosely attached to the body along the sides and belly. Individual muscles attach from the backbone and ribs to the broad belly plates, and these can be moved forward and backward outside the body. By sliding sections of these plates forward, anchoring them, and then drawing the body up to them, the snake progresses forward in a straight line. With a progressive sequence of alternate series of anchored, contracting, and extending belly plates, the snake moves smoothly forward, somewhat like a crawling caterpillar. In fact, this method is sometimes called "caterpillar locomotion." This method is slower than the serpentine type of locomotion. It is found in other snakes besides those in the two families mentioned. However, it is best developed in these two and is not present at all in many Colubrids. For example, snakes like the Racers (*Coluber*) and Whip Snakes (*Masticophis*) cannot move in this manner because the skin is tightly attached to the body.

Another type of locomotion found in snakes is the concertina method. This is a rather specialized type of movement used under particular conditions, such as on a very slippery surface or in the confines of a limited space. Here the forepart of the body is extended until it can gain a secure purchase. Then the rear is drawn up and anchored. The forepart is again extended to get a new anchor point. Thus by alternately expanding and contracting the entire body like a concertina, the snake is able to move forward.

The final type of movement is another specialized locomotion that is employed on loose sand. This is a modification of the serpentine method, but the snake moves in a sideward direction from the main body axis. This method is known as "sidewinding." The complex movements involved are diagramed in Figure 14. The snake's body is held in an S-shaped position, with the head pointed in the direction in which the snake is progressing. The body in its

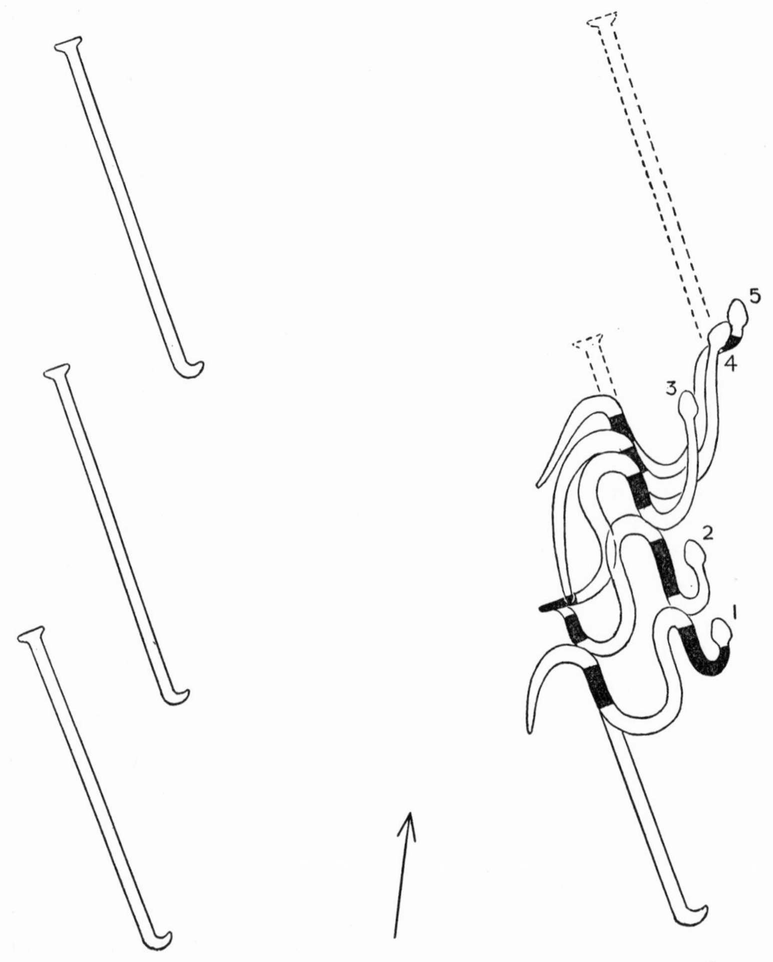

FIG. 14. Diagrammatic sketches showing on the right the sequence of movements, 1 through 5, involved in sidewinding locomotion by Sidewinder Rattlesnake (*Crotalus cerastes*). In this series of sketches the track already made is indicated in solid line, the track to be made is shown by a dashed line, and the part of the snake's body that is touching the ground is shown in solid black. Note that only two parts of the body touch the ground at any one time. On the left is shown a series of tracks. The arrow indicates the direction in which the snake is moving. (Adapted from Walter Mosauer)

S-shape position is held to one side of the head. The snake appears to roll its body along in a sideward motion of the body. Actually the body is in contact with the sand at only two places or sections at any time, but the entire length of the body is brought in contact with the sand as the snake moves along. The result of this locomotion is a series of parallel tracks, each equal to the length of the snake's body, with a hook where the neck began the cycle of body contact at the rear end of the individual track and a small mark left by the tail as it touched the ground. This method is very effective on loose sand and may be employed by a number of different species of snakes when on a loose or slippery substratum. However, the North American Sidewinder Rattlesnakes (*Crotalus cerastes*) and the sand-dwelling vipers of the Old World have developed this locomotion to its highest degree.

The foregoing methods are used by reptiles in moving over the surface of the ground. The same types of movements, with slight modification, are used in swimming, burrowing, or climbing, except that sidewinding is used only in moving on land and the concertina movement is not used in swimming. Fresh-water and land turtles swim with alternate movements of the legs in the same sequence as in walking. Those that live in the water characteristically have the toes of the hind feet jointed by a fleshy web that gives the feet greater driving power. The tail in all turtles is too small to be of assistance in swimming. Marine turtles have the front legs enlarged and modified to form expanded paddles or flippers. These are moved simultaneously in swimming, so that their movement is gracefully like the flying of a large bird. The hind legs are used as rudders and brakes.

Crocodilians use the large, laterally compressed muscular tail as the propelling force in swimming. The tail is moved from side to side, and the limbs trail at the sides. In stalking prey or moving in shallow water, a combination of walking and swimming movements may be used. Lizards and snakes swim by lateral undulations of the body and tail. None of our North American lizards possesses special modifications for life and locomotion in water, but all can swim. Because of the elongation of the body, all snakes are agile swimmers both on the surface and beneath the water. The Mangrove Water Snake (*Natrix sipedon compressicauda*) has the tail somewhat laterally compressed, making it a more effective organ of propulsion.

Lateral undulations of the body, accompanied by a sharply

pointed head, enable several of our sand-dwelling species to burrow rapidly in the sand. Thus such forms as the Florida Sand Skink (*Neoseps reynoldsi*) and the Shovel-nosed Snake (*Chionactis occipitalis*) literally "swim" into and through the sand by means of lateral undulatory movements. The Fringe-toed Lizards (*Uma*) bury themselves in the sand by lateral movements of the head and neck, with the forelimbs pressed to the sides of the body and propulsive action from the hind legs. As the lizard settles into a final position, the hind legs are flexed and the tail is vibrated laterally, causing it to be buried in the sand. Except for the sand dwellers, burrowing can hardly be classed as a locomotor performance.

Turtles and crocodilians can scarcely be considered climbing reptiles, although on occasion one may see a turtle or a young Alligator basking on a log or tree branch, which required a fair climbing ability. Some of our lizards and snakes, however, are respectable climbers, even though none is so well adapted to an arboreal life as are some species in the tropical forests. Only lizards with legs exhibit any climbing ability. These are aided by sharp, strongly curved claws; or they possess expanded, frictional adhesive pads. Most geckos have expanded adhesive pads on the fingers and toes, which are an aid in climbing on smooth trees, rocks, or walls of buildings. The Tubercular Gecko (*Phyllodactylus tuberculosus*) is an inhabitant of rocky areas in the extreme southwestern United States. It possesses greatly expanded pads and sharp claws at the very tip of each digit (Figure 15, left). The introduced Turkish Gecko (*Hemidactylus t. turcicus*), which is now found in southern Florida and the Keys and in the vicinity of New Orleans, has the base (but not the tip) of each digit expanded and a sharp claw at the tip. This form occurs around human dwellings and may be seen agilely running up the smooth wall of a house. In contrast, the Ground Geckos (*Coleonyx*) have no such expanded pads and are not climbers. In the Family Iguanidae the Anolis (*Anolis*) have the next to the last joint of the digits expanded to form an adhesive pad (Figure 15, right). These are arboreal or semiarboreal lizards that climb bushes, trees, and the walls of dwellings. In all these lizards with adhesive pads there is no suction involved as in the Tree Frogs. Rather, adhesion is gained solely through friction increased by the presence of numerous minute hairlike cells on the soles of the pads. These fine projections are forced into the microscopic irregularities of the surface and give the animals secure purchase.

Iguanids, skinks, and some Alligator Lizards (*Gerrhonotus*) that climb yet do not possess adhesive pads, climb by means of strong, curved claws. Some species of Alligator Lizards forage in low bushes or shrubs; they are the only North American lizards with a prehensile tail. The tail is not prehensile in all species, but is definitely so in members of the species *Gerrhonotus coeruleus*. Some arboreal lizards have the same ability to parachute as the tree-dwelling hylids. Thus the Green Anolis (*Anolis c. carolinensis*),

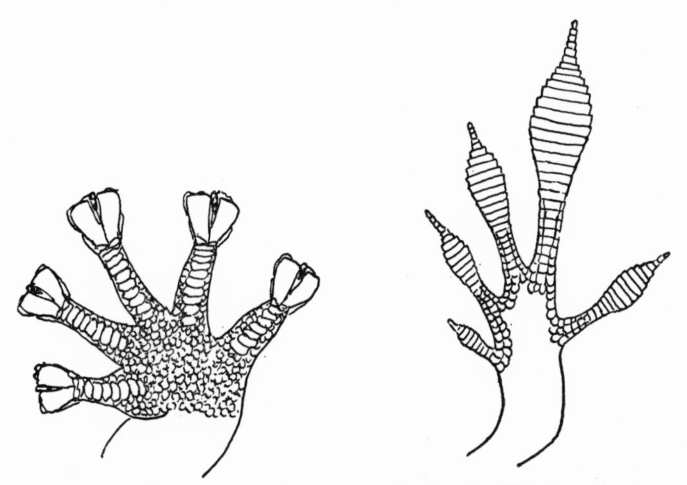

FIG. 15. Lefthand figure shows the expanded adhesive disks on the toes of the Tubercular Gecko (*Phyllodactylus tuberculosus*). On the right is the hind foot of the Green Anolis (*Anolis carolinensis*) illustrating the expanded adhesive portions on the next to last joints of the toes.

with its expanded digital pads, has been found to parachute from heights of 30 feet or more. Several specimens of the semiarboreal Southern Fence Lizard (*Sceloporus u. undulatus*) were tested for this and found to fall in a nearly straight line. Unlike the Anolis, they did not assume a constant position, but wiggled violently all the way down.

Several species of North American snakes can climb with ease. Whip Snakes (*Masticophis*), Racers (*Coluber constrictor*), Ribbon Snakes (*Thamnophis sauritus*), Watersnakes (*Natrix*), and others climb readily in low shrubs and small trees, using the serpentine method of locomotion. Chicken Snakes (*Elaphe*) and some King Snakes (*Lampropeltis*) climb trees of considerable diameter by taking advantage of small irregularities in the bark and using a combination of serpentine and rectilinear locomotion. The Chicken Snakes are the most proficient climbers in North America. The belly scales are so constructed as to form a small keel or ridge down each side of the belly. In climbing, this ridge can be held against minor irregularities, allowing the snake to proceed easily. When the diameter of the tree is small enough, the snake may wrap a loop of its body completely around the tree and go up in a modified concertina fashion—gripping at one point, extending the body to a new purchase point, drawing up to that, anchoring, and extending up again. The Corn Snake (*Elaphe guttata*) is one of the most expert climbers in the country. It has been observed to climb a 40-foot smooth-barked Coconut Palm, and a Sweet Gum three feet in diameter. A group of skeptical naturalists were amazed to see the ease with which a three-foot Corn Snake crawled headfirst down a large Elm Tree three and a half feet in diameter. The snake performed without a slip.

Rate of Movement

In this age of high speeds we tend to think in terms of how fast things can go. Our technological skill has produced airplanes and rockets that far exceed any living organism in speed. To consider the speed of amphibians and reptiles, we must come down to low rates of movement compared with other vertebrates. Despite the popular tendency to overestimate the speed at which snakes travel, these reptiles are slow by comparison with most mammals, including man. Because of the slowness of their movement, few records are available of actually measured rates of speed.

The fastest of North American salamanders are probably the large, eel-like aquatic Amphiuma (*Amphiuma*) or Siren (*Siren*). I do not know of any measurement of movement for either of these, but an estimate of the rate would be under two miles per hour. In studies of the movement of frogs, the length of the leap has received more attention than actual rate of speed. The leaping ability has been a point of considerable popular interest in connection with frog jumping contests. Newspaper stories indicate that this fad has spread to South Africa, where an entrant named "Leaping Lena" is claimed to have "beaten the American and broken the world's frog-jumping record at the Frog Olympics at Capetown." In these contests the distance covered in three consecutive leaps is used as the measure, rather than the longest single leap. Leaping Lena's championship performance measured 24 feet 3 inches, although she is reported to have done 32 feet in an unofficial exhibition performance. In the California contest most of the contestants are Bullfrogs (*Rana catesbeiana*). The record performance is a reported 16 feet 4 inches for three consecutive hops, or an average of approximately 5 feet 5 inches per leap.

While we are most often interested in maximum accomplishment —what species can jump the greatest distance—individual jumping ability measured in relation to the size of the animal gives a better indication of actual jumping ability. Therefore distance jumped expressed in terms of body or leg length gives a more useful standard of comparison. Jumping ability is clearly related to the bulk of the body, the length of the hind legs, and the surface from which the jump is made. Probably the most accurate method of evaluation would be in terms of body weight rather than body length, but the few observations available have utilized body or leg length and distance jumped.

A. Stanley Rand, who has made the most extensive study on this matter, has presented his observations on the jumping ability of six species of North American frogs. His results point out the important factors that influence the length of the jump. Measuring tracks of Fowler's Toads (*Bufo woodhousi fowleri*) on sand, Rand found the normal distance covered per hop to be between 5 and 6 inches. When individuals of this genus were captured and tested on similar sand, they jumped from 6 to 14½ inches per hop. The same toads, when tested on a grassy lawn, jumped 12 to 22½ inches per hop. Rand's observations on the length of jump for the six species studied are summarized in Table 3, which presents distances covered per jump, averages, and the relative lengths of jump in relation to the head-body length. The latter figure is an average of all the observations for a particular species and indicates its relative jumping abilities measured in terms of body size. The figures show that the small Cricket Frog (*Acris gryllus crepitans*) is by far the best jumper in relation to *relative* jumping ability—36 times its own body length—and is up near the top in actual distance covered. The Bullfrog (*Rana catesbeiana*) may be famed in frog jumping contests, but actually is a poor third among the three species of True

Frogs in both actual and relative jumping abilities. The Leopard Frog (*Rana pipiens*) of the open wet meadows and marshes is the best jumper of the group in terms of total distance covered.

TABLE 3

JUMPING ABILITY OF FROGS (AFTER RAND)

Family and Species	Distance per Jump (Range in inches)	Average (inches)	Relative Jumping Ability Distance Jumped/Body Length (inches)
Family Bufonidae			
Fowler's Toad (*Bufo woodhousi fowleri*)	12 to 22½	20	7.8
Family Hylidae			
Cricket Frog (*Acris gryllus crepitans*)	12¾ to 41¼	33¾	36.2
Spring Peeper (*Hyla c. crucifer*)	2½ to 20¾	17½	17.9
Family Ranidae			
Bullfrog (*Rana catesbeiana*)	7 to 37¾	26¾	8.9
Green Frog (*Rana clamitans*)	15¾ to 42¼	32½	11.5
Leopard Frog (*Rana pipiens*)	20¾ to 44¼	36¾	12.9

Rand's figures for the Cricket Frog leave little doubt of its proficiency in comparison with the other frogs that he tested. Clifford H. Pope records leaps by this frog of up to four feet, and he says that it can jump 40 times its own length. Albert H. Wright credits it with leaps of three feet on the surface of water. I can add a few observations on two introduced species of frogs that now live in the southern United States. Neither has exceptional jumping abilities unless the small Greehouse Frog (*Eleutherodactylus ricordi planirostris*) is to be a candidate for limited relative jumping ability. One specimen—with a head-body length of 1¼ inches—in five trials jumped 2½ to 4¾ inches per jump, for a relative jumping ability of only 2 to 4. Leaps of a Cuban Tree Frog (*Hyla sep-*

tentrionalis) were measured in five trials and found to vary from 23 to 41 inches per hop, for a relative jumping ability of 10.6 to 18.9.

Rand also studied the factor of jumping endurance and obtained some very interesting results. A Spring Peeper jumped 120 consecutive jumps, but the distance per hop gradually decreased. The Cricket Frog also decreased the distance covered as the number of hops increased. No True Frogs were tested for endurance, but three toads showed little decrease in length of jump at the end of their trials. Both the Cricket Frog and the Spring Peeper customarily jump only short series of jumps, whereas toads often move several hundred feet in their nightly activities.

Tortoises are known in legend and folktale for their leisurely ways and slow gait. That this reputation is justified is clearly shown by the records. The fastest of our land turtles is either the Desert Tortoise (*Gopherus agassizi*) or the Florida Gopher Tortoise (*Gopherus polyphemus*). Angus M. Woodbury and Ross Hardy have studied the Desert Tortoise in Utah and report a series of five tests in which it walked at a speed of .13 to .30 mile per hour. I have measured the Florida Gopher Tortoise on several occasions. A large individual with a shell length of 9½ inches walked between .27 and .50 mile per hour in several trials. Only at the "higher" speed did the animal seem to be exerting itself. On another occasion this tortoise was clocked as it walked 36 feet through a pine woods to its den. It covered the distance in exactly two minutes, which is a rate of .2 mile per hour. By comparison, a smaller individual of the same species with a shell length of 5⅛ inches walked at the rate of .17 to .26 mile per hour. W. D. Klimstra clocked two Common Snapping Turtles (*Chelydra s. serpentina*) on an overland jaunt of 1,830 feet. This distance was covered in two and a half hours. Including two short stops during the trip, the rate was .138 mile per hour.

Large fresh-water turtles can move faster on land than the land tortoises. Several observations were recorded on the speed of a large female Suwannee Terrapin (*Pseudemys floridana suwannensis*) crawling on grass. This turtle measured 16 inches in shell length. In the fastest trial it went 1.07 miles per hour for a distance of eleven feet. The fastest of our turtles are the large marine species. In fact, some herpetologists claim that they are the fastest of all reptiles. It is extremely difficult to obtain accurate rates of speed for these large turtles because of the necessity of having fixed points on which to base the measurement of the distance covered. The turtles are usually encountered far from land—where no fixed landmarks exist and where the speed of small boats is not accurately known. Even in large enclosures it is difficult to stimulate the turtles to maximum effort.

I have recorded twenty-three observations on a large Green Turtle (*Chelonia mydas*) as it cruised leisurely in a large salt-water stockade. This individual had a shell length of three and a half feet. At no time during the observation did it make any noticeable effort of haste, but cruised at a speed of between .88 and 1.4 miles per hour. Similar observations were made on the cruising speed of a medium-sized Hawksbill Turtle (*Eretmochelys imbricata*) and a large Loggerhead (*Caretta caretta*), both of which moved at a rate of around one mile per hour. The large Leatherback Turtle (*Dermochelys coriacea*) is said to be the fastest swimmer of any of the marine turtles, but no record of an actual speed has been recorded. Raymond B. Cowles, Edwin H. Colbert, and Charles M. Bogert made incidental observations on the speed of walking of a small American Alligator on land. They found that an individual 32¼ inches long walked at a rate of .6 mile per hour. A large individual would go at a faster rate, and all individuals can swim faster than they walk.

The speed of snakes is a subject about which there is a great deal of misinformation and exaggeration. This is not at all surprising in the general public since snakes are usually feared and the very sight of a snake to some people is enough to separate them temporarily from their reason. However, it is disturbing to note that even herpetologists have had difficulty in accurately assessing the speed of moving snakes. This is owing in large part to the optical illusion one frequently gets when viewing the long, smooth-flowing body of a moving snake, particularly when it is seen in relation to small, closely placed plants, rocks, or sticks. The tales of speedy snakes that could overtake a galloping horse, keep pace with a fast car for more than a mile, or outdistance a running man are all pure exaggerations. It is disappointing to see how slow they really go when a stop watch is put on such performers.

The late Walter Mosauer made extensive studies on the locomotion of snakes in the arid southwest. The results of his studies are summarized in Table 4.

TABLE 4

SPEED OF SNAKES (AFTER MOSAUER)

Species	Number of Trials	Prowling Speed (miles per hour)	Maximum Speed (miles per hour)
California Boa (*Lichanura r. roseofusca*)	7	.09	.22
Sierra Coral King Snake (*Lampropeltis zonata multicincta*)	12	.17	.72
Gopher Snake (*Pituophis* spp.)	36	.13	1.18
Desert Patchnosed Snake (*Salvadora h. hexalepis*)	12	.22	1.43
Sidewinder Rattlesnake (*Crotalus cerastes*)	41	.31	2.04
Colorado Desert Whipsnake (*Masticophis flagellum piceus*)	39	.29	3.60

Charles C. Carpenter noted the speed of three species of Garter Snakes (*Thamnophis*) in southern Michigan while he was studying their ecology. He found that Butler's Garter Snake (*Thamnophis butleri*) was the slowest and the Eastern Ribbon Snake (*Thamnophis s. sauritus*) the fastest. The range of speed was 0.75 to 2.00 miles per hour.

In Florida my wife and I made a few tests on the Four-lined Chicken Snake (*Elaphe obsoleta quadrivittata*) and the Florida Racer (*Coluber constrictor priapus*). The fastest speed that we recorded for the Chicken Snake was .37 mile per hour, and for the Racer 3.7 miles per hour. Incidentally, the speed of this last trial was *estimated* by several observers to be about three times what it actually turned out to be.

For really fast land reptiles we must turn to the lizards. As with all the other groups, we need a great many more factual records, but we do have enough to show that some of them can really move rapidly. J. Southgate Hoyt has reported a speed of the Six-

TABLE 5

SPEED OF REPTILES

Family and Species	Method	Maximum Reported (miles per hour)
Turtles		
Emydidae		
Suwannee River Terrapin (*Pseudemys floridana suwanniensis*)	Walking	1.07
Testudinidae		
Desert Tortoise (*Gopherus agassizi*)	"	0.30
Gopher Turtle (*Gopherus polyphemus*)	"	0.50
Chelonidae		
Green Turtle (*Chelonia mydas*)	Swimming	1.4
Crocodilians		
Crocodilidae		
American Alligator (*Alligator mississippiensis*)	Walking	0.60
Lizards		
Iguanidae		
Fringe-toed Lizard (*Uma notata*)	Running	15.0
Common Gridiron-tailed Lizard (*Callisaurus draconoides gabbi*)	"	15.0
Teiidae		
Six-lined Racerunner (*Cnemidophorus sexlineatus*)	"	18.0
Snakes		
Boidae		
California Boa (*Lichanura r. roseofusca*)	Crawling	0.22
Colubridae		
Butler's Garter Snake (*Thamnophis butleri*)	"	0.75
Ribbon Snake (*Thamnophis s. sauritus*)	"	2.00
Four-lined Chicken Snake (*Elaphe obsoleta quadrivittata*)	"	0.37
Sierra Coral King Snake (*Lampropeltis zonata multicincta*)	"	0.72

TABLE 5 (Continued)

Family and Species	Method	Maximum Reported (miles per hour)
Gopher Snake (*Pituophis* spp.)	Crawling	1.18
Desert Patchnosed Snake (*Salvadora h. hexalepis*)	"	1.43
Florida Racer (*Coluber constrictor priapus*)	"	3.7
Colorado Desert Whip Snake (*Masticophis flagellum piceus*)	"	3.6
Crotalidae		
Sidewinder Rattlesnake (*Crotalus cerastes*)	Crawling (Sidewinding)	2.04

lined Racerunner (*Cnemidophorus sexlineatus*) at 18 miles per hour. This measurement was made while the lizard was running in front of a moving automobile. Western herpetologists cite the Common Gridiron-tailed Lizard (*Callisaurus draconoides gabbi*) as probably the fastest lizard on the desert. Charles C. Camp *estimated* the speed of one individual to be about 90 feet in 4 seconds, or 15 miles per hour. Kenneth S. Norris has measured the speed of a Fringe-toed Lizard (*Uma notata*) at 15 miles per hour when running in front of his car. These are the fastest speeds reported for any North American lizards. The fastest speed recorded by me in eight observations on the Six-lined Racerunner was 10.5 miles per hour. The lizards were running on open sandy soil, and the speed was measured with the help of a stop watch.

The foregoing remarks cover our scanty information on the rate of movement of amphibians and reptiles. Manifestly there is great need for many more factual records of measured speeds. Present knowledge is so fragmentary that we have little more than a scant hint of actual speeds. The information for reptiles is summarized in Table 5. It must be emphasized that the figures do not indicate the *maximum possible* speeds, but only the presently *known maximum* speeds of a few North American species.

Movements

In a Monterey, California, newspaper in 1953 appeared the picture of a Desert Tortoise under the caption, "Oh, my aching back." Allegedly, the tortoise had just completed, under its own power, a 400-mile trip in four years, returning to its former home after having been taken away and liberated in the desert. This would be a great accomplishment for a turtle, but the story involves too many improbabilities to be seriously considered by anyone who knows reptiles. Tales of this sort are told at frequent intervals. They are based on uncritical observation and wishful thinking, flavored with a strong dose of romanticism.

Studies on the movements of marked individuals in the wild, and experiments on the homing ability of a number of species, indicate that most amphibians and reptiles do not move long distances at any time during their lives. For amphibians and for terrestrial and fresh-water reptiles the total distance moved in a lifetime rarely exceeds one mile. Marine turtles are a notable exception to this general rule; they move considerable distances that often exceed several hundred miles.

The types of movement may be random wandering or more or less regular travels to and from a given location, such as a breeding site, hibernating den, feeding station, or source of water. In both the random and the regular movements, the distances covered vary considerably with the species and the type of country inhabited.

Little is known about the movements of salamanders except for their large-scale breeding migrations and hibernating congregations. The scarcity of information on these amphibians results in large part from the difficulty in marking individuals so that they can be recognized with certainty. Robert E. Gordon found that the Green Salamander (*Aneides aeneus*) tended to remain in a limited area of not more than 300 feet in maximum length. On the other hand. the Eastern Newt (*Diemictylus v. viridescens*), in its land stage, may wander up to half a mile from the nearest water. Regular non-breeding movements of salamanders have been noted in relation to cold weather and changes in water level. Thus the numbers of individuals sometimes found on damp nights in the fall or following a prolonged drought may rival those seen in the spring breeding migrations. W. J. Breckenridge reports finding in one night during such a movement 142 individuals of the Eastern Tiger Salamander (*Ambystoma t. tigrinum*) on one-quarter of a mile of paved road.

The best-known movements of salamanders are their breeding migrations. Such movements are most pronounced in land species that breed in or near water, but they are also seen in some aquatic species that move from one part of a lake or stream to another part of the water body—for example, the Hellbender (*Cryptobranchus alleganiensis*) and the Northern Mudpuppy (*Necturus m. maculosus*). Large numbers of salamanders collect around the breeding pools or may be observed crossing an open area, such as a paved road, en route to the breeding locations. The movement *toward* the breeding pools is more concentrated than that away from the area. The maximum distances moved during the breeding migrations are not known with certainty, but in some cases appear to be up to half a mile. More commonly they are in the nature of a few hundred feet.

More information is available on the movements of frogs because they are relatively easy to mark for subsequent identification of individuals. Also, because of their less secretive habits, they are recaptured more readily. Information is available on the normal movements for several species, and homing experiments have been made on their ability to return to the point of original capture. From this information it is indicated that the movements of most frog species are confined within an area of under one mile, and this area seems never to exceed two miles in diameter. Here again large-scale movements are sometimes found in relation to hibernation sites.

As in salamanders, the most prominent movement of frogs occurs during the breeding migrations. Large numbers of individuals take part in these movements, sometimes attaining spectacular proportions, to be numbered literally in the thousands. In most frogs the adults move to one breeding site only, remaining there until they have completed their reproductive functions or until the drive to reproduce has passed away. This is the case, for example, in True Frogs (*Rana*) and in the American Toad (*Bufo terrestris americanus*) in the northeastern part of the United States. However, in Oklahoma, A. P. Blair found that male American Toads sometimes moved short distances from one pond to another. A similar movement was observed in male Green Frogs (*Rana clamitans*) studied in southern Michigan by Bernard Martof. The movement of the adults away from the breeding areas is not on such a large scale as that toward the area. However, under adverse weather conditions large-scale movements away from the breeding pools may occur, as noted by Charles F. Walker in the case of the Eastern Wood Frog (*Rana s. sylvatica*) in Ohio. In some species, particularly Toads (*Bufo*) and Spadefoot Toads (*Scaphiopus*) the nearly metamorphosed young may move away within a short period, forming large-scale movements away from the water. On several occasions I have encountered such mass movements by newly transformed American Toads (*Bufo terrestris americanus*). For example, at New Hampton, New Hampshire, on July 21, 1938, it had rained all day and that night the ground around the ponds was "alive" with little toads moving out from the water. Arthur N. Bragg has recorded an interesting case of mass movement of newly transformed Hurter's Spadefoots (*Scaphiopus holbrooki hurteri*) in Oklahoma. He noted that the nearly developed tadpoles were gathered into two masses one evening. All emerged that evening and moved away from the pond, so that none remained in the water the following morning. H. Elliott McClure observed a band of small Great Plains Spadefoots (*Scaphiopus couchi*) hopping along a gravel road in Nebraska on July 18, 1942. These were in such numbers that they passed the observer at the rate of 100 per minute. The weather was warm, partly cloudy, and the time around noon. McClure continued the count for twenty minutes, during which the toads left the road and went into the grass when the sun came out from behind a cloud. They returned to the road when the sun was again obscured by clouds.

W. T. Stille studied the activity of Fowler's Toad (*Bufo woodhousi fowleri*) in a sandy beach area of southern Lake Michigan. He found that the daytime retreats of the toads were 200 to 700 feet back from the beach. On the beach at night the toads were active within a definite area on repeated occasions, and this area never exceeded 500 feet in width, averaging only 26.7 feet. Thus the greatest distances moved by the toads were perpendicular to the beach rather than along it. The nightly movements of the toads in this situation were primarily to obtain moisture.

Several people have made tests to determine the homing ability of toads. These tests assume that the animals are familiar with the details of the local habitat, and that when they wander beyond their regular haunts they can find their way back by means of recognized landmarks. The basic principle involved here has been demonstrated many times over, not only for toads, but for many amphibians and reptiles, both experimentally and by repeated observation. For example, these creatures can learn to run an artificial maze in the laboratory and can retain the ability to do so for some time after being trained. Ability to return to a familiar "home" area from different distances provides indirect information on the size of normal wanderings of the individual. A behavior pattern that also provides us with information here is the frequent tendency of the animal to remain where released when placed in a totally unfamiliar region.

Ray J. Nichols marked and released 570 Fowler's Toads (*Bufo woodhousi fowleri*). The maximum distance from which any toad returned was 2,175 feet, but one toad had travelled 3,450 feet moving toward the point of capture and another individual that was not removed from its "home" area travelled 4,200 feet spontaneously. The greatest speed noted in any of the returning toads was about one-tenth of a mile per hour. Charles M. Bogert performed a similar experiment with the Southern Toad (*Bufo t. terrestris*) in Florida. He found that the percentage of toads recaptured varied in direct relation to the distance at which they were released:

36.8 per cent returned from 1,350 feet
20.6 per cent returned from 2,250 feet
16.6 per cent returned from 2,550 feet

In another experiment he obtained some returns from as far away as one mile. He also found a difference in ability to return correlated with the type of country in which they were released, showing a higher percentage of returns from cleared than from uncleared land. On the basis of his studies and other published data, he concluded that the normal range of an individual toad may encompass an area a mile wide.

Edward C. Raney has studied the natural movements of the Bullfrog (*Rana catesbeiana*) in New York State. He found considerable variation in the amount of individual activity. Some frogs remained in an area less than 100 feet in diameter, with a maximum width of 300 feet. In his study of toads on a sand beach on southern Lake Michigan, W. T. Stille also recorded observations on the Bullfrogs present in the area and found the nature of their movements to be similar to those of the toad. Thus they occupied a definite area along the beach of less than 500 feet and they moved 200 to 700 feet perpendicular to the beach to their diurnal retreats.

Charles M. Breder and his associates observed the movements and homing ability of the Green Frog (*Rana clamitans*) in New Jersey and in New York. They noted that the maximum distance from which frogs could return was approximately 350 feet. More recently Bernard Martof has made extensive observations on the natural movements of this frog in southern Michigan. He studied Green Frogs living along a clear, actively flowing stream, at a point about 66 feet from an artificial lake. The frogs migrated to the lake only for breeding, and, except for the more prolonged movements to the lake and other breeding sites, they remained within very restricted areas. The daily activity movements of individuals studied were less than 3¼ feet for half of the frogs and less than 32¾ feet for five-sixths of them. The home-range area varied considerably, as indicated in Table 6.

TABLE 6

HOME-RANGE AREA OF GREEN FROGS (AFTER MARTOF)

	Number of Frogs	Size of Area in Square Feet		
		Minimum	Maximum	Average
Subadults	14	66	361	173
Adults	29	66	656	213
All Frogs	43	66	656	200

Martof found that adults characteristically returned to their home range after the more extensive breeding migrations, but females did so more regularly than the males. Olive and Coleman J. Goin have reported a Squirrel Tree Frog (*Hyla squirrella*) that had its nightly station on the same holly tree for some months.

Alligators and water turtles perform somewhat seasonal movements in response to fluctuating water levels, moving from drying-up water holes to more permanent or deeper bodies of water. In turtles these treks usually involve distances of from several hundred feet up to half a mile, but in the case of the 'gators the distance may be a mile or two. Fred R. Cagle has made an excellent summary of the information on turtle movements, contributing much of the knowledge about fresh-water turtles from his own studies. He has studied all the species occurring in southern Illinois, western Tennessee, and Louisiana, but has obtained more data on Slider Turtles (*Pseudemys*) and Painted Turtles (*Chrysemys*) than on any other groups. About these he concludes that they "(a) live within selected areas that may be designated home ranges within which they seek their food, basking sites, and mates; (b) have home ranges that may include parts of two or more water bodies; (c) make frequent overland movements."

On the subject of overland movements Cagle observed some interesting differences in behavior among turtles of different genera. He recognized the following conditions relating to the overland movements of fresh-water turtles in the region studied:

<table>
<tr><td>Frequently on land; movements between adjacent water bodies; home range may include parts or all of several water bodies.
Examples: Chrysemys
Pseudemys</td><td rowspan="2">Seasonal migration may be overland</td><td rowspan="3">Forced migration may be overland</td></tr>
<tr><td>Occasionally on land; no regular overland movements; home range probably confined to one water body. Examples: Chelydra
Sternotherus</td></tr>
<tr><td>Very rarely on land; home range probably confined to one water body.
Examples: Trionyx
Graptemys</td><td></td></tr>
</table>

By removing turtles from the point of capture and releasing them at another point, Cagle was also able to demonstrate a well-developed ability in homing for distances under two miles. Snapping Turtles (*Chelydra serpentina*) have been seen making overland jaunts of close to two miles. These turtles may follow the last remnant of water or may wander at random. M. M. Wickham has reported the most extensive movement of any nonmarine turtle. He marked an individual Alligator Snapping Turtle (*Macrochelys temmincki*) and three years later found it 17 or 18 miles upstream from the original point of release.

Eastern Box Turtles (*Terrapene c. carolina*) have been studied by a number of people, but John T. Nichols has marked more individual turtles of this species than anyone else. He concluded that in Long Island, New York, the normal range of the turtle has a diameter of 750 feet. The actual boundaries shift somewhat with the passage of time. Approximately 90 per cent of the turtles that were moved from one point to another returned to the territory from which they were moved—up to a distance of three-quarters of a mile. Grown turtles showed a more marked homing ability than did young individuals. Lucille Stickel made an intensive study of populations and movement of these turtles in Maryland, where she found the average home range of males to be about 330 feet and of females 370 feet. She also noted that turtles may have two home ranges and that they travel between them at infrequent intervals. A number of interesting long-term observations have been made on this turtle as a result of human beings carving their initials on the shells of the turtle. Two such records can be cited here to illustrate the sedentary habits of the Box Turtle. Oliver P. Medsger reported a turtle bearing initials that was recaptured 18 years later within 100 yards of the point of original capture. The same turtle was taken again after 35 years from the original date, and it was within 150 yards of the point of first capture. J. Schneck has recounted the taking of a turtle within half a mile of the place where it was captured 62 years earlier.

Angus M. Woodbury and Ross Hardy have studied a population of Desert Turtles (*Gopherus agassizi*) in Utah. They found that the turtles had a regular seasonal migration between the winter den area and the summer foraging range. This migration involved relatively short distances, and these workers estimated that the total range of the individual turtles was within 10- to 100-acre areas. Less detailed observations on the Gopher Turtle (*Gopherus polyphemus*) suggest that they are more sedentary than their western relatives. These turtles dig deep burrows and seldom wander more than 50 to 100 feet away from the burrow, although an individual will sometimes shift from one burrow to another for no apparent reason. The new burrow may be 200 to 400 feet from the former location.

Marine turtles appear to be not only the fastest of our aquatic reptiles but the greatest movers. In some regions they may remain within more or less definite areas, and the females are known to return to the same beaches year after year to lay their eggs. However, there are strong indications that they may wander over considerable distances between times. For example, turtles of several species appear from time to time far north of their usual haunts, being reported from the New England Coast and as far away as the British Isles. These wanderers have been aided in their travels by the strong Gulf Stream current and possibly by storms. During World War II, while serving aboard a destroyer, I kept a record of all the marine turtles that were sighted. Individuals were seen on several occasions 200 to 300 miles from the nearest land. On one occasion hundreds of Pacific Ridley Turtles (*Lepidochelys olivacea remivaga*) were seen in a large aggregation 50 miles off the west coast of Mexico. Nothing is known of the nature of the movements of these turtles except that some are probably breeding migrations.

Virtually all species of lizards are highly restricted in the areas where they occur. The home range usually centers around some log, rock, tree, or other vantage point, and in some species a defended territory may be maintained. Because of the frequent occurrence of colonies or groups, there are no large-scale migrations to particular breeding sites or to find mates. Lizards may move in large numbers in relation to food or inclement weather, but most movement consists of individual wanderings.

The Rough-scaled Lizards of the genus *Sceloporus* have been studied more thoroughly in this connection than any others. Henry S. Fitch studied the Pacific Fence Lizard (*Sceloporus o. occidentalis*) and concluded that individuals were extremely localized in their movements, living their entire lives within a radius of a few hundred feet. The activity sphere shifts from time to time, with males moving more than females, but remains confined to a restricted area. Robert C. Stebbins found a similar condition in the Sierra Pine Lizard (*Sceloporus graciosus gracilis*). His study indicated that males move about more than females. During the brief summer activity period the average distances moved were 59 feet for the females and 82 feet for the males. He found that the same territories may be maintained from one year to another.

In the southeastern United States the Southern Fence Lizard (*Sceloporus u. undulatus*) and the Green Anolis (*Anolis c. carolinensis*) may maintain territories and occupy home ranges that vary in size in relation to the population density and the thickness of the cover. For example, in a scrub oak and pine woods around an old sawdust pile, territories only 10 to 15 feet in diameter were guarded, whereas in an open woodlot nearby the size was 50 to 100 feet in diameter. In the open woodlot the territory and the range appeared to be approximately the same size. The Six-lined Racerunner (*Cnemidophorus sexlineatus*) in the same region does not appear to maintain a definite territory, but wanders over a fairly large home range of 200 to 300 feet in diameter, perhaps more. Few data are available for the fast and agile Gridiron-tailed Lizards (*Callisaurus draconoides*) in the United States, but Lloyd Tevis has studied the species in the adjacent Mexican state of Baja California. He estimated that each individual had a small range of about 50 feet in diameter.

Unlike many lizards, snakes do not seem to maintain territories and appear to wander more at random. Even here the maximum diameter of the area covered does not appear to exceed two miles and is usually much less. Walter Mosauer utilized tracks to study the daily range of three species of snakes inhabiting the sand dunes of the Colorado Desert in California. He found that the little Shovel-nosed Snake (*Chionactis occipitalis*) rarely exceeded 100 feet in area covered in one night, whereas a Sidewinder Rattlesnake (*Crotalus cerastes*) ten inches in length traveled approximately 1,000 feet. Frank N. Blanchard and E. B. Finster observed a Common Garter Snake (*Thamnophis s. sirtalis*) that moved 1,800 feet in one hour. They experimented with the movements of marked individuals in their natural range and when released in a new area. Garter Snakes under the latter condition moved up to two miles through rough, dry areas. Charles C. Carpenter studied the movements of three species of Garter Snakes (*Thamnophis*) in southern Michigan. The distances that these three species covered between points of capture are shown in Table 7.

Henri C. Seibert and Charles W. Hagen, Jr., studied a dense population of the Prairie Garter Snake (*Thamnophis radix*) and the Smooth Green Snake (*Opheodrys vernalis*) on a 3.2-acre plot in Chicago. The size of the home range and the distances covered by individuals were amazingly small, with no snake moving more than 300 feet. Half of the recaptured individuals had moved less than a total of 30 feet or had traveled at a rate of less than 6 feet per day. This seems to represent an unusual situation even for snakes, and the explanation for it is not clear. Perhaps the study was made in a location with an overabundant supply of food and shelter. The small DeKay's Snake (*Storeria d. dekayi*) is known in some situations to move over much greater distances—for example, 3,960 feet in one week.

William H. Stickel and James B. Cope studied the wanderings of snakes in Maryland. Most of their observations were on the Pilot Black Snake (*Elaphe o. obsoleta*) and the Black Racer (*Coluber c. constrictor*), both large, active snakes. The distances between points of capture varied from 130 feet to 1,760 feet, with an average of 816 feet for the Pilot Black Snake and 802 feet for the Black Racer. The study was carried on over a two-year period; and since there was no increase in distance traveled with elapsed time, Stickel and Cope assumed that the average figures indicate the size of the home range.

Henry S. Fitch studied the snake population on the San Joaquin Experimental Range in central California. The Northern Pacific Rattlesnake (*Crotalus viridis oreganus*) was the most abundant species in the area. Fitch could find no set pattern for the activities or the rate of movement, but where sufficient recaptures occurred over a period of time, some indication of size of range was apparent. The most typical condition was a male range of nearly three-quarters of a mile in diameter and a female range of about one-sixth of a mile. Several individuals were recorded to have moved more than one mile, but most were within a few hundred feet of the point of original capture even after months and years had passed. The Pacific Gopher Snake (*Pituophis c. catenifer*) appeared to be about as limited in movements as the Rattlers, but the California King Snake (*Lampropeltis getulus californiae*) seemed to be even

TABLE 7

Distances Moved by Garter Snakes (After Carpenter)

	Maximum Distance Covered (feet)	Maximum Width of Area (feet)	Estimated Average Range (feet)
Common Garter Snake (*Thamnophis sirtalis sirtalis*)	984	224	600 x 150
Ribbon Snake (*Thamnophis sauritus sauritus*)	912	160	600 x 150
Butler's Garter Snake (*Thamnophis butleri*)	1,000	56	900 x 100

more restricted than the other two. In contrast, the Fitch's Garter Snake (*Thamnophis sirtalis fitchi*) apparently wandered more extensively than any of the other species in this study, although limited to small intermittent creeks.

Wilfred T. Neill has recorded a puzzling and, in the light of the foregoing observations, unusual condition in relation to the Canebrake Rattlesnake (*Crotalus horridus atricaudatus*). Studying the snakes of Georgia, Neill reported movements up to 20 miles for this snake. Such long distances are so much greater than anything observed elsewhere that it seems hard to accept them without question. Neill was not studying marked individuals, but he has told me in conversation that the region in which the snakes were found is such that they could not survive the winters without migrating to the nearest den sites, which in some instances were 20 miles distant. Furthermore, he reports that there are well-used travelways radiating to and from the dens.

The foregoing observations show how amphibians and reptiles move, what their locomotor abilities are, and how effective they are in covering various distances. They also show something of what use the animals make of these abilities in their daily activities. Most species of amphibians and reptiles live their lives in limited areas, usually under a mile in diameter. Few ever move much beyond a single day's journey away from the center of their home range.

CHAPTER 8

Activity

As HUMAN BEINGS WE CARRY ON activities that are arranged according to the calendar and the clock in some orderly fashion. There are occasional moments of indifference to these measures of time, but by and large our affairs are arranged on more or less precise schedules. Most recurrent events fit a cyclical pattern according to time of day, week, month, or year. Sometimes we become impatient with the pressure of living according to rigid schedules and envy the carefree creatures of the wild with their apparent obliviousness of time. But are they completely indifferent to time? Do they not have some sort of schedule of their own? Is their life made up solely of random activities?

The answer to these questions is that animals too have their activities regulated, and that the recurrent events of their lives frequently fit cyclical patterns. Though they have no computed time schedules, their activities are influenced by the same rhythmical phenomena on which we base our time scales—day and night, light and dark; yearly seasons, warm and cold, wet and dry.

Hibernation and Estivation

The seasons of the year are generally characterized by changes in weather conditions affected by solar movement, which in turn influence plant and animal life. Thus every region in the world has its characteristic seasonal changes. They may be extreme, as in the so-called temperate regions of the world, particularly in the continental interiors; or very slight, as in some tropical localities. Regardless of the scope of seasonal change, the animal life in each region is adjusted to the weather conditions of that particular region. Amphibians and reptiles, because of their lack of internal heat regulating mechanisms and their moisture requirements, are more directly influenced by weather conditions than are mammals and birds. When temperatures vary far from the optimum for amphibians and reptiles, they must seek shelter. If exposed to freezing or very high temperatures, they soon die. Because of their sensitivity to low temperatures, amphibians and reptiles are normally inactive during the winter months throughout most of the United States and all of Canada, being abroad only during the warmer spring, summer, and fall. However, high summer temperatures and drought may cause another period of inactivity, resulting in two peaks of activity —in spring and fall. Regular, prolonged inactivity of wintertime is termed hibernation; and that of summertime, estivation. The former is a reaction to adverse low temperatures, the latter to deficiency of moisture or harmful high temperatures. Hibernation in most parts of North America is more regular and a more distinct phenomenon than the summer inactivity. In some northern species it is such an inherent seasonal occurrence that it takes place regularly even in the absence of lowered temperatures. Ruth A. Holzapfel found that Northern Leopard Frogs (*Rana p. pipiens*) in Wisconsin had an inherent seasonal cycle not fundamentally dependent on the environment. In winter the body functions and behavior of the frogs were modified. Exposing the animals to low temperatures, inadequate food, and low moisture conditions in summer did not produce the same changes. One of the interesting characteristics of the frogs observed in this study was a seasonal difference in length of life at low temperatures. Individuals exposed to low temperatures in July and August lived less than half as long as they did if exposed to the same temperatures in January or February. A similar change takes place in the ability of amphibians to remain submerged under water at low temperatures. Frogs breathe by means of lungs, and at high temperatures they must come to the surface to breathe at frequent intervals, but at a temperature of 40° F. they can remain totally submerged for days. In fact, some frogs habitually hibernate on the bottom of cold streams or springs. F. John Vernberg has recorded a seasonal change in body water content in the Red-backed Salamander (*Plethodon c. cinereus*), with a decrease in the wintertime. Such a change is doubtless of adaptive value in enabling the animal to withstand lower temperatures without freezing.

In hibernating and estivating, the animal must seek a location that provides not only adequate protection from temperature ex-

PLATE V. A Corn Snake (*Elaphe g. guttata*) climbing up a large tree. Note how the body grips irregularities of the bark. (New York Zoological Society photograph)

PLATE VI. A real mouthful! A Mexican Tree Frog (*Hyla baudini*) in the act of swallowing a grasshopper about as long as the frog. Note the use of one fore leg helping to get the food in and the use of the adhesive pads in holding on to the branch. (Photograph by Robert C. Hermes)

tremes but also sufficient moisture. Usually these conditions are obtained by burrowing underground, going deep into rocky chasms, digging into the mud at the bottom of ponds and streams, or entering a spring or cave. In such situations the temperatures are fairly even, usually above freezing in winter and not too high in summer. Also, moisture conditions are generally good in such places.

The species present in a given locality will differ in the length of hibernation period. Some enter hibernation earlier and remain longer in the spring than others. For example, in the northeastern United States the Northern Spring Peeper (*Hyla c. crucifer*) emerges from hibernation a month or two before the Bullfrog (*Rana catesbeiana*), and the Eastern Garter Snake (*Thamnophis s. sirtalis*) is out of hibernation long before the Timber Rattlesnake (*Crotalus h. horridus*). Since hibernation affords protection from harmful low temperatures, the duration of hibernation increases toward the north of the continent and toward higher altitudes. Amphibians as a group can tolerate lower temperatures than reptiles and thus hibernate for shorter periods. For the same reason they also occur farther north and at higher altitudes than reptiles. Because of the need for hibernation sites in the north, amphibians and reptiles cannot occur in regions where the ground is perpetually frozen. Within a single species, adults usually enter hibernation earlier and leave later than young or juvenile individuals. Reptiles are more resistant to moisture loss than amphibians and may remain active longer during higher summer temperatures and low moisture conditions than amphibians.

In the southern part of the country, hibernation may be so incomplete as to be difficult to recognize or define. The bodily changes that occur in hibernating animals in Canada, for example, either do not take place or are on a much more limited scale in the animals of the extreme south. In some southern localities, certain species may undergo a definite, prolonged hibernation, whereas others may remain active throughout the year on days when the temperature is high enough to permit them to be abroad. For example, in northcentral Florida, Olive B. and Coleman J. Goin found a quite definite period of hibernation in the Greater Five-lined Skink (*Eumeces laticeps*). In several years of observation they found this lizard entering hibernation between September 22 and October 10. The spring emergence date varied from March 26 to April 7. They concluded that there was no relation between temperature and the onset of hibernation in the fall, but emergence in the spring was influenced by temperature. In the same area the Six-lined Racerunner (*Cnemidophorus sexlineatus*) has a definite period of hibernation that begins in October and terminates in March or April. Neither of these species is active in warm periods during this time. However, the Green Anolis (*Anolis c. carolinensis*) and the Southern Fence Lizard (*Sceloporus u. undulatus*) living in the same region remain active throughout the winter months and can be seen abroad on days when there is sufficient warmth for them to be active. During short cold periods they remain inactive in some sheltered place, but come forth as soon as the temperature rises. The intermittent, short winter periods of inactivity of these lizards cannot be considered hibernation in the sense that it occurs in northern species. At the present the extent of bodily changes that take place in the wintertime is not known for these two lizards, as compared with the true hibernators like the Greater Five-lined Skink and the Racerunner. In the winter, chemical changes do take place in the body of inactive Anolis in Louisiana. These changes are somewhat similar to those observed in hibernating animals in the north, but it is not clear whether they are simply seasonal changes that enhance survival during inactivity or whether they are in part influenced by inactivity at low temperature.

Some species are known to hibernate regularly in the colder part of the range and not in the warmer part. For example, Tracy I. Storer has pointed out that the Red-legged Frog (*Rana aurora*) undergoes regular hibernation in the northern part of its range and at higher elevations, but remains active all winter or has only brief periods of inactivity in the southern part of the range at low elevations. Similarly the Box Turtle (*Terrapene carolina*) hibernates in the northern United States, but may remain active all winter in southern Florida. Thus in the winter there may be complete activity, brief periods of inactivity, or the prolonged inactivity of true hibernation. This results in a geographical gradient from the southern parts of the country to the northern, with an increase in the length of the inactive period toward the north.

During the period of low-temperature inactivity, the animal must retire to adequate shelter from temperature extremes in order to survive. Some individuals fail to gain such shelter and are killed by the freezing temperatures. Species with well-developed inherent rhythms that are not dependent on a temperature stimulus to enter hibernation are in less danger of being caught by a sudden drop in temperature than those stimulated only by a temperature change. That many fail to reach adequate shelter each year is shown by the individuals found dead as a result of winter mortality. All groups are sometimes represented in these casualties. In experiments on hibernation in the Red-backed Salamanders (*Plethodon c. cinereus*) and Two-lined Salamanders (*Eurycea b. bislineata*), F. John Vernberg found 57 per cent and 50 per cent mortality, respectively, showing a high loss during hibernation. In northern Florida the nonhibernating Anolis and Fence Lizard live with a dangerously slight margin between them and freezing temperatures. The margin is sufficient, however, for the survival of the species, but occasionally many individuals are frozen. At night large numbers of these lizards retire to the tops or upper level of trees, gaining shelter under loose bark, in dead limbs, or in clumps of Spanish Moss. I have seen them retire to such sparse shelters on nights when frost appeared on the ground, but they were out basking in the sun the following day. Wilfred T. Neill has found them on a cold day under loose bark with frost crystals on their backs. If the cold is not much lower than freezing and remains for only a few hours before it warms up, such protection serves adequately and enables the lizards to emerge as soon as the warm temperatures return. On the other hand, a period of severe cold weather lasting several weeks will kill off all such tree-retreating individuals and leave only those that seek shelter below the surface of the ground or in large brush piles. That some individuals do seek greater protection during cold weather is indicated by the fact that Arnold B. Grobman dug up a live Anolis buried in the ground about 12 inches deep during a cold snap in Florida on December 4, 1949. Ross Allen provides an example of how tree-climbing specimens may be caught: A sudden ice storm at Silver Springs, Florida, numbed many individuals, causing them to fall from the trees, and within an hour Allen picked up more than 70 individuals that had been caught by this cold wave.

Reeve M. Bailey has recorded interesting observations on hibernation and winter mortality in two species of snakes. He excavated a denning site of DeKay's Snakes (*Storeria dekayi*) in Iowa on March 22, 1939, at the time that some of the snakes were emerging from the den passageways. All the live individuals were found between the surface and 18 inches down. Twenty dead individuals were found between the surface and a depth of ten inches, indicating that they had not succeeded in reaching sufficient depth for protection in that locality. Bailey performed a series of experiments to learn something of the conditions necessary for successful hibernation in the Great Plains Garter Snake (*Thamnophis radix*) in Iowa. He took careful temperature readings at various depths in the soil, and on November 4 he buried healthy, live snakes at depths of 6, 12, 18, 24, and 36 inches. The animals were dug up the following April. Those at the 6- and 12-inch depths were dead, whereas all but one at the 18- to 36-inch levels had survived. On the basis of his temperature recordings, he estimated that the frost line reached a maximum depth between 25 and 27 inches below the surface of the ground. This meant that survival at a depth of 18 inches required a toleration of minimum temperatures of 3½° F. below freezing.

Species that possess an inherent tendency to hibernate in the fall apparently move into the hibernation shelter well before the arrival of dangerously low temperatures. Whether these species have a more sensitive response to slight temperature changes or to changes in the duration of daylight—or just what the stimulus might be—is not known. Other species exhibit a marked reaction to falling temperatures by moving into hibernation sites. Thus Toads (*Bufo*) will dig into sandy or loamy soil with a decrease in temperature. The same change causes Leopard Frogs (*Rana pipiens*) to seek shelter beneath objects at the bottom of pools. Paul Anderson has described an interesting experience with Prairie Rattlesnakes (*Crotalus v. viridis*) in the vicinity of a den in South Dakota on October 18, 1942. He observed about 35 individuals sunning themselves in a large hole. A sudden strong wind caused a drop in temperature from 79° F. at 1 P.M. to 46° F. at 2 P.M. With the decrease in temperature many rattlers that were out of sight of the den began coming in rapidly and in considerable numbers along three distinct routes.

Hibernation sites vary considerably from species to species and from one locality to another. Some amphibians hibernate on land in deep holes, in and under rotten logs or stumps, or under deep piles of leaf litter. Northern Dusky Salamanders (*Desmognathus f. fuscus*), which normally occur along the borders of streams, move under rocks and logs in deeper water. The Two-lined Salamander (*Eurycea b. bislineata*) hibernates under logs and stones in some localities, but in other regions is never found out of water in midwinter. The Spotted Salamander (*Ambystoma maculatum*) usually hibernates on land, whereas the Eastern Tiger Salamander (*Ambystoma t. tigrinum*) has been found in the bottom of ponds in winter. Land species such as the Red-backed Salamander (*Plethodon c. cinereus*) and the Green Salamander (*Aneides aeneus*) hibernate below the surface in the soil in deep rock crevices.

F. John Vernberg has shown that there is a vertical seasonal movement in the soil, with the animals digging deeper during low temperatures and moving toward the surface in warm temperatures. He found Red-backed Salamanders and Two-lined Salamanders from 4 to 15 inches down in the soil. Frank N. Blanchard found 18 Eastern Four-toed Salamanders (*Hemidactylium scutatum*) in and around a single, six-foot-long log in southern Michigan in November. In association with them, in the same log, he found 12 other salamanders belonging to four species and one Eastern Garter Snake (*Thamnophis s. sirtalis*). On another occasion, also in November, he found large numbers of the Four-toed Salamanders and other amphibians in little clusters of individuals under the leaf litter in small depressions. In an area only a few square feet in size, he found the following numbers of amphibians:

Eastern Four-toed Salamander (*Hemidactylium scutatum*)	Nearly 200
Northern Spring Peeper (*Hyla c. crucifer*)	114
Western Chorus Frog (*Pseudacris nigrita triseriata*)	88
Northern Wood Frog (*Rana sylvatica cantabrigensis*)	48
Jefferson's Salamander (*Ambystoma jeffersonianum*)	In small numbers
Red-backed Salamander (*Plethodon c. cinereus*)	In small numbers
Red-spotted Newt (*Diemictylus v. viridescens*)	In small numbers

The Northern Leopard Frog (*Rana p. pipiens*) characteristically hibernates under water, often in sizable aggregations in certain pools or springs. Lawrence Hope tells of a Wisconsin frog hunter who got 280 pounds of Leopard Frogs in four hours without moving, simply by collecting them as they hopped toward their winter pool. W. J. Breckinridge records an interesting winter aggregation of this species of frog in Minnesota. On January 1, 1939, in the clear outlet stream below the dam of a lake, he found the clear sand bottom "literally paved with hundreds of closely crowded Leopard Frogs." These individuals were not entirely dormant and would occasionally swim to the surface and move to a new position. Kurt Bohnsack has presented detailed information on the terrestrial hibernating site of a Green Frog (*Rana clamitans*) in southern Michigan. This frog was in a very shallow excavation beneath two inches of compact litter. While the temperature of the air went as low as −4° F., the inside of the frog's shelter never went below 32° F. Toads (*Bufo*) dig down in the earth to depths of 3 feet. Roy Latham reports frequently plowing up hibernating Fowler's Toads (*Bufo woodhousi fowleri*) in the winter and early spring on Long Island, New York. The toads were found individually in small chambers from 6 to 12 inches below the surface.

Alligators (*Alligator mississippiensis*) usually hibernate in winter dens which are scooped out of the mud by the animal and may be ten or 15 feet deep. Aquatic turtles find suitable hibernation sites in the mud at the bottom along the margins of ponds and lakes. Sometimes the hibernation is interrupted, and they are seen swimming about under the ice of frozen ponds. Aquatic turtles also retire into muskrat burrows and sometimes hibernate on land not far from water in hollow logs, stumps, and shallow holes. Box Turtles (*Terrapene*) dig into loose earth or vegetable litter and generally hibernate singly, but occasionally small groups may congregate at the same spot. Angus M. Woodbury and Ross Hardy found the Desert Tortoise (*Gopherus agassizi*) in Utah hibernating in regular winter dens which are reused year after year. Occasionally tortoises move from one den to another, even during the period of hibernation, but this is a rare event. The dens are large tunnel burrows that extend back for more than 20 feet in some instances and accommodate a number of turtles.

Lizards hibernate on land in a variety of situations that provide slight to very great protection. This may be under loose bark, in rotting logs or stumps, under rocks, under leaf litter, or down in the soil to an extreme depth of 8 feet. Raymond B. Cowles observed 14 species of western lizards hibernating from just below the surface to a maximum depth of 30 inches. Young individuals tended to hibernate at shallower depths than adults. Ninety-six specimens were found in a limited area, suggesting that they hibernate in groups. Other species may be found in isolation at varying depths below the surface. In Florida the Six-lined Racerunner (*Cnemidophorus sexlineatus*) has been found hibernating individually 6 inches below the surface in an abandoned deer-mouse burrow, and 13 inches underground in a small cavity apparently dug by the lizard itself.

Hibernating aggregations of snakes have long been known and studied in many parts of the country. The numbers of individuals and species that utilize a particular den may be quite high, in some instances exceeding several hundred individuals. Sometimes the dens are located in rocky cliffs, where the snakes retire into caves or deep fissures; in other instances the den may be in an abandoned mammal burrow, a shallow cavern, the rotted root channels of a stump, or the chambers of a large ant hill. The more populated dens usually are situated on slopes facing south or west. G. K. Noble and H. J. Clausen studied the aggregation behavior of several species, particularly DeKay's Snake (*Storeria d. dekayi*). They reported a hibernating group of 76 DeKay's Snakes, 10 young Eastern Garter Snakes (*Thamnophis s. sirtalis*), and 1 young Northern Water Snake (*Natrix s. sipedon*)—found at Flushing, New York, in an old rat burrow only 11 inches deep and facing south. On another occasion they excavated a den containing 97 DeKay's Snakes that were distributed in smaller groups in the passages of an ant hill.

Stuart Criddle discovered one of the most interesting aggregations of hibernating snakes that has been reported. From a single ant hill near Treesbank, Manitoba, Canada, in September and October of 1934, he excavated a total of 257 snakes. There were 148 Smooth Green Snakes (*Opheodrys vernalis*), 101 Red-bellied Snakes (*Storeria occipitomaculata*), and 8 Great Plains Garter Snakes (*Thamnophis radix*). The snakes were in the passages and cavities of the ant hill, which was occupied by small black ants thought to be of the genus *Formica*. In the den the ground water level was 4 feet 9 inches below the surface; and while no snakes were found below the water level, some had parts of the body submerged. In all of these the heads were out of the water and directed upwards. As in most cases, the adults were at a greater depth than the young, indicating an earlier arrival.

Robert C. Schroder studied a small den located in a sand dune in northern Illinois. This den was in an abandoned mammal burrow, a long tunnel extending back into the dune for a horizontal distance of about 8 feet and with a maximum depth of 4 feet below the surface of the dune. It contained two enlarged chambers, one 12 inches and the other 7 inches in diameter. The den was excavated on February 11, 1950, and in the larger chamber were found 5 Blue Racers (*Coluber constrictor foxi*) and 2 Bull Snakes (*Pituophis catenifer sayi*). These were all adult individuals and were tightly intertwined in a ball. The second chamber had another "ball" of closely intertwined snakes, consisting of 2 Blue Racers and 3 Bull Snakes. These were all juveniles, and this is one of the few den aggregations in which the smaller individuals have been found at a greater depth than the adults. Perhaps the adults simply occupied the first chamber when they retired; and because of lack of room the later-arriving juveniles were forced to go farther into the burrow. "Balls of snakes" are sometimes uncovered during road excavations and other building operations. They generally attract considerable interest in the newspapers. Actually they consist of hibernating aggregations.

Hibernating dens used by rattlesnakes have received a great deal of attention and have been reported from virtually all parts of the country except the far south. Usually these dens are utilized by other species than rattlers, but they are popularly called "rattlesnake dens." Angus M. Woodbury has been studying reptile dens in Utah since 1935 and, with the aid of several associates, is carrying on the most extensive studies on snake dens that have been reported in this country. He states that "there are no earmarks by which a snake den, per se, can be recognized." He has found them in loose cobblestone rocks, in gravel banks, in lava beds, in dry spring channels, in rock slides, in fallen clay banks, in deep rock crevices, and in artificial hibernating places such as garbage dumps, rock walls, and open house foundations. The one he is now studying is located on a slope facing east (an exception to the general rule) in a heavy stand of sagebrush. Since 1940 the following total number of snakes have been caught at this den and marked for study: 930 Great Basin Rattlesnakes (*Crotalus viridis lutosus*), 632 Striped Whip Snakes (*Masticophis taeniatus taeniatus*), 127 Western Racers (*Coluber constrictor mormon*), 36 Great Basin Gopher Snakes (*Pituophis catenifer deserticola*), and 5 individuals belonging to three other species. From these studies Woodbury and his associates are amassing a great deal of interesting information on the habits of snakes.

The most frequent reports on hibernation of snakes involve

aggregations of individuals in or around dens. Some species appear to hibernate individually in isolated locations. Wilmer W. Tanner has reported two observations on the Western Milk Snake (*Lampropeltis doliata gentilis*) in Utah. One individual was dug up in sandy soil 4 feet below the surface; another, 6 feet down in a gravel pit. Both were hibernating singly.

Estivation in North American amphibians and reptiles does not appear to be a very clear-cut phenomenon, and there is some question whether true estivation occurs at all in our species. In some localities and in some species there are annual periods of inactivity to escape drought and heat, but the duration and intensity of the processes are not well recognized. Some species respond to adverse dry or hot weather by changing their habits and becoming inactive under such conditions. In still others the inactivity is strikingly similar to that occurring in response to low temperatures. As the Toad (*Bufo*) is stimulated to dig into the ground by falling temperatures, it and other amphibians will do the same thing in response to decreasing moisture. Terrestrial salamanders retire deeper into the ground as the surface soil dries out. They remain until the advent of rains that replenish the surface soil moisture. During hot and dry periods fresh-water turtles frequently burrow in the mud at the bottom of pools, and Box Turtles (*Terrapene*) burrow in the mud at the edge of streams, ponds, and bogs, with only their heads exposed. In Utah, Desert Tortoises (*Gopherus agassizi*) have summer holes that are different from their winter dens, and they retire to these to seek shelter from extreme heat. Farther south this turtle is reported to occupy a single burrow all year. The summer inactivity is unlike hibernation in that a single heavy rain usually activates the animals immediately, whereas prolonged warm weather is generally necessary to bring the animals out of hibernation. The extent of the changes in body chemistry are not known at present.

Seasonal Activity

The seasonal activity cycle is affected by the necessity, or lack, of a period of hibernation and, if present, the duration of it. In southern Canada and at high elevations in the western mountains the period of activity may extend only for a few months, whereas in southern localities it may last for twelve months. Regardless of the duration of this period, the activity is not uniformly distributed throughout, and marked variations occur. In North America most of our amphibians and reptiles have the highest peak of their activities in spring, regardless of whether or not they undergo a period of hibernation. The activity gradually dwindles from this maximum peak to a summer low; and generally, but not invariably, there is another minor resurgence of activity in the fall. This is the general pattern for most of our species, but there are numerous variations of it resulting from species and environmental differences.

The more or less regular activities of amphibians and reptiles appear to center entirely around the following functions:

1. Reproductive functions
2. Eating
3. Obtaining moisture
4. Basking (in diurnal species)

Added to these would be the miscellaneous irregular activities resulting from the animal's efforts to escape harmful features of the environment. Few people have had sufficient time to watch individual amphibians and reptiles of many species going about their daily activities. The information on seasonal activities is based largely on chance encounters with individuals in the field, trapping results, observations of numbers of individuals seen on highways, collection dates, and condition of preserved specimens in museums. A few excellent field studies carried on over a long period have augmented our knowledge on this subject. Admittedly such information reflects not only activity but also population abundance; it is more accurately considered to be information on seasonal incidence of the species rather than simple activity. Although it is incomplete, it does, however, give some indication of the periods of greater and lesser activity.

J. D. Ives studied the fauna of a twilight cave in Tennessee, visiting the cave every month of the year and recording all the animals seen on each visit. The animal inhabitants of the cave included a few salamanders, principally the Cave Salamander (*Eurycea lucifuga*). During the months of March, June, November, and December he saw no salamanders. In January, April, and May, and from July to October, he saw between one and ten salamanders per visit. February was the peak month, with between 11 and 20 individuals being recorded. Fred R. Cagle has reported his turtle trapping results in Louisiana, where he has caught Red-eared Turtles (*Pseudemys scripta elegans*) in every month of the year except January. Turtles were caught in abundance from mid-March until late October. Stomachs of turtles taken during the winter months seldom contained food, suggesting that the activities consisted mainly of basking. The same worker has reported the results of his turtle trapping studies in Illinois. In that state he trapped Red-eared Turtles in every month of the year except January, February, and December. Figure 16 shows the number of turtles caught per trap

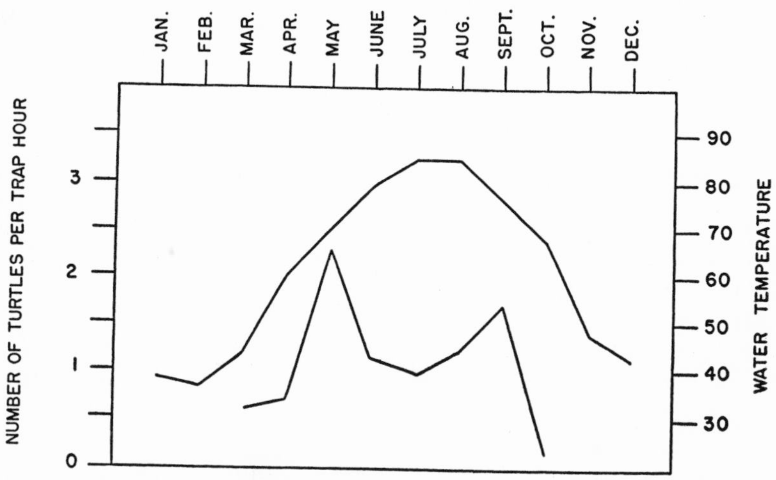

FIG. 16. The number of turtles caught per trap for each month in southern Illinois. The upper curve indicates the mean monthly temperature in degrees Fahrenheit; the lower curve shows the number of turtles caught per trap hour. (After Fred R. Cagle)

per hour in each month. The monthly figures reflect the seasonal activity of the species in that region. Roger Conant found that Painted Turtles (*Chrysemys picta*) were active during every month of the year in Ohio and were even observed occasionally swimming beneath the ice in winter. Angus M. Woodbury and Ross Hardy found the Desert Tortoise (*Gopherus agassizi*) out of the winter dens and on the summer range usually from early April to early October, with the maximum number of individuals observed in August. None was found on the flats of the summer range from November to the first of March. In contrast to this, the Gopher Tortoise (*Gopherus polyphemus*) can be found abroad in Florida during every month of the year, with a peak of activity occurring probably in May or June.

The Green Anolis (*Anolis c. carolinensis*) does not hibernate in Florida. In a study of marked individuals on a two-acre plot, the following total number of specimens were recorded for each month over a three-year period:

Jan.	Feb.	Mar.	Apr.	May	June	July	Aug.	Sept.	Oct.	Nov.	Dec.
25	31	21	25	12	7	26	28	84	48	37	23

The low peak in May and June is associated with a decrease in the population and not solely inactivity. The peak in September and October also indicates the large addition of newly hatched young.

H. Elliott McClure traveled 77,000 miles in Nebraska in three years and kept a careful record of the 6,723 animal traffic victims encountered in his travels. Amphibians comprised 17.4 per cent and reptiles 18.2 per cent of the total. Forty-one per cent of all amphibians and 25 per cent of all reptiles were found in July. He presents the following additional breakdown in figures:

66 per cent of all frogs were found in August
94 per cent of the Tiger Salamanders (*Ambystoma tigrinum*) were found in March
30 per cent of the Toads (*Bufo*) were found in July
45 per cent of the lizards were recorded in June
24 per cent of the Yellow-bellied Racers (*Coluber constrictor flaviventris*) were encountered in October
29 per cent of the Western Hog-nosed Snake (*Heterodon n. nasicus*) were found in September
25 per cent of the Bull Snakes (*Pituophis catenifer sayi*) were encountered in May

The figures give the months in which the maximum numbers of individuals were recorded, but do not indicate the pattern of activity during the year. Frogs (*Rana*) appeared on the highways in May and June, reaching a peak in August. Toads (*Bufo*) also appeared in May, reached a peak in July, and disappeared in October. Lizards, which reached their peak numbers in June, were absent in September, but appeared again in small numbers in October. Yellow-bellied Racers appeared in May, but showed peaks of numbers in June and October. The Hog-nosed Snakes also appeared in May and had two peaks, one in July and again in September. It is interesting to note the similarity in pattern between this snake and the toads that comprise its chief food. Great Plains Garter Snakes (*Thamnophis radix*) appeared a month earlier than the Hog-nosed Snakes, but showed the same pattern as that species. Bullsnakes were fairly uniform from June through October, with the maximum number recorded in May. Ornate Box Turtles (*Terrapene o. ornate*) appeared in May, had a peak of abundance in June, and were not found after the end of August. These figures for highway mortality do not accurately indicate the animal's total activity, but they do provide a quantitative indication of seasonal variation in the number of animals found on highways.

Snakes have been studied in connection with their seasonal incidence more than other reptiles and amphibians. Figure 17 indicates the data for all snakes observed at four localities in the United States. Comparison of activity periods at different localities for individual species would indicate variations from those seen when all forms at the different localities are lumped together. The strong peak in the spring followed by a decline in the summer is shown at all of the localities and probably occurs with the arrival of suitable temperatures. Three localities show a secondary peak in the fall. This partly results from a resurgence of activity as well as the increase in population with the appearance of the young of the year. The spring peak is influenced by the aggregation of species in the vicinity of winter dens, mating activity, increased appetite for food following winter inactivity, and basking during periods of near-minimal environmental temperatures of early spring. The fall peak appears to be related to a lowering of high summer temperatures and the arrival of drought-ending rains.

Henry S. Fitch, in his studies on the Northern Pacific Rattlesnake (*Crotalus viridis oreganus*), pointed out the differences in seasonal activity among adult males, adult females, and young individuals. Adult males reach their greatest abundance in April and gradually decrease almost to the vanishing point in July, but then have a resurgence in August and September. Females attain their maximum abundance in early May, dwindle in June, and are almost entirely absent for the rest of the season. The young are most abundant in May, remain fairly so in June but less so in July, and gradually dwindle in number until hibernation in October.

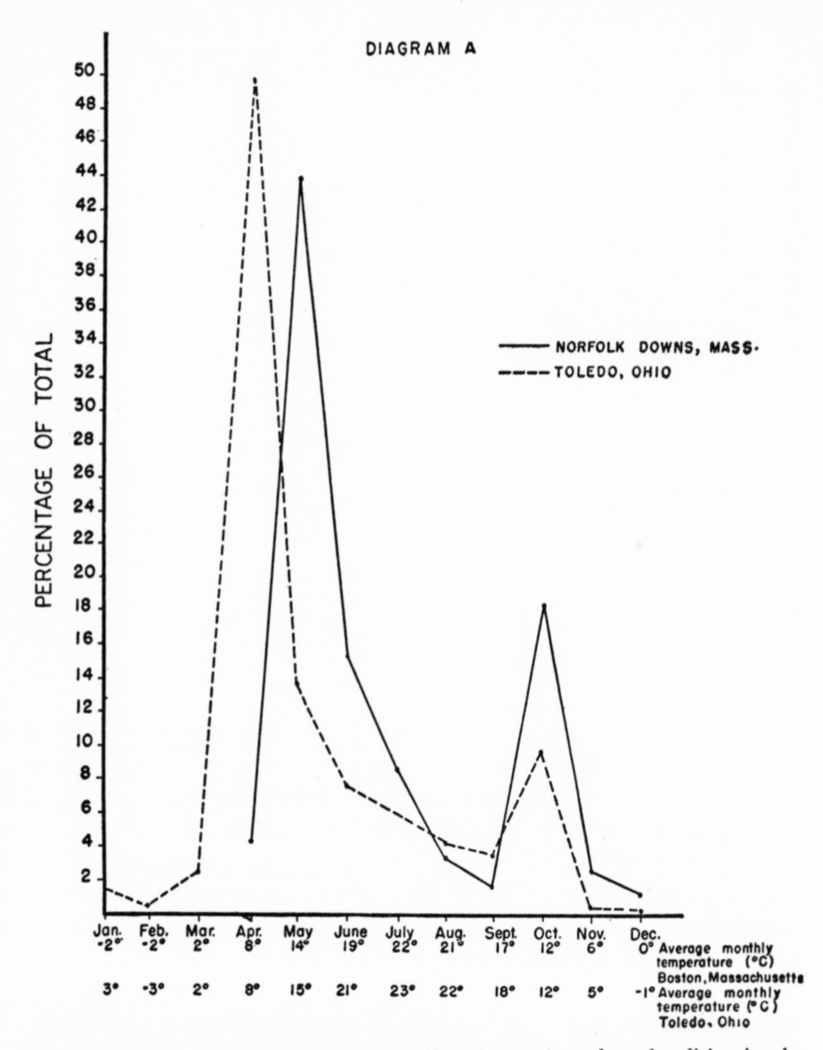

FIG. 17. The seasonal incidence of snakes observed at four localities in the United States. Diagram A records the conditions for Norfolk Downs, Massachusetts (data from Arthur Loveridge) and Toledo, Ohio (data from Roger Conant). Diagram B (p. 131) presents the conditions for Raleigh, North Carolina (data from Clement S. Brimley) and San Diego, California (data from Laurence M. Klauber).

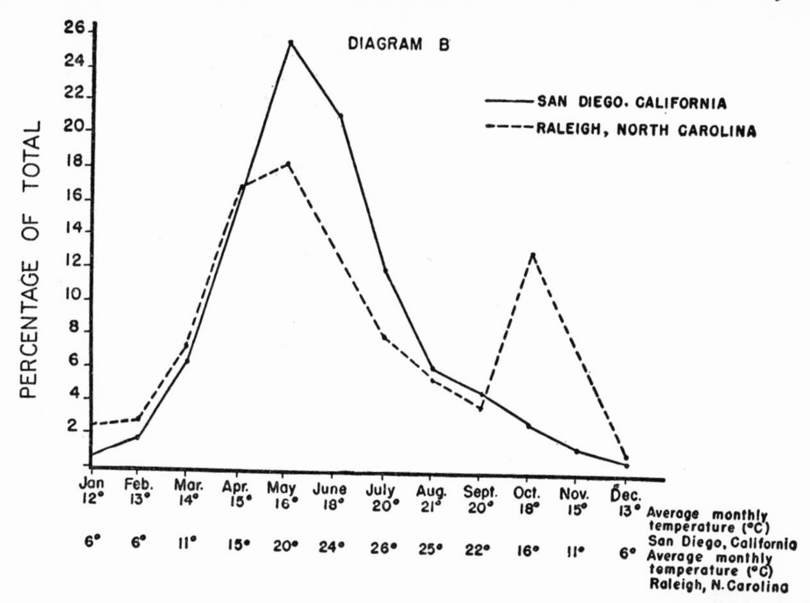

FIG. 17 (cont.)

DAILY ACTIVITY

Seasonal activity reflects the sum total of the daily activities throughout the season. The same factors that influence seasonal activity—the primary types of activity influences—also pertain to daily activity. Sleeping must be added to this list, for it marks the primary period of daily inactivity. Depending on what time the animal is active within the 24-hour period, the animal can be designated as follows: diurnal, or active during the daylight hours; crepuscular, or active at dusk; and nocturnal, or active at night. Most species are characteristically active only at one or another of these periods and thus can readily be designated by one of the three terms. For example, most amphibians are either nocturnal or crepuscular, or both. By being active at such times they avoid the heat of the day with its low relative humidity and consequent danger of desiccation. Most of our reptiles are diurnal, but a few are crepuscular and some nocturnal.

The daily activity cycle is in large part a response to temperature and moisture conditions rather than to light, although the latter is important in many species. Because of the temperature factor, the cycle of daily activity may change from one season to another or from one geographical region to another. For example, many species are diurnal in the early spring, when temperatures are mild and the sun is not at its maximum strength. At such times reptiles may be seen abroad in the middle of the day. Later in the summer, when the sun is stronger and temperatures are higher, the same species may be active only early in the morning and late in the afternoon. They may become crepuscular or nocturnal. Some of our southwestern rattlesnakes are diurnal in spring and fall, and crepuscular or nocturnal in the summer. In Utah, Angus M. Woodbury and Ross Hardy observed a similar pattern in the Desert Tortoise (*Gopherus agassizi*), which becomes active in summer only at night and early morning. Its southeastern relative, the Gopher Tortoise (*Gopherus polyphemus*), may forage at dusk in hot, dry weather, but is virtually never nocturnal.

Though amphibians are mainly nocturnal or crepuscular, they are active only in the middle of the day in the far north and at high elevations. Bayard H. Brattstrom has recently called attention to observations reporting essentially nocturnal reptiles abroad in the daytime. Most such occurrences seem to take place at low temperatures or on overcast days.

Whether the animal is diurnal or nocturnal, there is usually a definite period in the day or night when the peak of the activity occurs. In his studies of nightly activity of Fowler's Toads (*Bufo woodhousi fowleri*) on the beaches of Lake Michigan, W. T. Stille found the toads active from after sunset to shortly before sunrise. Their appearance on the beach after sunset was related to their moisture content; toads of lighter weight had less body water and appeared earlier than heavier ones. After replenishing the water, the toads returned to the diurnal retreats, remaining near the surface and feeding on whatever was available until near sunrise. In contrast to this night-long period of activity are observations on reptiles of the arid southwest.

Laurence M. Klauber has kept careful records of the times that nocturnal reptiles have been encountered on the highways in southern California. His records give an interesting indication of the time of activity for several species. Two examples can be cited to indicate the definite time pattern of activity:

171 Colorado Desert Shovel-nosed Snakes (*Chionactis occipitalis annulatus*) were recorded between 5 P.M. and 2:30 A.M. Of these, 84 per cent were active between 7:30 and 10:30 P.M. Only 6 per cent were active before 7:30 P.M. and 10 per cent after 10:30 P.M.

403 Desert Banded Geckos (*Coleonyx v. variegatus*) were observed between 5:30 P.M. and 4 A.M. Six per cent were encountered before 7:30 P.M., 77 per cent between 7:30 and 10:30 P.M., and 17 per cent after 10:30 P.M.

D. L. Jameson and Alvin G. Flury were able to find specimens of the Trans-Pecos Rat Snake (*Elaphe subocularis*) only between sunset and 10 P.M. In Florida in April, the Green Anolis (*Anolis c. carolinensis*) is most active from about 8 A.M. to 10 or 11 A.M., and again from about 4 P.M. to 6 or 7 P.M. In the same place the Six-lined Racerunner (*Cnemidophorus sexlineatus*) becomes active later in the day, around 9:30 or 10 A.M., and remains more or less active until about 4 P.M. Later in the summer, when midday temperatures are higher, the Anolis may not be seen except in thick, damp woods, while the Racerunner is abroad in the early morning and late afternoon.

During the warmer period of the activity season some salamanders, many frogs, many turtles, and most lizards appear to feed daily if food is easily obtained. Many amphibians and reptiles, however do not feed every day and may go for fairly long periods without food even during their active period. Such animals may remain in seclusion for days without being stimulated to stir themselves. W. T. Stille found Fowler's Toads (*Bufo woodhousi fowleri*) coming to the beach for moisture on the average of once every five nights. Others may come out to bask in the sun in the case of diurnal species, or to obtain moisture or warmth in the case of nocturnal forms. During the cooler parts of the year, daily activity may consist solely in basking. Turtles may be seen basking throughout the year in the southern states, but in the winter few are found with food in their stomachs. Lizards that are active in the winter months have been observed to bask all through the middle of the day without moving except to retire as soon as the temperature dropped or solar radiation was reduced. Sleeping is generally done in seclusion where the animal is protected from adverse changes in the weather and from predators. Characteristic positions may be assumed, affording maximum protection to the head and protruding parts of the body. Occasional species sleep pretty much exposed, however. The Red-spotted Newt (*Diemictylus v. viridescens*) may be found sleeping on the stems of submerged water plants. Some Tree Frogs (*Hyla*) may sleep in fairly exposed leaf axils. Crocodilians sleep either in a secluded spot on the bank while basking or in their den hole. Fresh-water turtles sleep either submerged on the bottom or floating on the surface. Most lizards and snakes sleep in the seclusion of some protected nook. There are a few exceptions: the Green Anolis (*Anolis c. carolinensis*) sleeps completely exposed on bushes, trees, and fence posts. Exceptions are found among the snakes also. These include many of the Water Snakes (*Natrix*), which sleep in branches over water or on logs and stumps. Rough Green Snakes (*Opheodrys aestivus*) and the Florida Ribbon Snake (*Thamnophis sauritus sackeni*) are frequently found sleeping in small trees, bushes, and large herbaceous plants.

Snakes have an advantage over most of the other reptiles in that the eye is covered with a transparent immovable lid and cannot be closed like the eyes of other reptiles and of mammals and birds. Thus movement within range of the eyes may quickly awaken them. The eyeball itself does relax in position, and the pupil of a sleeping snake may sometimes be directed up or down, backward or forward, out of the normal position.

CHAPTER 9

Relation to Environment

THE IMPORTANCE OF THE ENVIRONmental relationships between the animal and its environment have already been mentioned in connection with the occurrence of amphibians and reptiles. It was there stated that the relationships were mutual in many respects and that the environment had a marked indirect effect on the nature of the animal. The basic features of the environment are considered here in the light of their primary effects on amphibians and reptiles, and the animal's adjustments and reactions to the different environmental elements. The successful animal is one that has attained a harmonious balance with the factors of its environment. In a sense, every living animal has achieved a measure of success up to the moment it is living, but it also needs constant adjustment to maintain itself and remain alive. The study of the relations of an animal to its environment, called ecology, is one of the most fundamental fields of biology because it covers such a wide scope of vital life processes.

THE PHYSICAL ENVIRONMENT

For ease of comprehension and analysis, the environment may be divided into the nonliving or physical elements and the living or biotic elements. Each of these groups may be further divided into its various component parts, which are indicated in Table 8.

This table indicates in the simplest terms the complexes that comprise the environment of amphibians and reptiles. The exact influence or effect of most of these factors is still relatively unknown or only slightly known at best. To be sure, we know the effect of extreme conditions and some of the gross results of certain variations in these factors, but we do not know the exact require-

TABLE 8

ENVIRONMENTAL FACTORS

Environment	Major Factors	Primary Features
A. Physical	Climatic	Temperature Humidity Light Atmospheric pressure Wind
	Aquatic	Salt water Brackish water Fresh water
	Edaphic	Exposed rocks Sand Soil
	Physiographic	Altitude Latitude
B. Biotic	Plant	Food Shelter Environmental force
	Animal	Food Enemies Parasites Competition Cooperation Environmental force

ments of a single species for any one factor throughout the life of that species. This is a fertile field of investigation, and the studies that are now being made are revealing many fascinating results and problems.

In most cases a species can tolerate a particular range of conditions for each physical factor. In some species the range may be very narrow or very wide, but for each there are limits outside which it cannot operate or at which the "cost of living," so to speak, is too high for prolonged survival. The limits of toleration vary from species to species. For example, the Red-legged Frog (*Rana aurora*) cannot tolerate the low relative humidity encountered by the Colorado River Toad (*Bufo alvarius*). Therefore it must live where it is not exposed for a long period to the aridity resulting from such low humidity. The Yucca Night Lizard (*Xantu-*

sia vigilis) is killed by the high temperatures at which the Chuckawalla (*Sauromalus obesus*) is normally active.

Temperature

Studies made by Raymond B. Cowles, Charles M. Bogert, Robert C. Stebbins, Lamont C. Cole, and others are yielding a considerable amount of information about the relations of amphibians and reptiles to temperature. It has long been known that these animals are dependent on external environmental sources of heat, in contrast to mammals and birds, which produce sufficient internal heat for their needs. Early workers touched the bodies of fish, amphibians, and reptiles; finding them cooler than their own bodies, they called them "cold-blooded" animals. Mammals and birds, on the other hand, felt warm to the human touch and were called "warm-blooded" animals. These terms have become well rooted in our textbooks and in popular accounts. It was later realized that these designations were not accurate, that the body temperature of some reptiles is sometimes higher than that of man and other mammals, and that some mammals at times have low body temperatures. It is now known that fish, amphibians, and reptiles are able to produce very little heat inside their body and that the heat is quickly lost unless they have an outer source of warmth. Instead they utilize outside sources of heat to warm the body to whatever temperature is required for its effective operation. Because of this dependence on outside heat, they have been designated "ectothermic" animals. The mammals and birds, which produce their required heat inside the body by muscular activity and retain it within their protective coats of fur or feathers, are called "endothermic" animals.

Since amphibians and reptiles derive their body warmth from outside, it was long believed that their temperature would be within a degree or two of the surrounding air. The statement expresses the general condition for amphibians and nocturnal reptiles, but for diurnal reptiles it would be more accurate if expressed in relation to the temperature of the substratum. The exceptions and complexities involved in the temperature conditions of both amphibians and reptiles make even a general statement of little value. The first statement still appears all too frequently in books about these animals.

From the studies of Cowles, Bogert, Stebbins, and Cole we have learned that reptiles, when they are active, move about and regulate their body temperatures through their behavior. By basking or lying on a warm rock, they can raise the body temperature; by retiring into the shade, under a rock or into the ground, they can lower it. Therefore, by moving about, exposing itself to warmth or coolness, the animal can maintain a fairly constant body temperature. If the source of warmth is the surrounding air, the body temperature may approximate that temperature. However, if the animal is lying in contact with a warm substratum when the air is cool or if it is basking, the body temperature may be considerably above that of the surrounding air. A lizard basking in the sun on a cool day when the temperature of the air is only 55° F. may have its body temperature at approximately 100° F. The animal's body more effectively absorbs solar heat than does the air. As an aid to controlling the temperature of the body, most lizards and frogs can vary the color of the body, making it dark when the animal is cold or light when it is warm. The dark-colored body absorbs more heat, whereas the light-colored body reflects a larger percentage of heat and hence absorbs less.

Because of differences in behavior and structure, several species of reptiles active at the same time in a single habitat may be maintaining their bodies at quite different temperatures. When reptiles are inactive or in a stable thermal environment, their body temperatures approximate the temperature of the surroundings. The activity temperature of the body in amphibians is much lower than that in reptiles. This is partly owing to the evaporation of moisture through the skin in amphibians. At 100-per-cent relative humidity there is no evaporation, but at humidities below that degree of saturation the evaporation is sufficient to make the body temperature of an amphibian approximately equal to the temperature indicated on a wet-bulb thermometer. There is little or no evaporation from the skin of a reptile, and consequently no variation with changes in the relative humidity. However, if the reptile's body temperature is approaching the critical maximum, it can cool its body by forced respiration through the open mouth. This process of cooling operates more efficiently at low relative humidity than it does if the humidity is high. Studies by Charles M. Bogert indicate that salamanders apparently lack the ability to control their body temperatures through their behavior and are relatively insensitive to changes within the range of temperatures tolerated. That this is not true of frogs is indicated by the frequent observations of these animals basking in the direct sunlight at low temperatures to warm their bodies.

Temperature studies on western amphibians indicate some of the difficulties involved in making general statements on the temperature relations of ectothermic forms. The studies of Robert C. Stebbins indicate that the body temperature of the Mountain Salamander (*Rhyacotriton olympicus*) is usually slightly below that of the water in which it is found. Thermometer readings of the water and the salamander both varied from about 40° to 50° F. In contrast, Stebbins' temperature observations on the Black Toad (*Bufo boreas exsul*) show that when in water its body temperature was 1° to 3° F. above the temperature of the water. The body temperature of this toad when on land, like that of other amphibians, was below that of the air and substratum. In the water the toad's temperature varied from 70° to 73° F., whereas the water temperature was 69° F. On land the toad's body temperature was 71.5° to 76° F., the temperature of the substratum was approximately 77° to 83° F., and that of the air between 75° and 80° F.

Raymond B. Cowles and Charles M. Bogert studied twelve diurnal and seven nocturnal species of reptiles inhabiting the arid southwest. A summary of their findings indicates the general conditions of temperature adjustment in our North American reptiles. Voluntary activity occurred between body temperature extremes of 60° and 108° F., with the average activity range being below those found in many mammals. An interesting result of this study was the demonstration that the average activity temperature is close to the critical maximum that can be tolerated. A difference of less than 11° F. between the two seems like a slight margin. Their studies demonstrated the fallacy of the popular belief that reptiles are heat-loving animals, some being killed at body temperatures of approximately 98° F., close to the average body temperature of human beings. No reptile was able to stand temperatures above 118° F. Nocturnal species could tolerate lower temperatures and had lower average activity temperatures than diurnal reptiles. Smaller individuals of the same species acquire and lose heat more rapidly than do larger ones. This is an important factor in the earlier emergence and later retirement of the young at hibernation, as compared with the adults. The ability of reptiles in their normal habitats to avoid extensive temperature fluctuations was clearly shown by a Sidewinder Rattlesnake (*Crotalus cerastes*). The body temperature of this snake was recorded frequently during the day while it was at the mouth of its burrow. By exposing varying amounts of its body in the early morning and moving deeper into its burrow as the air and soil surface temperature rose, it maintained its body temperature between 88° and 90° F.

Cowles and Bogert found that the average activity temperature of diurnal lizards was approximately 98° F., higher than the average for the snakes tested. The highest activity temperature of lizards represents the upper limit of body temperatures tolerated by reptiles. An Old World lizard of the Family Agamidae has been reported at slightly higher temperatures than those recorded for any North American lizard, but the Chuckawalla (*Sauromalus obesus*) is known voluntarily to tolerate a body temperature of 108° F. And recently Kenneth S. Norris has recorded the activity body temperature of the Desert Iguana (*Dipsosaurus dorsalis*) to be as high as 117° F. Extremely high temperatures not only kill the individual, but cause sterilization. Cowles has recorded such results in the Yucca Night Lizard (*Xantusia vigilis*) when it is forcibly kept at temperatures that are high for the species but not lethal.

The studies that have been made clearly demonstrate the difficulty of measuring environmental temperatures for reptiles. As already pointed out, in the case of a basking individual the air temperature may be quite different from the animal's body temperature. If the animal is resting (but not basking in the sun) on a warm rock, the temperature of the rock may be more important than that of the air. In most field studies now being carried on, the temperature of the animal, the air, and the substratum are all recorded. In earlier studies only the temperature of the air was recorded. Large numbers of observations on air temperature, however, do provide an indication of the air temperature at which the species is abroad. Bogert observed several species of eastern salamanders to be active in moist conditions with a substratum temperature range of 59° to 65° F. Toads usually are not active when the air temperature is below 59° F., but may be out at air temperatures of 80° F.

Laurence M. Klauber recorded the air temperatures at which 286 Desert Banded Geckos (*Coleonyx v. variegatus*) were collected. The temperatures ranged from 60° to 99° F., but 74 per cent were collected between air temperatures of 75° and 89° F. By comparison with these figures for air temperatures, Cowles and Bogert found this lizard to have an average activity body temperature of 86° F.

Temperature is one of the most important of all physical factors of the environment, particularly for the ectothermic forms. They can live only within certain temperature limits that are more restricted than those tolerated by the endothermic mammals and birds. Within the limits of toleration, most life processes take place more rapidly at higher than at lower temperatures. Below an optimal body temperature, amphibians and reptiles cannot carry on the vital processes. E. G. Boulenger observed that the salamander Amphiuma (*Amphiuma means*) would not feed at a temperature of 56° F., but fed as soon as this was raised to 65° to 70° F. Cowles and Bogert observed that the Desert Spiny Lizard (*Sceloporus m. magister*) commonly fed at a body temperature of 86° F., but defecation was most frequent at a body temperature of approximately 98° to 100° F. Eastern Garter Snakes (*Thamnophis s. sirtalis*) and Great Plains Garter Snakes (*Thamnophis radix*) kept at a constant temperature of 80° F. fed, defecated, and shed the skin more frequently than did individuals of the same species kept at 70° F. This temperature relationship is shown over and over again in the study of virtually all amphibians and reptiles. However, we do not now know the details of the temperature requirements at different times in the life cycle nor for all of the life functions.

Humidity

Humidity is a factor that is intimately related to temperature, and the requirements for this element vary proportionately with the temperature. Amphibians are more dependent on humidity than reptiles, but both have definite toleration limits for humidity. Because of their limited toleration to conditions of low humidity, many amphibians are aquatic or semiaquatic, rarely moving far from moist situations. Even toads (*Bufo*), which have adjusted to life on land about as successfully as any amphibians, cannot move far from moisture. W. T. Stille has recorded the nocturnal visits of frogs (*Rana*) and toads (*Bufo*) to the beach in the dunes area of southern Lake Michigan. The visits are related to the moisture requirements of these amphibians. Frogs enter the water to absorb moisture, while toads do not go in the water but sit on the wet sand. Both absorb water through the skin of the groin, but neither can obtain moisture from the air by absorbing it through the skin of the back. Stille found that the toads visited the beach on an average of once every five nights. He found a greater concentration of individuals and an earlier arrival time on the beach in toads adjacent to higher (and presumably drier) elevations than in toads in low and presumably wetter areas. He assumed that toads living in such areas lost moisture more readily and hence needed to replenish it more frequently than did those from lower elevations.

A number of studies have been made on the toleration of moisture loss in amphibians and reptiles. In general there is a correlation between the amount of moisture that can be lost without death and the habits of the animal. Land-dwelling forms can lose more water without harm than can the aquatic species; those living in drier places can lose more than the species occurring in damp habitats. Robert E. Gordon's recent studies on the Green Salamander (*Aneides aeneus*) and the Highlands Salamander (*Plethodon jordani melaventris*) illustrate this point. The former lives in drier rock crevices than the latter. In measuring the percentage of water loss that could be tolerated under experimental conditions, Gordon found that the Highlands Salamander lost 12.7 to 25.6 per cent of the original weight, with an average of 18.8 per cent; whereas the Green Salamander sustained losses of 25.0 to 34.2 per cent of original weight, with an average of 30.4 per cent.

Charles M. Bogert and Raymond B. Cowles ran similar tests on eleven species of reptiles from Florida. They found the same general relationship between the moisture loss that a species could tolerate and its habitat. They stressed the important point that in such studies it is necessary to restrict comparisons to species of the same order and not contrast, for example, a turtle with a snake. The structural and physiological differences between members of the different orders are too great to permit accurate comparisons. Within a single order, marked differences were observed in the rate at which the loss occurred under identical conditions. In a thermal chamber with a constant temperature of 100° F. and relative humidity of 37 per cent, the Indigo Snake (*Drymarchon corais couperi*) lost moisture at the rate of 1.3 per cent of its original weight per hour and survived only 9.5 hours. In contrast, the Coachwhip (*Masticophis f. flagellum*) lost moisture at a rate of less than .2 per cent per hour and was still surviving at the end of 99.5 hours.

In these two snakes the percentage of moisture loss in terms of the original body weight was virtually the same, approximately 12 per cent. The Indigo Snake is abundant in warm, damp habitats, frequently foraging in water and never encountering humidities as low as those in the experiment, whereas the Coachwhip occurs in hotter, dry habitats, where it more frequently encounters conditions similar to those in the thermal chamber.

Within the habitat of the species, individuals move about to keep themselves in suitable moisture conditions. With the seasonal changes that take place in soil moisture, land salamanders and burrowing frogs move up and down to remain in moist soil. V. E. Shelford showed that both frogs and salamanders responded to very slight changes in moisture, avoiding low humidity and moving toward high humidity. The summer aggregations of amphibians and reptiles are usually in situations that afford high humidity or moisture conditions compared with the surrounding areas. Charles E. Lowe, Jr., found a group of 14 estivating California Newts (*Taricha torosus*) in a shallow, damp hole in June. The tendency of aquatic species to dig into the mud of drying ponds and lakes brings them into contact with moisture and usually lower temperatures. The aggregations of individuals at times of low humidity and warm temperatures enable the individuals to conserve more body moisture than if they retired separately. Amphibians are most active at times of high relative humidity; warm rains invariably stimulate an increase in amphibian activity. Reptiles respond similarly to moisture changes but tolerate lower humidities. Both amphibians and reptiles undergo a considerable loss of body moisture just before and during the shedding of the skin. Because of this they require higher moisture conditions at this time, and there is actually a greater intake of water during the shedding process. Land reptiles frequently soak themselves in water at this time, and there is some indication that there is a general correlation between the frequency of shedding and the humidity of the habitat, with greater frequency of shedding in the more moist habitats.

Other Physical Factors

The role of the remaining physical features of the environment is not so well recognized as are the roles of temperature and humidity. Here the importance is only generally indicated. For example, we know that light plays an important part in the life functions of amphibians and reptiles; but in exactly what ways and how, we still don't know. Light, of course, is a very general term that covers all the visible wave lengths. Actually, the light from different wave lengths must be of importance in varying ways. Light is important in regulating many of the physiological functions of the body. Some, but not all, of these functions can be carried on under artificial light as well as sunlight. What types of light are absent from artificial light? Which types are important for different functions? Is one wave length alone responsible, or is it effective only when present with other wave lengths?

It has been shown experimentally that tadpoles of certain species receiving only artificial light soon die, but those that get a small amount of sunlight and long periods of artificial light develop faster than those receiving the same amount of sunlight but no artificial light. On the other hand, tadpoles of other species can complete development when exposed only to artificial light. It has also been shown experimentally that turtles and lizards can be stimulated to reproduce at an earlier time in the year by increasing the length of the daily light period. This response can be produced solely with artificial light.

Atmospheric pressure is another factor about which we know relatively little in relation to its effects on amphibians and reptiles. The altitudinal distribution of these forms may be influenced by the decrease in pressure at higher elevations, but our present information indicates that temperature is the critical limiting factor for these animals at high altitudes. The most interesting effect of pressure on North American amphibians or reptiles that has been noted is that observed by William Beck on the Spadefoot Toad (*Scaphiopus h. holbrooki*) in Florida. It had long been known that this species breeds only after or during very heavy rainstorms. Beck tried stimulating them to mate in the laboratory, but was unsuccessful until he put specimens in a vacuum jar and lowered the pressure. Under the conditions of reduced pressure, mating behavior was stimulated.

The effects of varying chemical conditions of water on amphibians and reptiles is another aspect of the physical environment about which precise relationships are poorly known. Amphibians as a group are notably sensitive to salt water and are quickly killed when immersed in it, yet the eggs of some species can develop in brackish water. Adults of the Green Tree Frog (*Hyla c. cinerea*) have been found on sedges in salt marshes at considerable distances from dry land. Larvae of several western races of the Tiger Salamander (*Ambystoma tigrinum*) have been found in strongly alkaline water. Marine turtles are inhabitants of the oceans and only rarely go into fresh water, yet they can live entirely in fresh water. Land and fresh-water reptiles infrequently enter salt water, but most species can survive fairly long periods of immersion in the sea. A few species live in the brackish-water zone between fresh water and the seas. Differences in toleration and frequency of occurrence in waters of marked acidity or alkalinity have been reported but have not been studied in detail in our North American species. Interesting studies have been reported on the reactions of amphibians to differences in concentration of dissolved gases in water. The Red-spotted Newt (*Diemictylus v. viridescens*) is attracted during the breeding season to stands of aquatic vegetation where a high oxygen concentration exists.

Land reptiles may be adapted to living in or on particular types of soil and may be found only on such soils. For example, the Sand Skink (*Neoseps reynoldsi*) is restricted to the loose sandy soil of the interior high pine and rosemary scrub area of the central Florida Peninsula. Charles M. Miller found that Footless Lizards (*Anniella pulchra*) were limited to fine-textured sandy soils in southern California. Robert C. Stebbins studied the adaptations of the Fringe-footed Lizard (*Uma notata*), which is highly specialized for life on the shifting sands of desert dunes and is found only on loose sand.

Reactions to Physical Environment

The reactions of species to the various physical factors of the environment may involve physiological, structural, or behavioral responses. Since we are concerned here primarily with the natural history aspects of amphibians and reptiles, we will consider primarily their behavioral reactions.

In studying the response of animals to the physical features, we use the term "tropism." This term is given a prefix to indicate the specific physical factor being designated. Thermotropism indicates a response to temperature; hydrotropism, to humidity; phototropism, to light; barotropism, to pressure; rheotropism, to current; geotropism, to the pull of gravity or the slope of a surface; thigmotropism, to contact; and chemotropism, to a chemical substance. The animal's response is either to move away from (negative tropism) or toward (positive tropism) the physical factor present. Through such responses the animal tends to keep itself in an environmental situation suitable to its needs. Many of an animal's tropistic responses automatically move it into a proper location for some specific function, such as reproduction; or remove it from unsuitable or dangerous situations. The tropism of a species for a particular physical feature may always remain the same or may vary with the physiological condition of the animal and other physical factors of the environment. For example, the Texas Blind Salamander (*Typhlomolge rathbuni*) is always negatively phototropic, whereas Toads (*Bufo*) are negatively phototropic at high activity temperatures and low humidity, but may be positively phototropic at low activity temperatures. A gravid female Spotted Salamander (*Ambystoma maculatum*) exhibits a positive geotropism and moves downhill, but this is reversed after she has completed her mating activity. Many amphibians can locate water by being sensitive to a moisture gradient in the air or soil and move toward conditions of increasing moisture. Hatchling fresh-water and marine turtles are assisted in finding their way from the land nest to the water by means of first a negative geotropism and a positive phototropism that gets them out of the ground. Once in the light, the positive phototropism is retained, but the negative geotropism becomes positive. This takes them downhill or toward the maximum concentration of light, which is usually over open water. Through this series of responses, or tropisms, the animal moves away from less suitable to more suitable situations.

Biotic Environment

Plants and animals that live in the same area are part of the environment. Amphibians and reptiles have important relations with their environment that will be discussed in the present section. The complex role of the organic environmental elements can be subdivided into various categories. A simple outline is given in Table 8.

For amphibians and reptiles the most important roles of plants are to serve as food, as shelter, and as a general environmental force. As a source of food, plants are of less importance to amphibians and reptiles than animals, because most species are carnivorous. However, many turtles and a few lizards utilize some plants in their diets. Living and dead plants, or plant remains, provide shelter for amphibians and reptiles. Rotting logs and stumps, particularly, serve as protective retreats. Some terrestrial salamanders may spend most of their lives within a single large log. Reptiles may live in or under logs; other species may lay their eggs in logs; and still others may use logs as shelters in which to bring forth their young. In Missouri, I once found a total of 22 Northern Copperheads (*Ancistrodon contortrix mokeson*) and Timber Rattlesnakes (*Crotalus h. horridus*) in a six-foot hollow log. Here a mother Copperhead had her young at one end of the log and a mother rattler had hers at the opposite end. I had discovered them before the young had moved away to shift for themselves. The log was a veritable nursery.

The term "environmental force" is a general one that covers all the roles not easily categorized without a more detailed consideration. It includes the important role of plants in making up a major part of the habitat in which the animals live. In this role living plants not only form one of the primary features of the habitat, but contribute to the formation of the soil and influence the physical features, such as temperature, moisture, light, and wind conditions of the habitat. Plants largely determine the visible characteristics of the habitat and hence give each habitat its general appearance.

Plants play other roles of a more special type in some cases. Molds or fungi may grow as parasites on terrestrial eggs, bringing about the death of the developing embryos. Algae frequently grow on the shells of aquatic turtles, making them more difficult to see in their aquatic habitat. One of the most interesting relations with plants is the relation of algae that grow *inside* the outer egg membrane of the eggs of some amphibians. Here the algae, like those on the shells of turtles, are beneficial. Perry W. Gilbert studied this relationship in eggs of the Spotted Salamander (*Ambystoma maculatum*) and found that the alga-egg relationship is another of the interesting mutually beneficial arrangements found among a number of living organisms. Alga inhabited eggs produce larger embryos, hatch earlier, and have a lower mortality than eggs without algae. He also found that the alga grows more vigorously in eggs containing embryos than in eggs from which the embryos have been removed.

The relations of amphibians and reptiles to the other animals of the environment can be considered under several different headings. First is food. Since most amphibians and reptiles are meat eaters, the animal life of the environment represents the primary source of food. Not all species are eaten, and those that are preyed upon will be utilized in different measures by the species of amphibians and reptiles occurring in any one environment. The details of the food habits are considered in Chapter 10 and therefore need not be considered here except as they pertain to competition.

Enemies

Just as amphibians and reptiles prey upon other animals in their environment, they, too, fall prey to members of other animal groups and their own classes. Thus frogs may be eaten by fish, larger frogs, crocodilians, turtles, snakes, birds, and mammals. Snakes may be eaten by fish, frogs, crocodilians, turtles, other snakes, birds, and mammals. Virtually all classes of vertebrates may prey upon amphibians and reptiles, or on their eggs. Some species may eat them only occasionally, when other supplies of food are limited, but other species may feed regularly or solely on these animals. The chapter on food habits discusses cannibalism, or the eating of members of the same species. Here the remarks pertain only to preying upon members of another species, even when prey and predator belong to the same order. The eating of a Water Snake by a King Snake is not cannibalism in the strict sense of the word.

Man is doubtless the most important enemy of amphibians and reptiles. He represents an enemy who kills for food, to obtain materials for use as ornaments or in clothing, simply to get rid of animals that he finds objectionable, or merely for the "sport" of killing. Other enemies kill the animals in defense or for food. The numbers that are killed in defense are insignificant compared with

PLATE VII. Head-on view of a male Fowler's Toad (*Bufo woodhousei fowleri*) calling with vocal pouch fully inflated. Note that the toad is in shallow water, only partly submerged, when calling. (Photograph by Dr. Charles Stine, Jr.)

PLATE VIII. A female Eastern Tiger Salamander (*Ambystoma t. tigrinum*) in the act of laying eggs underwater. This remarkable picture shows how the eggs are attached to submerged vegetation. (Photograph by Dr. Charles Stine, Jr.)

those eaten as food. No large group of amphibians or reptiles is free from predation. What methods are utilized in avoiding, or in reducing the probabilities of, being eaten? It is of interest to examine in some detail the major types of protection used by North American amphibians and reptiles.

The first and most widely used protective method is simply to escape by fleeing—relying on locomotor skill, agility, and the nearness of some type of shelter. A frog sitting on the bank of a pond jumps into the water and quickly swims to the bottom, where it buries itself in the plant debris or mud. A turtle basking on a log in the pond does the same thing. A lizard basking on a rock runs down and under the rock. A snake crawls into the nearest hole or under the nearest shelter, or crawls quickly through the brush out of harm's way. The success of this method depends on the nearness of protective shelter and the locomotor ability of the individual. Inhabitants of open habitats are usually faster than those of the thicker brush. Exceptions to this generalization possess other protective methods. Some of the fastest lizards and snakes simply rely on their speed to remove them from danger. Often these species remain motionless after coming to rest at a point removed from the original encounter. The Coachwhip (*Masticophis f. flagellum*) crawls away with considerable speed when encountered, frequently climbs into a low shrub or tree when a good distance away, and remains motionless watching the intruder from its point of vantage. It will stay in this position almost until touched.

Another method is to escape detection through one of three types of adaptation:

1. Structural features that create a similarity to inanimate objects of the environment.
2. Coloration that obscures the outline of the animal's body or blends with or simulates some object of the environment.
3. Behavior that orients the animal's body so that it enhances the effectiveness of the two foregoing adaptations.

One or all three of these adaptations may occur in the same individual. The Horned Lizards (*Phrynosoma*), with their flattened bodies and ability to change color, blend very closely into the sandy or rocky substratum on which they may be found. Some Tree Frogs (*Hyla*), when flattened in the axils of large leaves or on the bark of rough-barked trees, appear as part of the objects on which they rest. The Mexican Vine Snake (*Oxybelis aeneus auratus*) of southern Arizona looks strikingly like a narrow twig, and when approached it moves gently back and forth, resembling a twig blown by a breeze.

Another type of protection is obtained by the presence of strictly defensive structures. The shells of turtles are among the classical examples of such structures. It is interesting to note that the land species have the hardest and most protective shells found in turtles. Archie Carr has pointed out that there is a general correlation between the amount of protection offered by the shell and the viciousness of the species—those with less shell being more vicious. The horns on the head of the Horned Lizards (*Phrynosoma*) provide protection against small predators, but are of little effect against larger prey. Many species of these lizards squirt blood from the eyes when disturbed. The blood is reputedly irritating when it comes in contact with the eyes of mammals, possibly permitting the escape of the lizard from small mammal predators. The poison glands in the skin of amphibians are effective in protecting them from many would-be predators. The secretions of the parotoid glands (above and behind the ear membrane; see Figure 20, upper) in toads protect them from molestation by dogs. The same glands protect them from many other mammalian and some reptilian predators. The skin of all amphibians contains glands that secrete a poisonous substance. The effectiveness of the secretion varies from species to species and with different predatory species. The Pickerel Frog (*Rana palustris*) looks superficially like the Leopard Frog (*Rana pipiens*), but the two differ considerably in the toxicity of the skin secretions. The Leopard Frog is eaten by many species of snakes. The same snakes may grab a Pickerel Frog, but they almost immediately release it and act as if the secretion caused an unpleasant sensation.

Marian Hubbard studied the effectiveness of skin secretions in protecting three western salamanders from being eaten by two western snakes, the Western Garter Snake (*Thamnophis elegans*) and the Western Ring-necked Snake (*Diadophis amabilis*). The snakes would not accept the California Newt (*Taricha torosus*), which has well-developed and abundant skin glands. Once when a snake was induced to bite a newt, it let it go and went about for an hour opening its mouth in apparent distress. The Northern Pacific Red Salamander (*Ensatina eschscholtzi oregonensis*) has poison glands concentrated in the dorsal region of the tail. This salamander was seen to strike an investigating snake with its tail—an action that effectively discouraged the snake. When the salamanders had their tails intact, the snakes would not eat them, but if the tails were removed, the salamanders were voluntarily eaten by the snakes. Worm Salamanders (*Batrachoseps*), on the other hand, have little or no toxic skin secretions and were readily taken by the snakes. The foul-smelling musk glands of some turtles and snakes are not poisonous, but are repugnant to mammalian predators.

The Worm Salamanders and a few other salamanders, and some lizards, have very fragile tails that readily break off. The disjointed tail wriggles violently when just detached and frequently distracts an enemy while the owner crawls away to safety. The tail is then regenerated, not so long as the original but a tail nevertheless. Many of the species in which this ability is well developed have brightly colored tails that add to the distracting effect. Not all lizards have tails that break easily, and some cannot regenerate a tail if the original is injured. In the species where the tail is fragile, the break occurs at one of many fracture planes, where the muscles are so arranged that they immediately close the blood vessels at that point and reduce the amount of blood lost.

Many species have effective offensive weapons that can be employed in defense when the occasion demands. The venom and venom apparatus of all venomous species can be used in this way. When a venomous snake bites a dog, cow, horse, man, or any large animal, it is using an effective offensive weapon in defense. The sharp jaws of the Snapping Turtles (*Chelydra*) and the Soft-shelled Turtles (*Trionyx*) represent similar weapons. The painful, but not serious, bite of our large aquatic salamanders is the result of the same type of defense.

Another type of protection is a behavior response designed to discourage further molestation. In this defensive response the animal may flash a bright color that is normally concealed. The Ring-necked Snakes (*Diadophis*) and the Mud Snakes (*Farancia abacura*) curl the tail so as to bring the bright orange or red undercolor into view. Bluffing, accompanied by an inflation or enlargement of part of the body and frequent loud hissing, is employed by many species. The Hog-nose Snakes (*Heterodon*) are the best proponents of this defensive response. If this fails, they then "play dead" by rolling over on the back with the mouth open. Many turtles, crocodilians, lizards, and snakes hiss or forcibly expel air from the lungs when disturbed. Such sounds may distract or repel an intruder or potential predator. A number of lizards and snakes twitch or vibrate the tail when excited by the presence of an intruder. This reaction reaches its peak of development in the rattlesnakes of the genera *Crotalus* and *Sistrurus*. Here the tip of the tail bears a series of loose horny rattles that are vibrated at a rapid rate. L. E. Chadwick and Hermann Rahn have demonstrated that the frequency of the rattle vibration varies from 17 cycles per second at a body temperature of about 47° F. to 88 cycles per second at a body temperature of about 97° F. The resulting sound from a large rattlesnake can be heard 100 feet away, but that of a small individual or species can be heard for only a few feet. The rattle is employed only when the snake is disturbed by a large or unseen intruder. It is not employed in mating, to attract prey, or as a signal to other rattlesnakes, and it is not an automatic reaction but is controlled by the snake. Contrary to popular belief, the rattlesnake is not a gentleman who always warns before he strikes. Sometimes the snake strikes and then rattles; other times it may not rattle at all. Effectiveness of the rattle on a would-be predator is indicated by the observation of Charles M. Bogert, who reported that a California Weasel refused to go near a rattling Sidewinder Rattlesnake (*Crotalus cerastes*) but did not hesitate to attack the snake when the latter's rattle was silenced. Bogert has also reported that the rattlesnake assumes a characteristic defensive position when approached by a King Snake (*Lampropeltis*), but never rattles on such an occasion.

There are a number of defensive positions assumed by amphibians and reptiles that make it more difficult for a predator to eat them. Most of these defensive responses would appear to be effective only against small enemies that could barely overpower the animal. Under such conditions the defensive position would make the swallowing of the animal so difficult that the predator abandons the project. Frogs frequently assume a tight, squatting position with the head pressed firmly against the substratum. Snakes and lizards assume a coiled position with the head protected under the body and tail. L. V. Compton reported an unusual reaction of an Alligator Lizard (*Gerrhonotus*): when attacked by a snake, the lizard grabbed its tail in its mouth, encircling a small branch with its body. Then the snake was unable to engulf the lizard.

Finally, the animals will fight to defend themselves against some predators. Often this is an ineffectual effort, but sometimes it proves of value. In a few surprising cases the creature fails to put up any resistance and is overpowered by a predator that it could easily destroy or avoid.

No fight can be launched against the parasites that attack amphibians and reptiles. A large number of internal and external parasites, ranging from one-celled viruses and Protozoans to insects and ticks, infest these animals. Salamanders and aquatic frogs appear to be free of external animal parasites, but may be infested by round and flat worm parasites of several different groups. In addition to these parasites, ticks and mites often infest toads.

Aquatic turtles and crocodilians are hosts to leeches and numerous internal worm parasites. Land turtles carry ticks and may be hosts to botfly larvae, which cause large swellings and open sores when the pupae emerge. Lizards and turtles are frequent hosts to internal worm parasites as well as external ticks and mites. Snakes are infested with the specialized arthropod parasites, the Linguatulids, most commonly inhabiting the respiratory tract and lungs. Bot and other flies parasitize several species of lizards. Most parasites are highly adapted to their hosts and do not bring about death. However, heavy infestations of fly larvae and mites frequently result in the demise of the host. Few amphibians and no reptiles are carriers of any human disease organism, and none of the parasites found on them is effective on human beings.

Competition and Cooperation

One of the relationships between animals that is difficult to evaluate accurately is competition. It is an easy term to call to mind when other explanations do not give satisfaction. Despite the fact that it has been overworked in some instances, competition is an important factor in the relationships between animals in the same area. Competition may be interspecific—that is, between the members of different species. Or it may be intraspecific—that is, between individuals of a single species. The more similar individuals are, the more their requirements are alike, and hence the more apt they are to compete. If there is an abundance of all the required elements, then there will be no competition. Where there is a shortage in one or more requirements, then competition will be important in the welfare of the species. Intraspecific competition is of importance in stimulating the spread of the species into unoccupied areas and in influencing the survival or failure of individuals with certain attributes. Interspecific competition may play an important role in the distribution of the species. Where one species competes with another, it must do so successfully if it is to continue in the area where the two occur together. The pressure of competition may cause a species to be absent from a region where suitable habitats exist for it if the habitats are already occupied by a successful species. Such competition may be important in the development of different modes of living through selection.

One way in which competition is reduced in one locality is by means of different feeding habits. Among individuals of the species, the young, being smaller in size, can eat only small prey, whereas the adults, being larger and stronger, can eat larger prey. In this way a greater variety of food can be used by the species without competition between young and adults. Austin Rand has suggested that this is an important factor in the development of sexual dimorphism in size. Competition between related species occurring in the same habitat is also avoided when they have different feeding habits. At Crater Lake, Oregon, Donald S. Farner observed the Crater Lake Newt (*Taricha granulosus mazamae*) and the Long-toed Salamander (*Ambystoma macrodactylum*) living side by side. In fact, they were frequently found beneath the same stone at the edge of the lake. Study of the food of the two species showed that they had quite different food habits and were not competing directly for food. The difference in food consumed is shown in Figure 18. The Long-toed Salamander is primarily a scavenger, but takes a few live aquatic insects, whereas the Newt feeds principally on live snails, amphipods, and insect larvae. In contrast to this situation, Richard G. Zweifel found a locality where the Monterey Salamander (*Ensatina e. eschscholtzi*) and the Arboreal Salamander (*Aneides l. lugubris*) occurred together and ate virtually the same food organisms. However, the Monterey Salamanders were three times as abundant as the Arboreal Salamanders, suggesting that the former were more successful in competition than the latter.

Charles C. Carpenter studied the ecological relationships of the three species of Garter Snakes occurring in southern Michigan. He found that differences in the type and size of food consumed reduced the competition between the species. The differences are

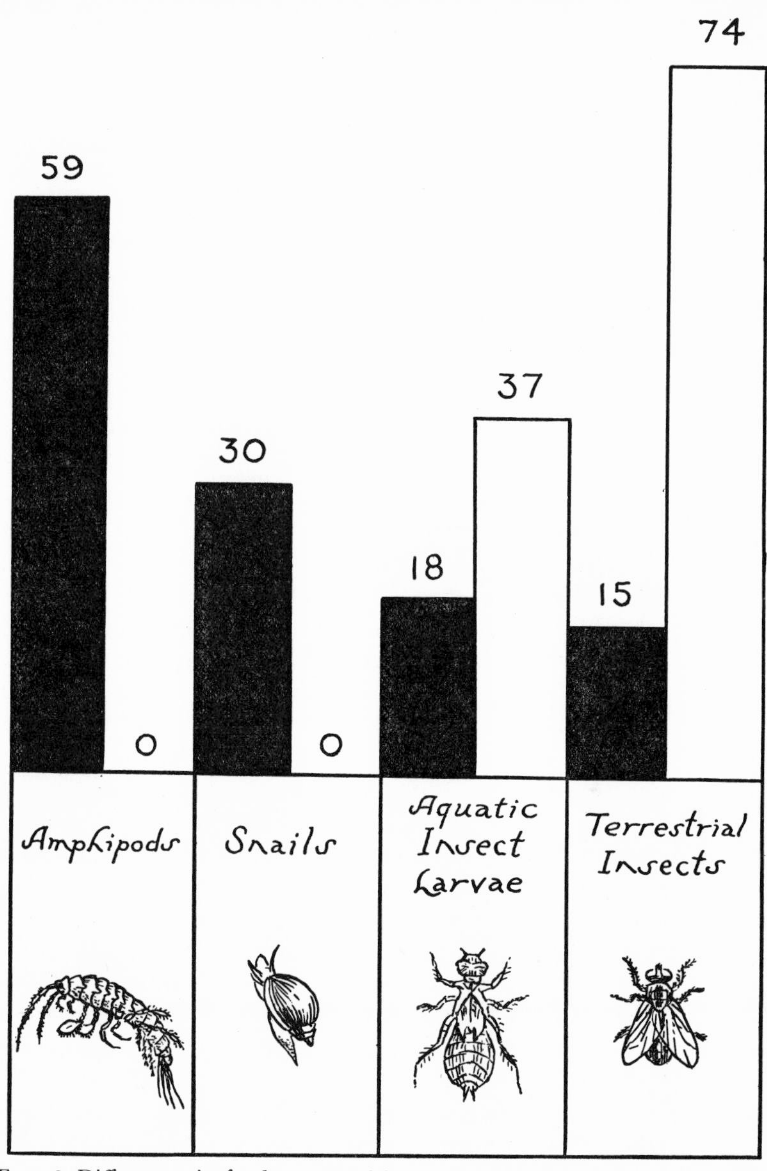

FIG. 18. Differences in food consumed by two salamanders found in the same habitat in Oregon. The figures above each column indicate the percentages of stomachs containing each item of food. The dark columns show the food of the Crater Lake Newt (*Taricha granulosus mazamae*) and the light columns represent that of the Long-toed Salamander (*Ambystoma macrodactylum*). (Data from Donald S. Farner)

shown in Figure 19. Where the two species eat the same food organism, the difference in size of prey minimizes the effect of utilizing the same food. In the spring and fall the three species were found together in large groups near the hibernation dens. In summer they exhibited differences in habitat preference, which further reduced competition.

Competition can occur for any of the requirements of life: food,

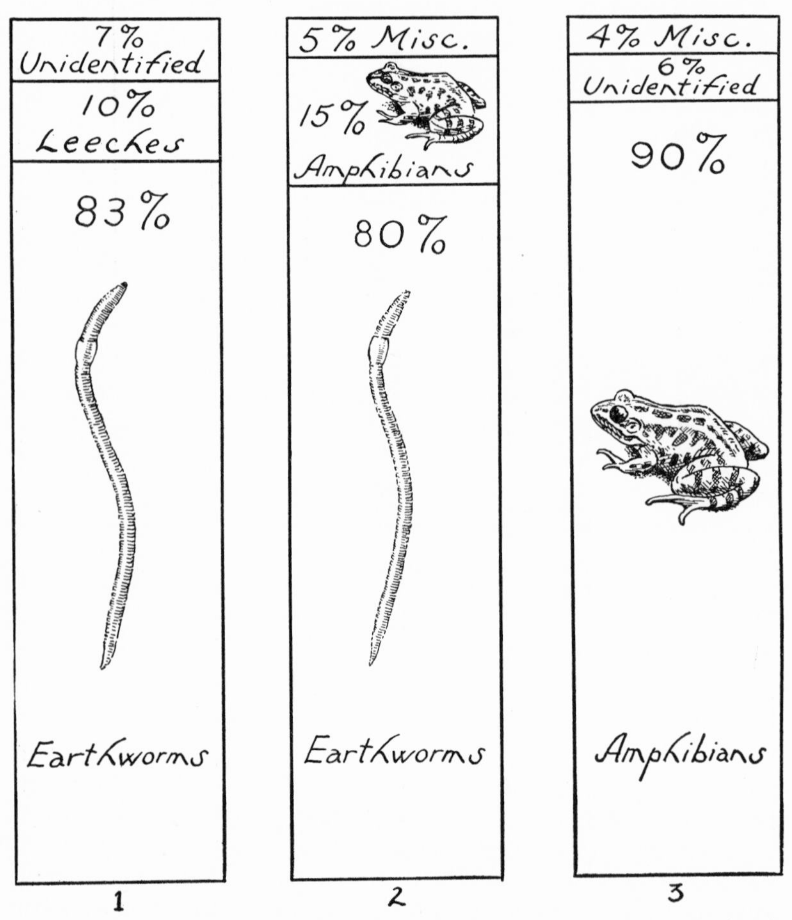

FIG. 19. The food consumed by three different species of Garter Snakes in southern Michigan. The percentages indicate the number of each item of food eaten. 1. Butler's Garter Snake (*Thamnophis butleri*). 2. Eastern Garter Snake (*Thamnophis sirtalis sirtalis*). 3. Eastern Ribbon Snake (*Thamnophis sauritus sauritus*).

shelter, basking sites, or mates. It may be of little consequence, or it may influence the success of the species. Where competition does exist, it has an important role in determining which individuals or populations will survive in that environment. Competition appears to be most important between related species that live in limited areas.

The opposite of competition is cooperation. In terms of human activities, we like to think of cooperation as a definite, positive contribution from two or more individuals aiming at a common goal. This is the end stage of cooperation, the ideal condition. Like most things, it starts in a simpler fashion or in simpler terms and gradually develops to that obviously beneficial stage that has just been mentioned. Among the lower animals "proto-cooperation" assumes the form of unconscious mutual aid or reciprocal responsiveness. Under these more generous terms, many types of mutually beneficial relations exist. W. C. Allee, in his stimulating book *Cooperation among Animals with Human Implications,* summarizes the various stages in the development of cooperative relationships in the Animal Kingdom. He points out that crowding is detrimental to both the individual and the species, but certain types of animal aggregations have definite survival value. He cites hibernating aggregations, breeding congregations, and migrating groups as illustrations of his point. From such aggregations of individuals have come the social organizations of animals, with their marked mutual dependencies and benefits.

In studying the aggregation behavior of snakes, G. K. Noble and H. J. Clausen found that DeKay's Snakes (*Storeria dekayi*) tend to form aggregations more often under disturbing than optimal environmental conditions. Individuals in aggregations lose water and weight less rapidly than isolated individuals. The beneficial effects of proto-cooperative aggregations may be confined to individuals of a single species or may be interspecific, as in the case of several species forming hibernation or estivating aggregations.

Numerous extensions of the proto-cooperation relationships can be cited. Other types of relationships exist in which one or more individuals derive benefit from the presence of other animals in the environment. It is sometimes necessary to differentiate between relationships that are beneficial to the individual and those that are of value to the species population. The latter may actually be harmful to the individual. Frequently the exact details of a relationship are not clearly known. The old tale of the happy home life of the Prairie Dog, the Burrowing Owl, and the Prairie Rattlesnake, all living cosily in one burrow and each deriving some obscure advantage from the presence of the other, has long been recognized as pure fiction. But the Prairie Rattler does obtain benefit from the Prairie Dog and the burrow constructed by this rodent. It may eat the young mammals or use the burrow for shelter. And the prairie-dog population, though not the individuals, actually benefits from the presence of the rattlesnakes, which serve as population checks and selective factors. Amphibians and reptiles are constantly utilizing burrows or other homes made by other animals. These may be abandoned or occasionally still occupied by their original owners. One of the most interesting cases of the latter is the burrow dug by the Gopher Turtle (*Gopherus polyphemus*) of the southeastern states. The burrow, which is 10 to 20 feet in length, is regularly occupied by a single turtle, but additional tenants customarily include the Florida Gopher Frog (*Rana c. capito*) and a number of insect species. Abandoned Gopher Turtle burrows are used for shelter by a variety of snakes, lizards, and mammals.

The relations of other animals referred to under the designation "environmental force" include all the contributions that these animals make to their environment—the burrows, the homes, the changes they make in the physical setting as a result of their activities. Each of these contributions has an important effect on the welfare of the species living in that environment.

Senses

In their comings and goings, amphibians and reptiles have daily relations not only with individuals of their own species, but also with other animals of the habitat. This makes them dependent on the efficiency of their sense organs. In order to understand the success or failure of these relations, we must know something about the sense organs that are present in amphibians and reptiles. All sense organs are properly considered a part of the nervous system of the animal, and since their function is solely to perceive stimuli of various types, they can be considered as receptors.

A Toad (*Bufo*) has eyes, or visual receptors; ears, or sound receptors; a nose, or chemical receptor (Fig. 20, upper). These we can see if we look closely, but they are not all the sensory receptors that a Toad has. Actually we are accustomed to think in terms of our own sensory abilities and do not look closely enough at those of other types of life. If we are going to list all the senses of the amphibians and reptiles, we will have to use a special classification:

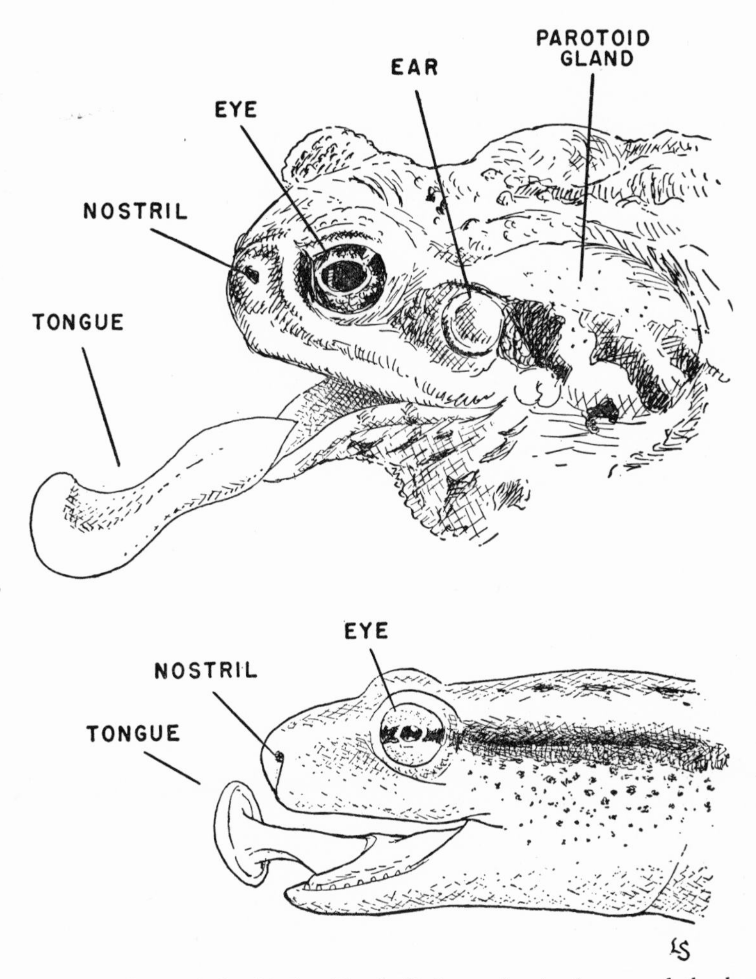

Fig. 20. The head of the Marine Toad (*Bufo marinus*), above, and the head of the Two-lined Salamander (*Eurycea bislineata*), below, with the tongues extended.

1. Mechanical and equilibrium receptors in the—
   a. Skin
   b. Muscles
   c. Inner ear

2. Vibration receptors in the —
   a. Ears
   b. Lateral line organs
   c. Body

3. Light or heat receptors in the—
   a. Eyes (light only)
   b. Light- and heat-sensitive cells of skin
   c. Facial pit of Pit Vipers (heat only)

4. Chemical receptors in the—
   a. Nose
   b. Jacobson's organ
   c. Tongue

5. Moisture receptors in the skin

6. Pain and hunger receptors in the—
   a. Skin
   b. Internal organs

The skin is listed under several different categories because it contains isolated or clustered sensory cells that function in a number of different capacities. Just as our own skins can perceive heat, contact, or pain, so can the skins of amphibians and reptiles. The skin of amphibians and reptiles is also sensitive to moisture—some parts being more sensitive than others. For example, the skin on the soles of the feet of Toads (*Bufo*) is highly sensitive to differences in moisture content of the substratum. Just as hunger is perceived by the nerve endings in our stomach, or as positional pressures are perceived by the nerve endings in our muscles, so, too, do perceptions occur in amphibians and reptiles. All amphibians and reptiles have three semicircular canals in the inner ear that serve to maintain equilibrium. Snakes have rather lightly constructed skulls and seem to be more subject to injury to the semicircular canals than other reptiles. When the canals are injured, the animal loses its ability to maintain its customary position and tends to topple over. A snake so injured may wind about like an animated corkscrew.

The human range of sound perception is from about 15 to nearly 15,000 cycles, covering a rather extensive variety of sounds. Accord-

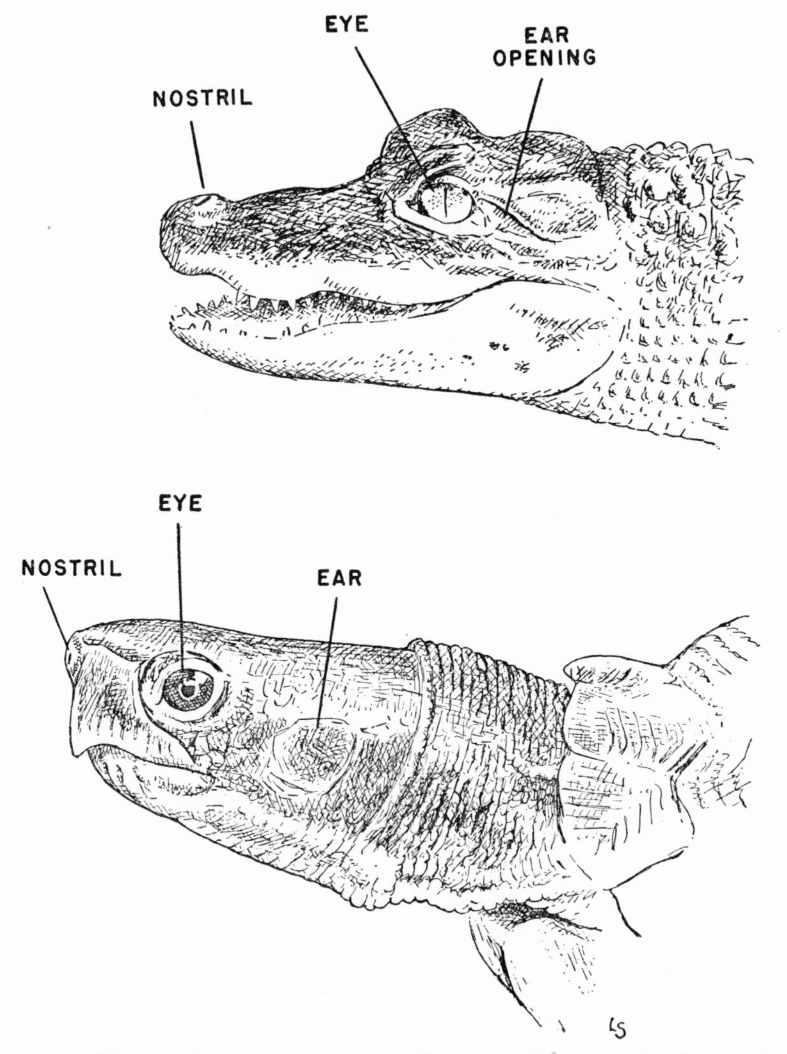

FIG. 21. The head of the American Alligator (*Alligator mississippiensis*), above, and the Wood Turtle (*Clemmys insculpta*), below.

ing to our present knowledge, no amphibian or reptile has such a great range of sound perception. The widest known in these groups is that recorded for True Frogs (*Rana*): 50 to 10,000 cycles. Salamanders have been thought to be deaf to airborne sounds, but recent work by S. Ferhat-Akat on salamanders of the genus *Ambystoma* indicates that they can perceive sounds up to a frequency of 244 cycles. Salamanders all lack a middle ear, with its eardrum, which is so important in the reception of air vibrations (Figure 20, lower). Under this anatomical handicap, it is not surprising that salamanders are either not responsive or responsive only to frequencies in the low range. Frogs, on the other hand, possess a middle ear, and most species have the eardrum exposed on the surface. Consequently frogs have a well-developed sense of hearing, and voice plays an important role in their reproductive behavior.

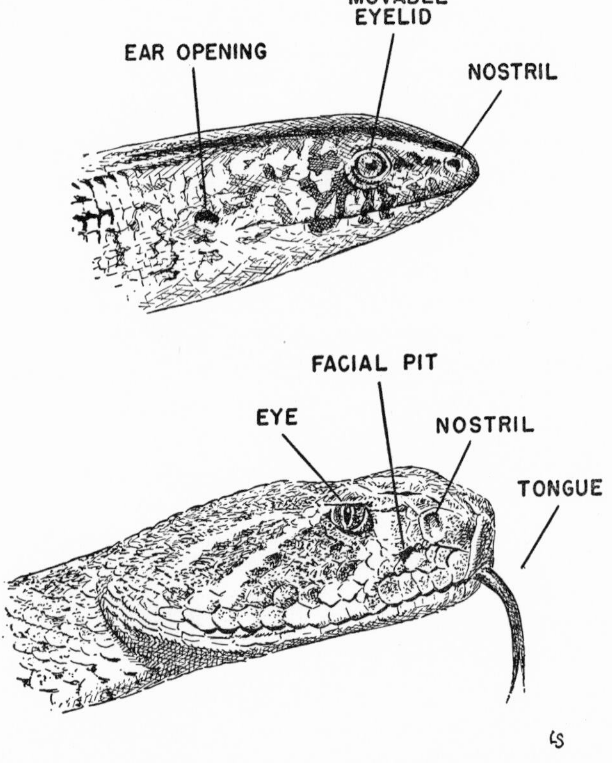

FIG. 22. The head of a Glass Lizard (*Ophisaurus attenuatus*), above, and the head of a Western Diamondback Rattlesnake (*Crotalus atrox*), below.

Crocodilians have well-developed ears (Figure 21, upper). The Alligator (*Alligator mississippiensis*) is known to hear sounds in a range of from 50 to 4,000 cycles. Voice also plays an important role in the territorial organization and reproduction of this reptile. Turtles have frequently been reported to be deaf to airborne sounds, but they usually have well-developed middle ears with prominent eardrums (Figure 21, lower). It is now known that they can hear sounds below an upper limit of about 2,000 cycles. Some species give no response above 300 cycles, but the Painted Turtle (*Chrysemys picta*) was found by E. G. Wever and C. W. Bray to give a response between 120 and 1,000 cycles, while E. D. Adrian noted that Box Turtles (*Terrapene*) were responsive from 50 to 2,000 cycles. Many lizards can hear well; and in a few species, such as the geckos, voice plays an important role in their social life. Some species have been reported to respond to sounds of almost as high frequencies as those reported for the True Frogs.

A great deal of controversy has been waged on the hearing ability of snakes. All snakes lack a middle ear, and they have no eardrum (Figure 22, lower). The ear bone is attached to one of the bones supporting the lower jawbone. Despite widespread popular beliefs, snakes cannot hear airborne sounds. However, they are sensitive to vibrations in the ground or the substratum on which they are resting. Other amphibians and reptiles that cannot hear airborne sounds or can hear them only to a limited extent are usually sensitive to vibrations in the ground. For example, in terrestrial salamanders the ear bone connects with the shoulder girdle; vibrations are picked up through the front limbs and conducted to the ear bone. In aquatic salamanders, such as the Hellbenders (*Cryptobranchus*) and the Mudpuppy (*Necturus*), the ear bone articulates with the lower jaw or a bone supporting it. Vibrations are picked up by the lower jaw and transmitted to the ear bone. These salamanders frequently rest with the lower jaw in contact with the bottom of the stream or pond in which they live.

Larvae and adults of some aquatic amphibians possess a system of external sense organs called the "lateral line organs" (Figure 23). Similar organs are present in fish. These are little clusters of sensory cells arranged in regular, symmetrical rows on the head and body. The arrangement and distribution of the lateral line organs varies greatly from species to species. The organs are sensitive to vibrations in the water and may be used in orienting the animal in the water, in positioning it in relation to another of its species, or in locating food. A hungry, blinded larval Newt (*Diemictylus*) will snap at a weak jet of air directed against the side of the body. The lateral line system of the larval amphibian is lost when it becomes an adult, except in the case of some aquatic species.

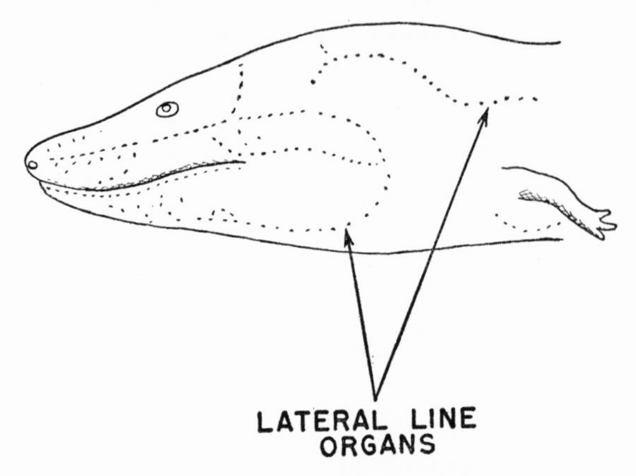

FIG. 23. The head of Amphiuma (*Amphiuma means*) illustrating the lateral line organs on the head. (After B. F. Kingsbury)

Amphibians and reptiles generally have well-developed eyes and fairly good vision. Some species, however, have secondarily lost the function of the eyes in their adaptation to a burrowing or underground existence. Gordon L. Walls has made extensive studies on the eyes of vertebrates, particularly the reptiles. He has found reptile eyes adapted for keen vision during daylight, as in diurnal lizards that have large eyes with rounded pupils and a yellowish colored lens that serves as a filter providing greater visual acuity in daylight. Some nocturnal species have eyes that are suited to vision under low light conditions. Many have an elliptical pupil that cuts down the light entering the eye in the daytime, keeping its vision sharp for nighttime. This pupil is expanded and round at night. A number of these nocturnal species have a highly reflective material, called crystalline guanine, either in the retina or on the inner back wall of the eyeball. This causes the eyes to shine at night in the presence of a light. It also gives the animal a greater visual sensitivity in dim light.

In many species, such as the Hellbenders (*Cryptobranchus*), the eyes are so located that there is no point in the visual field at which both eyes can focus on the same object. Other species have binocular vision only on objects at quite a distance in front of the animal. Many turtles have well-developed binocular vision, but the Vine Snake (*Oxybelis aeneus auratus*) has the fullest development of binocular vision of any North American amphibian or reptile. However, even this species does not see an object with both eyes at close range.

Our knowledge of the existence of color vision in these lower vertebrates is very incomplete—owing partly to the difficulty of definitely establishing the fact that animals do or do not perceive color in objects. Robert G. Smith, Jr., after investigating the color discrimination of the Florida Cricket Frog (*Acris gryllus dorsalis*), stressed the need to distinguish clearly between responses to different colors and to different intensities of brightness. The present state of our knowledge is limited. We do know that some lizards and turtles definitely have color vision, some frogs have limited color discrimination, and snakes may or may not have color vision. There is no experimental evidence to suggest that salamanders or crocodilians have any color-discrimination ability. The studies of R. Granit suggest that snakes lack the physiological basis for color vision. However, investigations in Europe by N. Grodzinska on the European Water Snake (*Natrix natrix*), a close relative of our water snakes, indicate that color discrimination does exist in these snakes.

Many of our lizards possess a parietal eye, sometimes called a "third eye." This organ is located in the top center of the head behind the eyes. It does not function as an eye in the sense of furnishing an image. In some species it may function simply as a light receptor perceiving simply presence or direction of light.

An interesting structure that is present in the side of the head of Pit Vipers of the Family Crotalidae is the facial pit (Figure 22. lower) from which they derive their vernacular name. This structure is generally referred to as a heat-sensitive organ, but Theodore H. Bullock and Raymond B. Cowles have shown that it also may function as an infrared receptor. By means of this organ alone a blindfolded Pit Viper can accurately locate and strike small mammals or birds. It does this by its sensitivity to the heat of the animal's body. G. K. Noble and A. Schmidt have investigated the function of the facial pits and have demonstrated the accuracy of the pit receptors in directing a strike when the snake was blindfolded and had its chemical receptors blocked. Moving a cold light bulb in front of such a snake produced no reaction, but as soon as the current was turned on and the light warmed up the snake struck at it. Noble found that the snake was sensitive to a difference of less than 1° F. between its body and that of the prey.

Chemical reception, for us, consists of smelling and tasting. Most amphibians and reptiles possess receptors for these two functions. In amphibians the smell receptors are located in the nasal chambers; those of taste, in the mouth. The chemical receptors of the nasal chambers appear to be of greater importance—and more frequently used—in aquatic amphibians and terrestrial salamanders than in toads and terrestrial frogs. Taste is of importance in the latter forms primarily for rejecting unpalatable food. Reptiles have an accessory chemical-receptor system in Jacobson's organ, which is a small sensory structure in the roof of the mouth (Figure 24). The tongue

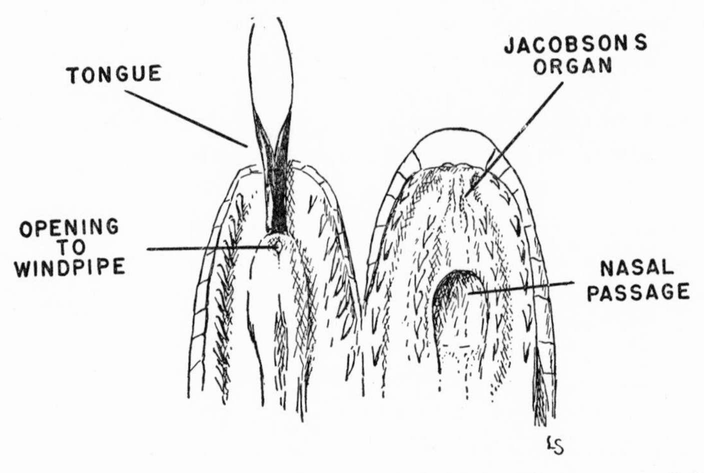

Fig. 24. The inside of the mouth of a Milk Snake (*Lampropeltis doliata*) showing the location of Jacobson's Organ and other internal structures.

is used as an adjunct of this organ, flicking out to pick up chemicals or particles and bringing them in contact with Jacobson's organ. Contrary to statements in some textbooks, the tongue itself has no known sensory function. Its relation to Jacobson's organ is merely to pick up and bring chemicals in contact with that receptor. It is the same as the function performed by a boy's finger when he picks up jam on it and puts both finger and jam in his mouth. The finger aids in tasting by bringing the jam into contact with the taste organs but has no sensory function of its own. When a snake flicks its tongue out rapidly, it is exploring the environment by testing the odors or chemicals that are around. In locating and investigating food, the tongue–Jacobson's organ system is used with the nasal system, but either may be employed separately. G. K. Noble has demonstrated this experimentally in DeKay's Snake (*Storeria dekayi*) and in several species of Garter Snakes (*Thamnophis*). Males of these snakes could follow a trail left by the odor of a female by means of either system. The same ability has been demonstrated in the location of food.

All snakes employ the tongue–Jacobson's organ system in testing food, but use it in varying degrees with other sensory organs. Lizards also use the system, but the long-tongued species, such as the Teids and Anguids, appear to rely on it more fully than do Iguanids, which appear to use vision primarily. All of the senses serve to orient the animals in relation to the various factors of the environment. Where one system is of less importance, one of the others is often highly developed. For instance, burrowing species generally have poor vision and no hearing, but they are very sensitive to vibrations in the earth, to touch, and to smell.

CHAPTER 10

Food and Feeding

HUMAN BEINGS ARE ACCUSTOMED to thinking of food in terms of three square meals a day. This is a rhythm of eating that has been inherited with little questioning. Actually it might be better for us to eat smaller and more frequent meals. This is a matter of conjecture, but there certainly are not many of us who would think of voluntarily eating fewer than three meals a day. Because of our eating customs, we tend to think that all animals require frequent meals.

Animals show wide variation in their nutritional requirements. Some small mammals and birds must eat almost continuously throughout their wakeful hours and may consume more than their weight in food daily. Such animals require a large amount of food to furnish the fuel necessary to keep their bodies warmed to a high temperature and to carry on their bodily functions. These animals are said to have a high rate of metabolism, which simply means that the physical and chemical processes of the body are carried on at a relatively rapid rate. The vast majority of mammals and birds, maintaining their bodies at relatively constant temperatures, require food at more or less regularly recurring intervals.

In contrast to mammals and birds, the ectothermic amphibians and reptiles may eat at less frequent intervals. They are noted for their ability to undergo prolonged periods of inactivity when no food is consumed. Because of their relatively low metabolic rates as compared with mammals and birds, and the lack of any need to furnish fuel for the maintenance of a high body temperature, a single large meal may suffice for a long period.

Types of Food

For our purpose we shall consider as food any of the necessary nutritive materials taken into the digestive tract. Very simply, in the case of an amphibian or reptile, food consists of plant material and living or dead animal material, including eggs. Those species that eat only plant food are referred to as herbivorous forms, or plant eaters. Those that feed on living or freshly killed animal food are spoken of as carnivorous forms, or meat eaters. Those that eat the remains of dead animals are called scavengers, or carrion eaters. And, finally, those that include more than one of these categories in their diet are termed omnivorous forms, or mixed eaters. The designation cannibalism is frequently used in a broad sense to include any animal that eats another similar animal, whether it is closely or remotely related. In precise usage the term cannibalism is used *only* when the prey belongs to the same species as the predator.

Amphibians and reptiles are predominantly carnivorous; a few are herbivorous or omnivorous or carrion eaters. In general they are fairly catholic in their tastes, feeding on a wide variety of animal life. Those with specialized diets—limited to but a few similar food species—are the exception rather than the rule. Most species feed on whatever type of food animal is of a size that is easy to capture and to swallow and that is palatable. Here the word "palatable" is best defined in negative terms, as "not unpleasant, not disagreeable, not distasteful, or not harmful." This definition does not imply that amphibians and reptiles do not discriminate in the food consumed, but simply indicates that many species appear to have a wide tolerance in taste. As will be shown, they do discriminate before swallowing and do reject unpalatable food.

Factors Determining Kind of Food

A number of factors operate to determine the kind of food that is consumed. Prominent among them are the following:

1. The primary feeding adaptations of the animal. For example, whether it is adapted to feeding on plant or animal food and what major types of these foods is most used.

2. The size of the animal and its methods of getting its food.
3. The habitat in which the animal lives and hunts for its food.
4. The relative abundance and size of food organisms available at the time of feeding.

The importance of these factors can be illustrated by considering the adult Leopard Frog (*Rana pipiens*). It is adapted for feeding on small live animals, such as insects, spiders, and small worms, which it catches on its sticky tongue. It has teeth only in the upper jaw; these are small, straight teeth that are used only to crush or hold larger prey organisms. It is not adapted for a plant diet nor for feeding piecemeal on animals too large for it to swallow. This frog is primarily an inhabitant of damp or wet grassy areas and meadows. It will feed on almost any of the animal life in this habitat, providing the prey is of a size that can be ingested, is moving, and is palatable. Throughout most of the frog's activity period and the time that it feeds, insects are the most abundant food items of suitable size in the habitat and will be eaten most frequently.

The frog seeks its food by slowly moving about a more or less definite area and waiting at some spots for food to appear. It is stimulated to feed by the sight of moving prey of an appropriate size. A potential morsel is viewed, possibly examined and stalked, but more often flicked immediately into the mouth on the sticky tongue and gulped down. If distasteful when in the mouth or distressing to the consumer when in the stomach, the prey may be thrown out and rejected. The size of the frog, of course, limits the prey organisms that can be swallowed whole. This is true of most amphibians and reptiles; few forms other than turtles eat their food piecemeal, particularly animal food.

From the foregoing it can be seen how various factors operate to determine the type of food consumed. Because of its structure and size, the frog must prey on small animals; in its particular habitat, insects are usually the most abundant suitable food; the species of insects that are actively moving about and exposed at the time the frog is feeding are taken more frequently than quiet or secretive forms; species that are too large, too powerful, or possessed of an effective defense are not eaten.

The importance of the availability of food is clearly shown in the studies of Karl F. Lagler and J. Clark Salyer II. They studied the food habits of a number of vertebrates in relation to predation on game fish. In their observations on the food habits of the Northern Water Snake (*Natrix s. sipedon*), they found that fish made up the following percentages of the bulk food in three different situations:

At fish rearing stations, 98%
In natural trout streams, 76%
In lakes and ponds, 47%

A similar variation has been shown in the diet of the Eastern Garter Snake (*Thamnophis s. sirtalis*). Under most circumstances this species eats little or no fish, but where fish are abundant, as in a fish hatchery, they are included in the diet.

Changes in Food Habits

The specific kind of food consumed by a given species usually does not remain constant throughout the lifetime of the animal. Two basic changes occur in many species. First, there are the seasonal changes that produce dietary variation as a result of (1) the temporal changes in the abundance of prey organisms and (2) seasonal movements of the animal or its prey from one habitat to another. In the case of a species that feeds on plant blossoms, for example, it is obvious that one type of plant does not have a sufficiently long blooming period to provide food throughout the yearly activity period of the herbivorous animal. A similar condition may hold true for species that feed on animals; the maximum abundance of a given prey species may last for only a brief period. When one prey species is at a peak of abundance relative to other prey species, it will usually be consumed in large quantities simply because its greater numbers make it easier to find. This is well illustrated by the studies of George F. Knowlton on the food habits of the Northern Side-blotched Uta (*Uta s. stansburiana*) in Utah. In the early spring this lizard feeds mostly on young grasshoppers and true bugs. In July and August, when the grasshoppers are becoming rather large for this lizard to master, the food consists mostly of true bugs and leafhoppers, which are beginning to be more abundant—especially the Beat Leafhopper (*Eutettix tenellus*), which is very abundant. By September and October more than half of the food consists of this leafhopper, with true bugs comprising a quarter of the total. This seasonal change is shown in Figure 25.

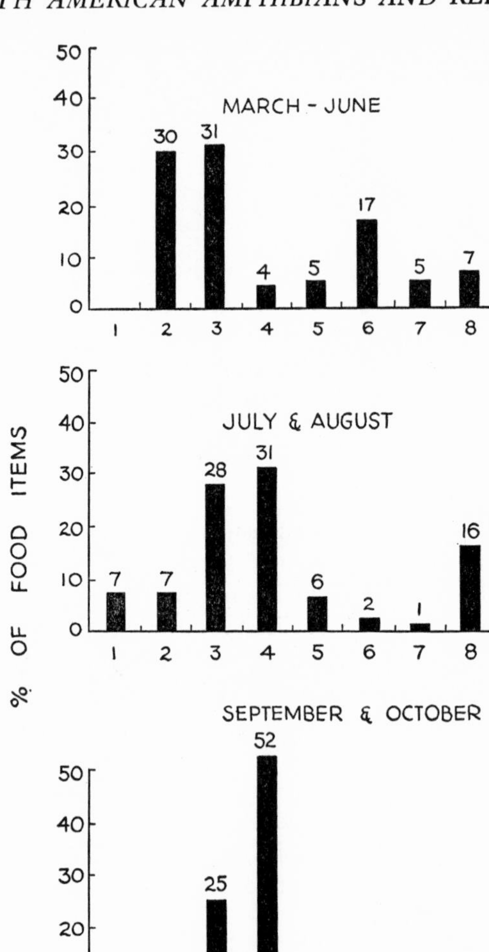

FIG. 25. Seasonal change in food composition of the Northern Side-blotched Uta (*Uta stansburiana stansburiana*) in Utah. Percentages are those of total number of items represented. Numbers below each graph represent insect groups as follows: 1. Springtails; 2. Grasshoppers and crickets; 3. True Bugs; 4. Leafhoppers; 5. Beetles; 6. Moths and butterflies; 7. Flies; 8. Ants, wasps and bees. Note particularly the increase in the leafhoppers (#4) consumed as the season progresses. This is due to the eating of large numbers of the Beet Leafhopper (*Eutettix tenellus*) as they become abundant. (Data from George F. Knowlton)

Henry S. Fitch found that young Ground Squirrels constitute the most important item of food for Northern Pacific Rattlesnakes (*Crotalus viridis oreganus*) in central California (Figure 26). The

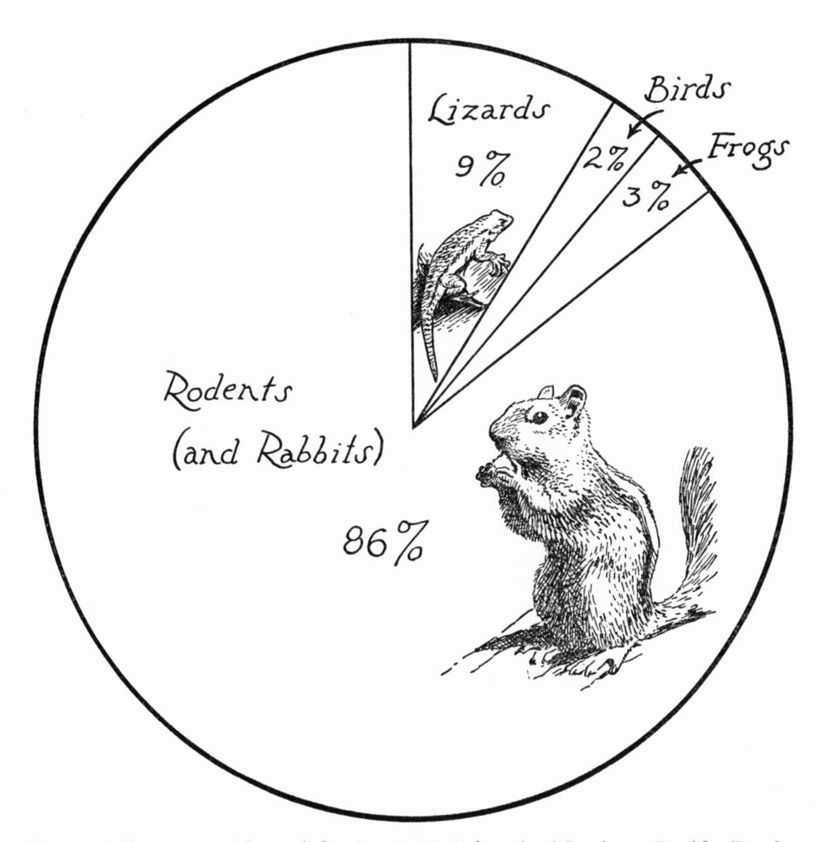

FIG. 26. The composition of food recorded for the Northern Pacific Rattlesnake (*Crotalus viridis oreganus*). Percentages are those of items recorded. (Data from Henry S. Fitch)

young Ground Squirrels appear above ground in April, but by late summer they are too large except for the largest rattlesnakes to swallow. Analyzing the number of these squirrels eaten each month in four different years, Fitch noted that 83 per cent of the ground squirrels were consumed in April and May.

A similar change occurs when an animal has a regular seasonal change of habitat. For example, in the spring the Northern Copperhead (*Ancistrodon contortrix mokeson*) occurs most frequently in wooded rocky hillsides, where it feeds mostly on mammals. As the temperatures rise in the summer months, these snakes move into the lowlands, where large numbers of frogs and insects are consumed in addition to mammals. Change in habitat, with resulting variation in food habits, may occur as part of a daily movement, such as in actual foraging for food, or it may take place at irregular intervals. John D. Kilby found that Green Tree Frogs (*Hyla c. cinerea*) feeding along lake margins in Florida ate mostly large midges (*Chironomus lobiferus*); but when feeding in the broadleafed woods (hammocks), they consumed mostly spiders. Movement from one habitat to another is frequently related to the abundance of food in the respective habitats.

Another important type of change that occurs in most, if not all, species is the change that takes place between young and adult stages. In some species, such as most True Frogs (*Rana*), this may involve a change from an essentially herbivorous tadpole to an entirely carnivorous adult. In other species of frogs, it may be a change from a predominantly piecemeal carnivorous diet to the consumption of whole prey. In a few amphibians and in most reptiles it is mainly a difference in prey species available to the young and to the adult. Obviously, a greater selection of food is available to a large animal than to a small one. Also, it is more efficient for a large animal to obtain all of its current nutritional requirements from the capture of a single food item than to have to catch, say, ten smaller morsels.

An ontogenetic or individual age difference in food habits has been noted in many species. In the Alligator (*Alligator mississippiensis*), for example, Remington Kellogg found that spiders comprised 3 per cent of the food consumed by Alligators of all sizes, whereas in those only two feet in length this food made up 10 per cent of the total. And E. A. McIlhenny, reporting on the food of 25 adult Alligators, found no spiders in the stomachs.

Henry S. Fitch, in his studies of the Northern Pacific Rattlesnake (*Crotalus viridis oreganus*), found that young snakes fed on mice, lizards, and Spadefoot Toads, but none of these food items was found in adult rattlers, which fed on larger mammals, such as the Ground Squirrel, Cottontail Rabbit, Kangaroo Rat, Pocket Gopher, and Wood Rat. This type of dietary change is probably of less importance—and more frequently absent—in turtles than in other reptiles or amphibians, because of the piecemeal method of feeding of most turtles.

The existence of ontogenetic differences in food habits has an important value for the survival of the species because it reduces competition for food between the young and adults of the same species. Feeding on different prey species makes a larger total source of food available to the predator species, thus insuring a greater likelihood of survival. The same is true, as pointed out by Austin Rand, where there is a marked difference in size between males and females of a species. The size difference allows the species a wider utilization of potential food resources in a given habitat.

Methods of Locating Food

The regularly herbivorous tadpoles of some species of frogs locate their food simply by foraging about in the water in which they live. Sight and chemical perception appear to be the most important means of locating plant food in the water. Salamanders do not seem to eat plant food regularly, but some aquatic species accidentally ingest fairly large quantities of such plants as filamentous algae. Herbivorous reptiles appear to locate their plant food mainly by sight, but it is not known to what extent odor may be used.

Aquatic amphibians, larval and adult, that feed on animal food may locate their food through sight, chemical perception, or touch, or by means of water vibrations, which affect the lateral line organs. One or more of these methods may be regularly used by a given species, and one or more may be employed in the larval stage with a complete change at metamorphosis. The hungry animal may actively seek food or may passively wait for it to come close enough to be caught. Some of the large aquatic salamanders apparently root around in mud or dense aquatic vegetation seeking food. They snap viciously at any slight movement near the snout, suggesting that touch either through actual contact or through the perception of vibration in the water is their primary method of finding food.

Most terrestrial and semiaquatic amphibians actively seek their prey, locating it by vision or smell. It is not known how extensively, if at all, sound may be utilized by these animals in locating potential food organisms. In hunting food, a definite area appears to be patrolled. The hunting periods are interspersed with prolonged periods of quiet waiting in particular spots. For example, toads and frogs are known to take up the same station regularly night after night in seeking food. Usually the station is in a location affording good visibility and abundance of food organisms. William J. Hamilton, Jr., found that in New York State the Green Frog (*Rana clamitans*) normally selects a stand and awaits its prey. He states that when small frogs are transforming from the tadpole stage and coming out of the water, the Green Frogs take a position near the pond's edge, usually at points where the newly transformed individuals are emerging in greatest numbers. J. E. Eckert reports that the Western Toad (*Bufo boreas*) will come after sundown and sit at the entrance of honeybee hives to feed on the bees.

That abundance of food attracts large numbers of individuals is frequently indicated. H. J. Pack has reported large congregations of Woodhouse's Toad (*Bufo w. woodhousei*) during outbreaks of the Sugar-beet Webworm in Utah. He estimated that in one field about a quarter of an acre in size there were no less than 100 of these toads. George F. Knowlton, also in Utah, has reported large concentrations of Northern Side-blotched Uta (*Uta s. stansburiana*) in fields when the Beat Leafhopper is abundant. He estimates the number of these lizards at such times to be between 200 and 700 per acre! This is an estimate; it seems to be rather high but brings out the point that large aggregations may develop where food is very abundant.

Alligators and crocodiles slowly stalk their prey or lie in wait partially secluded. They rely upon vision or a keen sense of smell to locate their food. Aquatic turtles also use smell and sight as the primary means of locating food, although they may utilize water vibrations to some degree. Terrestrial turtles use smell and sight exclusively. Turtles have very keen sight and can perceive a small insect or worm at some distance. A few aquatic turtles lie in wait for their food, either depending on their cryptic appearance to allow the prey to come within lunging distance or attracting the prey with a moving lure.

Lizards locate their food mostly by means of their keen eyesight, or, less commonly, by means of chemical perception, and occasionally by means of sound. Some species actively forage for food—exploring nooks and crannies and investigating odors and likely sounds, such as the fluttering of a moth on dry leaves. Others take up a lookout post and wait for food to come within visual range. These seem to rely almost exclusively on sight, since they grab the food so suddenly that chemical or auditory cues would seem of little use. However, chemical cues are certainly employed in the rejection of unpalatable items. It is not known what methods are most frequently employed by the specialized burrowing lizards. Here smell, touch, or the perception of vibrations are likely to be the most important senses.

Most snakes actively forage for food when hungry, although some appear to lie in wait for food and take suitable food that comes along. Whether these snakes habitually wait for prey, or whether they were approaching a point of hunger that would have sent them prowling if it had not been for the chance encounters, is not known. Chemical perception and vision appear to be their most important methods of locating prey. Active ground-dwelling and semi-arboreal snakes appear to use vision more than smell in locating food, whereas semiburrowers and secretive, semiaquatic, and aquatic species seem to use smell more than sight. This difference in cues utilized can be seen readily in captive specimens. The Black Racer (*Coluber constrictor*) is an active diurnal snake that relies primarily on visual perception in its feeding. When this snake gets ready to shed its skin and its vision is impaired, it will not feed. On the other hand, Garter Snakes (*Thamnophis*) and Water Snakes (*Natrix*), which rely to a large extent on chemical cues, will feed on dead fish even when their vision is impaired by the shedding process.

Wade Fox performed a series of experiments that clearly demonstrate the importance of odor as a food stimulus in Pacific Garter Snakes (*Thamnophis*). In these snakes the various aquatic and terrestrial forms exhibit marked differences in food habits. Both wild and captive specimens of the Red-striped Garter Snake (*Thamnophic ordinoides*) feed voraciously on a small gray slug (*Deroceras reticulatum*). Merely blowing a current of air across the slugs and into the snake's cage caused them to begin quick searching movements. Captive individuals of aquatic Garter Snakes of other species did not respond either to the odor or to the presence of the slugs. Fox could not get the Red-striped Garter Snakes to eat newborn laboratory mice unless he smeared the mice with the skin secretions of the slugs; then the snakes ate them quickly. He also found that the odor of the Pacific Tree Frog (*Hyla regilla*) produced violent feeding reactions in both terrestrial and aquatic snakes. In contrast to this, virtually all of these Pacific snakes showed an aversion to the odor of the introduced Bull Frog (*Rana catesbeiana*).

The venomous Pit Vipers possess another sensory receptor that is used in locating warm prey. Their facial pit is a heat-sensitive organ that can detect the presence and location of warm prey with a high degree of accuracy. Thus the Pit Vipers can locate their prey by means of visual, chemical and heat perception.

The tactile sense may possibly be employed by snakes in locating food; but it appears to play only a minor role compared with the other senses. In this regard there is some suggestion that aquatic species may rely to some degree on the perception of vibrations. This is not known with any degree of certainty.

Methods of Obtaining Food

In the case of the few herbivorous amphibians and reptiles, the method of obtaining food is a relatively simple matter. The species merely graze or crop the plant food in a leisurely fashion, moving about from one source to another. The scavengers are similarly uncomplicated in their feeding, locating food by smell and tearing off pieces that can be engulfed.

It is among the carnivorous species that we find many interesting and different methods of catching the organisms that comprise the food. The feeding process in these carnivorous forms is not a dainty matter; frequently it is based on the urgency of engulfing whole food animals with a minimum amount of chewing. Teeth, when present, are usually designed solely for grasping and holding the prey until it can be swallowed; they are not modified for the shearing, cutting, or grinding processes that we associate with the proper chewing of our own food (Figure 27).

In the amphibians the teeth are small, simple cones arranged around the edges of the jaws in one or more rows and in clusters or rows on several of the bones in the roof of the mouth. They may be absent entirely in the lower jaw, as in the frogs (Figure 27, no. 2); or absent around the rim of both jaws, as in the toads; or absent on some of the other mouth-roof bones, as in several species of frogs. In most terrestrial and semiaquatic amphibians the tongue is the important food-catching organ, and the teeth serve merely to crush or hold the food. The tongue is large and fleshy (Figure 20); it is kept sticky by the secretions of a gland or glands in the roof of the mouth. In some species—for example, the Purple Salamander (*Gyrinophilus porphyriticus*)—the tongue is attached at the middle and is free both in front and in back, whereas in some other species, such as the Dusky Salamander (*Desmognathus fuscus*) and the frogs, it is attached in front and is free in the back (Figure 20). The muscular tongue is flicked out on to the prey and quickly drawn in with the food adhering to the sticky surface. If small enough, the prey is swallowed immediately. If too large for im-

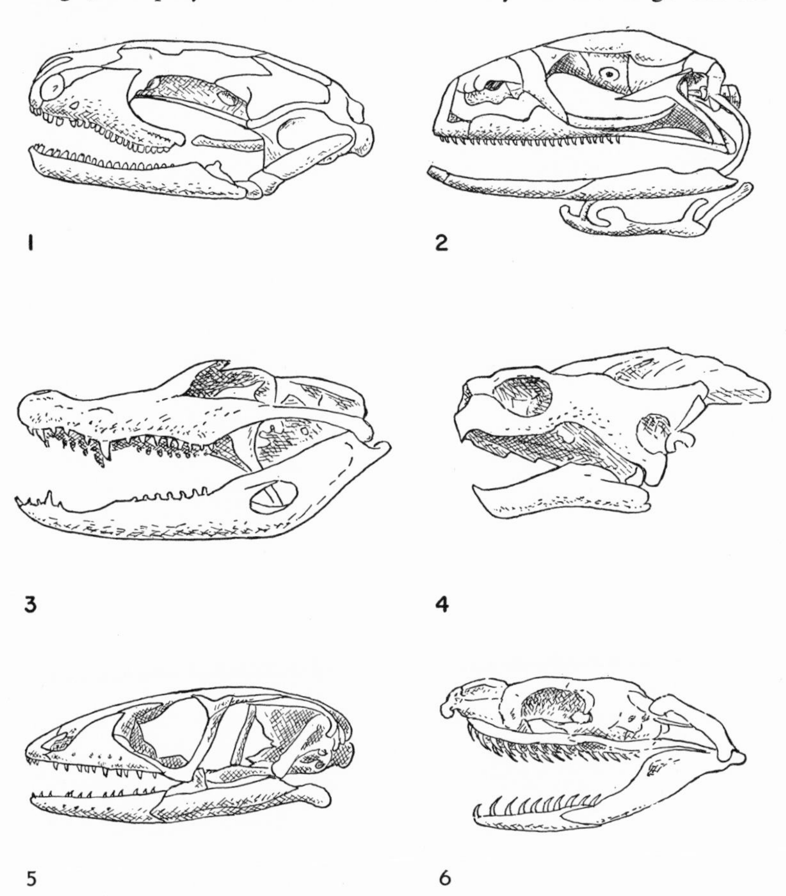

FIG. 27. The skulls of representative amphibian and reptile groups, showing examples of tooth and skull structure. 1. Salamander. 2. Frog. 3. Crocodilian. 4. Turtle. 5. Lizard. 6. Snake.

mediate swallowing, it may be crushed by the jaws and worked slowly into the gullet. The forefeet may be employed to retain or push in a particularly large morsel. The food organism may be stalked slowly and quickly flicked into the mouth by the tongue. Sometimes when the amphibian is waiting in an area of abundant food, a quick hop or lunge may be employed to grab up a food morsel.

In some of the aquatic amphibians the tongue is relatively small and the food is either seized with the teeth or engulfed with water and swallowed after the water is forced out. The animal is alerted by odor, movement, or vibrations in the water and lunges forward or sideward to grab the prey. If the prey is moving away, it may be followed until the predator is within striking distance. If the food is large and cannot be swallowed easily, it may be shaken violently back and forth, pressed against the substratum, or torn apart as the predator rotates its body rapidly in the water. This method of tearing flesh by rapidly rotating the body is used not only by some of the large salamanders but also by crocodilians and large lizards.

Alligators and crocodiles quickly seize live food and, if it is small enough, simply crush it in their powerful jaws. If the prey is too large to crush easily, it may be drowned or torn by the spinning method that has just been described. The large, sharp teeth and powerful jaws provide an effective grip (Figure 27, no. 3). The food is then gulped down whole or in pieces, depending on its size and condition. It is amazing how stealthily one of these large animals can stalk its prey and how quickly it can seize it. Large alligators in outdoor enclosures at the New York Zoological Park have been seen catching wild starlings. Alligators use their tails to fell large prey or to knock it into their jaws. The tail is a powerful organ in a large 'gator and can certainly stun a mammal the size of a large dog.

Turtles completely lack teeth, but they more than make up for this lack with their sharp, horny jaws that cut cleanly like curved scissors (Figure 27, no. 4). Small food may be engulfed whole, but more often it is grabbed by the jaws and cut or torn with the aid of the front feet. Large prey is always eaten piecemeal. Aquatic species usually pull their food into the water before swallowing it. A turtle usually stalks live food slowly and then makes a quick lunge at it with the head, grabbing the food in the mouth. Some turtles lie in wait and quickly snap the prey, engulfing it whole or killing it and eating it piecemeal.

One of the most unusual methods of food-capture found in reptiles is the method of the Alligator Snapping Turtle (*Macrochelys temmincki*) of the lower Mississippi Valley and the Gulf Coast. This turtle has a wormlike filament in the middle of its tongue (Figure 28). When the turtle is hungry and fish are nearby,

FIG. 28. Alligator Snapping Turtle (*Macrochelys temmincki*) "fishing" with worm-like lure of the tongue.

it opens its mouth and wiggles the filament in a very wormlike manner. When the fish swim over to investigate this lure, the turtle closes its mouth and the fish are trapped. The working of this lure can be seen readily in captive specimens kept in an aquarium.

Lizards may capture their prey with the teeth or by flicking it into the mouth with the tongue. All lizards possess teeth in both the upper and lower jaws, and some have small clusters of teeth on the roof of the mouth. The teeth are relatively short single or tricuspid cones with comparatively little specialization in structure (Figure 27, no. 5). None of our lizards shows the marked differentiation in tooth structure to be found in some of the South American or Old World lizards, as in some Teiids, Agamids, and Varanids, where the front and back teeth may differ markedly in shape and function. Unlike snakes, lizards cannot swallow whole food that is much larger than the head. When the food is grabbed, it is crushed with the teeth, worked into the mouth and swallowed. Large prey may be seized with the teeth and shaken vigorously until all movement stops; or the lizard may use his front legs to assist in tearing the prey. Where the food is caught by flicking it in with the tongue, it is usually crushed by the teeth. Some lizards, such as the Iguanids, have large, fleshy tongues that are effective in the capture of small food organisms. The food is stealthily stalked and seized, or may be rushed upon and grabbed. It may be crushed a few times and swallowed with the aid of the tongue.

Some species of American lizards are very adept at "lapping up" insect food with their tongues. However, the extreme development in this method of feeding is seen in the Old World Chameleons. In these lizards the tongue is greatly elongated and, by a complex system of muscles, can be quickly ejected for a distance approximately as great as the length of the Chameleon's body. Excellent coordination between keen eyesight and muscular control enables these lizards to capture prey at considerable distances with amazing accuracy.

Members of one genus of lizards, comprised of the Gila Monster (*Heloderma suspectum*) and the Mexican Beaded Lizard (*Heloderma horridum*), have a venom. Unlike the venomous snakes, the venom of these lizards is produced by a gland in the lower jaw and is secreted at the base of several teeth of the lower jaw between the teeth and the lips. As in snakes, the gland that produces the venom is a modified salivary gland, and the venom is composed, in part at least, of enzymes—those chemical agents that bring about digestion through chemical changes in the food. A number of the teeth in both jaws are grooved on both the front and back, but these grooves do not seem to be related to the venom ducts. The entire venom apparatus in these lizards is crude and seems to be of little value as an offensive weapon for the capture of food. The powerful jaws and sharp teeth appear ample for any prey that the lizard might choose. The presence of venom in these lizards is even more puzzling when considered in the light of the little we know about their food, which appears to consist primarily of eggs, fledgling birds, nestling mammals and small lizards. Perhaps this crude venom system was of greater importance to the ancestors of the present species of

Heloderma; in the modern forms it appears to have value solely as a defensive weapon used in biting large enemies.

With snakes the primary method of capturing food is by grabbing it with the teeth. In all our snakes the teeth are long, slender, sharply pointed structures that curve toward the rear of the mouth (Figure 27, no. 6). In most species there is a row of teeth along each side of the upper and lower jaw, with an additional inner row on each side of the upper jaw. The inner rows are formed by teeth on two pairs of bones in the roof of the mouth. This arrangement of teeth forms a series of opposing sharp spikes that hold struggling prey effectively; the harder the animal struggles, the more deeply the teeth become embedded.

The prey is overcome in one of several ways, depending on the kind of snake involved. Small prey may simply be grabbed and swallowed alive, being killed by the action of the digestive juices. In snakes such as the Whip Snakes (*Masticophis*) and Racers (*Coluber*), the prey may be seized and quickly suffocated by the jaws or by being pushed against the ground, the snake's body, or some object. Species like the King Snakes (*Lampropeltis*) kill their prey by constriction, wrapping several coils of the forepart of the body around the animal. In this method death occurs quickly as a result of suffocation.

A few species of snakes possess venom that paralyzes or kills the prey and also initiates the digestive processes. The venom is produced by the parotid glands located on each side of the head behind the eyes. This is one of the salivary glands in mammals, and the venom of snakes is a highly complex, modified saliva. The venom is injected into the prey by means of enlarged teeth, the fangs, Some snakes have a pair of hollow fangs in the front of the upper jaw (Figure 29), whereas others have two or three grooved teeth on each side at the rear of the upper jaw. Members of the first group, including our most dangerous snakes, are termed the front-fanged snakes, and those of the second group are called the rear-fanged snakes.

The front-fanged snakes are further divided into two groups on the basis of whether or not the fangs are movable or stationary. In the Pit Vipers and the Old World Vipers the maxillary bones, to which the fangs are attached, can be rotated backward, so that the fangs are placed against the roof of the mouth when not in use, or

brought forward into an erect position when ready for use. Each fang can be moved independently of the other, and the movements can be controlled voluntarily by the snake. Thus these snakes, the Solenoglyphs, are said to possess movable fangs. In contrast to this condition, the fang-bearing maxillary bones of the Cobras, Mambas, and Coral Snakes cannot be rotated, and the fangs are constantly in an erect position. These snakes, the Proteroglyphs, are said to have immovable fangs; however, the maxillary bones and fangs do have some movement, though they cannot be rotated up and down as in the other group.

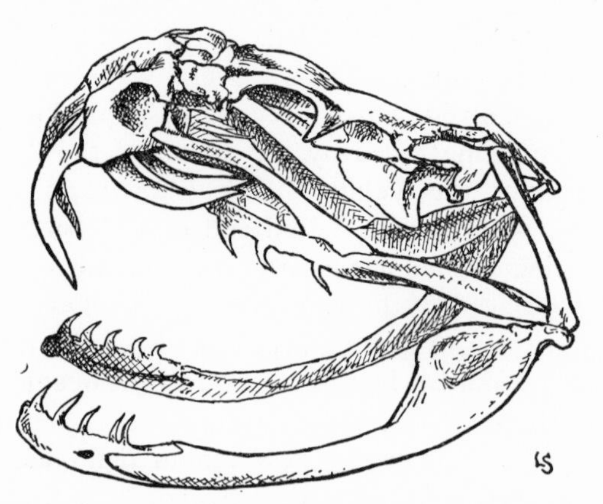

FIG. 29. The skull of a Rattlesnake (*Crotalus*). Note enlarged, hollow fangs in front of jaw and the small replacement fangs lying almost perpendicular to the raised functional fangs.

The venom gland is connected to the fangs by the venom duct. Normally there is a single functional fang on each side of the upper jaw. Immediately behind each functional fang is a graded series of small replacement fangs, with the largest of the series next to the functional fang and the smallest, a mere point, the farthest back. The fangs are replaced periodically with alternate occupancy of paired sockets in each maxillary bone; the replacement fang moves into the vacant socket beside the functional fang before the latter is lost. For a short time there may be two functional fangs on either side, or both sides, of the jaws. If a functional fang is broken off, a new replacement fang moves into place in a short time.

In the rear-fanged snakes two or three of the rearmost teeth on each side of the upper jaw are enlarged and grooved down the front or side. Frequently these fangs are separated from the other teeth by a short space or gap. The venom flows down the groove and into the victim. The rear-fanged snakes frequently must "chew" when they bite to get the venom into the prey.

The venom is a complex mixture of chemical substances including enzymes (see "Digestion" in the following section), toxic proteins, and other materials. The specific nature of the venom varies from one species to another. In a general way, venoms can be classed as nerve-affecting (neurotoxic) and blood-affecting (hemotoxic). Actually, venomous snakes contain both types of substances but usually have a preponderance of one or the other. There is some indication that the nerve-affecting type of venom is more efficient on the so-called cold-blooded animals and the blood-affecting type more efficient on mammals and birds, but actually both types can be highly efficient on either kind of prey.

The possession of powerful venom provides a number of advantages to its possessor. It enables the snake to strike dangerous prey quickly and from a distance with greatly reduced probability of receiving an injury. The venom takes effect, immobilizing the victim, which can then be swallowed without danger to the snake. It also enables the snake to overpower prey that might otherwise inflict a fatal wound on the snake. In this connection it is interesting to note that in striking small prey that might succeed in getting too far away before the venom has taken its effect, snakes may bite and hold on to the prey. The same snakes, however, in striking potentially dangerous prey, may stab or quickly bite and recoil. This, of course, is possible only for the front-fanged snakes, since the rear-fanged species almost always retain their original hold on the prey. Another important advantage in the possession of a venom is that the enzymes begin the digestive processes as soon as the venom is injected. Also, the injection of these digestive agents *into* the victim would seem likely to speed up the digestive action.

If the original bite is retained and the prey is small, the snake may begin swallowing almost immediately. Otherwise the snake will quietly retain the grip and wait for the prey to cease struggling before beginning to swallow. If the snake strikes the prey and recoils, it will remain in the coiled position and, if possible, watch the prey until the venom has taken effect and the animal stops moving. After a few moments, or as soon as most movement stops, the snake will slowly approach the victim, carefully investigating it with the tongue–Jacobson's organ system. If the food is acceptable, the snake will pick it up in the mouth and begin to swallow it. In this process the value of the remarkable flexibility of the snake's skull is seen as the snake swallows in one piece an animal several times larger than its head. The two halves of the lower jaw are not united firmly, as in the skulls of mammals, birds and the other reptiles, but are connected only by an elastic ligament, flexible muscles, and skin. Thus the outer ends of the lower jaws can be widely separated. In addition each lower jaw attaches to the skull not by means of a firm connection but through two movable bones that give additional flexibility.

Through the great accommodation of the skull the snake can perform amazing feats of ingesting prey of great bulk. By means of the recurved teeth and by working the two sides of the jaw independently, the snake literally pulls its body over and around its food. Once the food has passed the mouth, it is worked back to the stomach by a series of muscular contractions in the snake's body. The food is usually swallowed head first, but may be taken in any position.

Digestion

Once the food is taken into the mouth and swallowed, it begins to be digested. The process of digestion involves both chemical and physical changes that convert the ingested food into its simple components, which can be taken up and used by the body as the fuel for metabolism and the building blocks for growth and repair. These changes are brought about by the chemical agents, the enzymes, which largely make up the digestive juices. Enzymes themselves are not modified in the chemical changes, but they greatly speed up the process of change. One of the characteristics of these chemical agents is that any given enzyme can effect only a single specific change. Therefore a series of different enzymes is required to make the many changes involved in converting the different foods. For instance, one series of enzymes converts plant food by several small changes from starch to a simple sugar that can be utilized by the body. Another series of enzymes changes proteins to their simple amino acids. And still another group of enzymes is necessary to break down fats to their simple constituents.

The enzymes required to digest all types of food may be present in one species, or there may be only those necessary for the conversion of certain types of food. In addition to the enzymes present, there may be differences in the structure of the digestive tract associated with the characteristic diet of the species. For example, the intestine is usually very long in plant-eating forms, whereas it is generally short and simplified in the meat eaters. A given amount of plant food usually requires a longer time for digestion than an equal amount of animal food. Thus greater storage space is needed by herbivors than by carnivors. This difference in the length of digestive tube in plant eaters and meat eaters is readily seen in the long, watch-spring-like coiled intestine of the herbivorous tadpole and the short, simple, convoluted digestive tract of the carnivorous adult frog.

The amphibian and reptile meat eaters generally eat their food whole, soft and hard parts taken together. Because of the effectiveness of their digestive enzymes, virtually all of the animal food is digested. Some parts may be eliminated in a partially digested state; a few, such as enamel-covered teeth, are undigested. However, bone, egg shells, feather quills, and other hard parts may be completely digested in time.

Since digestion is essentially a chemical process, the rate at which food is digested will vary directly with the temperature as well as with the type of food eaten. Thus an aquatic salamander living in a spring at 70° F. will digest an earthworm faster than the same species living at 60° F. A lizard that basks in the sun warming its body to 90° F. after eating a moth will digest it faster than will a lizard that retires beneath a rock where the temperature is only 80° F. This temperature effect can be observed in captive animals and has been demonstrated in a number of laboratory experiments. Walter A. Kenyon has demonstrated this clearly in a series of experiments on fish, the amphibian Mudpuppy (*Necturus*), and three reptiles—the Common Snapping Turtle (*Chelydra serpentina*), the Painted Turtle (*Chrysemys picta*), and the Bull Snake (*Pituophis catenifer sayi*). He tested the rate of digestion for different food materials at room temperature, 76° F., and at 99° F., and found that both protein and carbohydrate foods were digested more rapidly at the higher temperature in all animals tested.

After eating to capacity, or at the end of the daily activity period, amphibians and reptiles usually retire to some secluded nook to digest their food quietly. Because of the importance of the temperature factor it is vital that they find a suitable temperature for efficient digestion. In nature they usually have a wide variety of temperatures available to them and can generally locate a secluded spot with a more or less suitable temperature for the digestion of their food. Animals in captivity may be unable to obtain appropriate temperatures for feeding and digestion. It has been a common observation on the part of zoo keepers that many nonfeeding reptiles can be induced to feed by the simple expedient of warming up their cages a little. It is also possible to get the cage too warm for digestion, which sometimes results in regurgitation.

In Kenyon's experiments, the digestion rates were determined by measuring the amount of the digestion products present. A rough indication of the effectiveness of digestion can also be gained by noting the regularity of feeding and elimination of the undigested food material. In a series of observations carried on for a year I kept one group of Garter Snakes (*Thamnophis*) at a constant temperature of 70° F. and another group at a constant temperature of 80° F. Both groups were maintained in the same type of cages and offered the same food at all times. As nearly as I could determine, the only difference was temperature. A careful record was kept on the frequency of feeding and eliminating for four snakes in each group. Food was offered regularly once a week. The snakes at the cooler temperature accepted food only 45 to 75 per cent of the time, whereas those at the higher temperature ate 90 to 100 per cent of the time. The snakes at the lower temperature exhibited a surprising amount of variation in the time of elimination. In this group, elimination occurred on the day after feeding 44 per cent of the time, as compared with 82 per cent of the time in the group at the higher temperature. Those at the lower temperature eliminated as long as 63 days after eating, whereas those at the warmer temperature eliminated within never more than 8 days beyond the feeding date.

If a variety of food has been consumed at one time, the softer animal foods will be digested more quickly than the hard-bodied animal food or the vegetable food. John D. Kilby fed one large, heavily sclerotized beetle to each of ten large Southern Leopard Frogs (*Rana pipiens sphenocephala*) and examined the frogs fifteen hours later. In four frogs, the beetle's abdomen and head had become separated from the prothorax; in one frog, the beetle's abdomen only was separated from the prothorax; and in the remaining five frogs, little digestive change could be noted. Kilby performed a similar experiment giving each of eight frogs of the same species one earthworm and examining the frogs ten hours later. He found that the earthworms were all reduced to small bits, attached together only by small strips of worm cuticle. In still another series of experiments, in which earthworms were fed to another lot of frogs and examined twenty hours later, only small bits of cuticle were found. As a result of the laboratory experiments and the study of wild caught frogs, Kilby concluded that "if only very soft food were eaten, it seems that the frogs could perhaps digest a stomachful once a day or in less time; but since very few individuals with full stomachs were collected, and since animals in all stages of digestion were found in most stomachs, it seems almost certain that feeding is a more or less continuous process that depends largely on the availability of food."

In studies of lizards, George F. Knowlton found a similar condition. Using the Northern Side-blotched Uta (*Uta s. stansburiana*) and the Sagebrush Lizard (*Sceloporus g. graciosus*), he found that the soft-bodied nymphs of the Beet Leafhopper were digested much more quickly than were the harder-bodied adults. Neither Kilby nor Knowlton recorded the temperatures at which their experiments were carried out, but their reports suggest that there was little variation in temperature. In Knowlton's experiments temperature variation would be of no importance, since the lizards ate both nymphs and adults at the same time.

Another important factor in the digestive process is the size of the meal consumed. Obviously, a small meal will be digested at a more rapid rate than will a larger one. Thus a snake that has consumed a meal equal to one-tenth of its own weight will require a considerable length of time to digest this food—longer than if the same snake had eaten a meal only one-twentieth of its weight. However, there is a direct relationship between the size of the meal consumed and the efficiency of the digestive processes as measured by the body heat produced—larger meals producing more heat and hence more effective digestion. The efficiency of the digestive processes in snakes is further indicated by the fact that these animals have a great capacity for the storage of excess protein and fat food materials. This is doubtless an important factor in enabling snakes to go for long periods without taking in additional food.

Frequency of Feeding

In large part, frequency of feeding is related to the rate of digestion and the need for food. The amount of activity, the reproductive state, the physiological condition of the individual, and the abundance of food are all related to the frequency of eating. When amphibians and reptiles are inactive for prolonged periods, as in hibernation or estivation, the need for food is reduced to a point that can be met by stored foodstuffs, and the animals do not eat until they again become active. The need for food is one of the principal factors in the activity patterns of amphibians and reptiles. Those that are active daily, usually feed daily; those that are active only weekly, usually feed only on a weekly basis.

Most salamanders, frogs, crocodilians, turtles, and lizards appear to feed more or less regularly every twenty-four hours during the season of activity. This is indicated by direct observations on the feeding habits of wild individuals and of captured individuals examined for food content. Some may feed almost continuously throughout the daily activity period—as food and temperature permit, of course—while others may feed only at a definite time or times during this activity period. Charles C. Smith and Arthur N. Bragg found that adult female toads (*Bufo*) eat more than males and that adults fill their stomachs once each day, whereas juveniles fill their stomachs twice a day.

In his study of the food habits of the Green Tree Frog (*Hyla c. cinerea*) and the Southern Leopard Frog (*Rana pipiens sphenocephala*), John Kilby found that the former species feeds mostly in late afternoons and at night, whereas the latter species feeds more or less throughout the day. In both species, feeding is usually continued as long as food is available or until the end of the activity period or until the stomach has been filled to capacity. In these animals the stomach is capable of a considerable amount of expansion, so that a full stomach is several times larger than an empty one. Because of this organ's ability to stretch, it is difficult to define the quantity of food that may be eaten at any one time. When food is unusually abundant, both amphibians and reptiles have been known to eat so much that they could move about only with difficulty.

When midday temperatures are too high for prolonged activity, there may be an early morning and a late afternoon period of feeding. Fred Cagle observed such a feeding pattern in the Red-eared Turtle (*Pseudemys scripta elegans*). I noted the same twice-a-day feeding period during the warmer months of the year in Florida for the Gopher Turtle (*Gopherus polyphemus*), the Green Anolis (*Anolis c. carolinensis*), and the Southern Fence Lizard (*Sceloporus u. undulatus*).

Snakes feed at less frequent intervals than other reptiles. This is related to their ability to engulf and store large amounts of food at one time. The ability to swallow large meals is a characteristic phenomenon of many snakes. Richard A. Lockwood had a 38-inch Chain King Snake (*Lampropeltis g. getulus*) that swallowed a 40-inch Corn Snake (*Elaphe g. guttata*). This accomplishment required five hours to complete, and on the same day this King Snake ate an 8-inch DeKay's Snake (*Storeria dekayi*) and a 15-inch Glass Lizard (*Ophisaurus ventralis*). Quite a meal! We have little direct information on the frequency of feeding in the wild. From indirect observations it appears that no snake feeds regularly every day, although a few feed as frequently as every two or three days. Most snakes, however, seem to feed irregularly—at intervals of a week or more. The time between feeding is partly influenced by the amount of food consumed at the previous meal. Karl F. Lagler and J. Clark Salyer II imply that the Northern Water Snake (*Natrix s. sipedon*) feeds daily during the activity season. In their study on the food habits of this species they state: "Specimens collected at midday and during the late hours of warm days usually contain little if any food. Individuals taken before noon, on the other hand, ordinarily have food in their stomachs." The high percentage of snakes without identifiable food remains in the digestive tract also bears out the infrequency of feeding. Animals feeding more frequently yield a higher percentage of individuals with food in the stomach. Approximately one-third to one-half of the individuals examined have such food. Perhaps the snakes collected in the early morning by Lagler and Salyer were taken solely because they had captured food the previous night and hence did not avoid capture so readily.

In contrast, Henry S. Fitch calculated that a minimum of five well-distributed meals of ordinary size was necessary to maintain an adult Northern Pacific Rattlesnake (*Crotalus viridis oreganus*) in good condition throughout the growing season of six to eight months. Fitch is speaking in terms of minimum requirements, and his figure is probably a conservative one on the lower side. In captivity it is generally assumed that a weekly feeding is adequate for most snakes. This is a good working rule, but must be modified and qualified for some species. For instance, a gravid female Garter Snake may eat every other day throughout all or most of the period the young are developing.

Specific Food Habits

In considering some of the specific food habits that have been recorded for amphibians and reptiles, bear in mind the remarks in

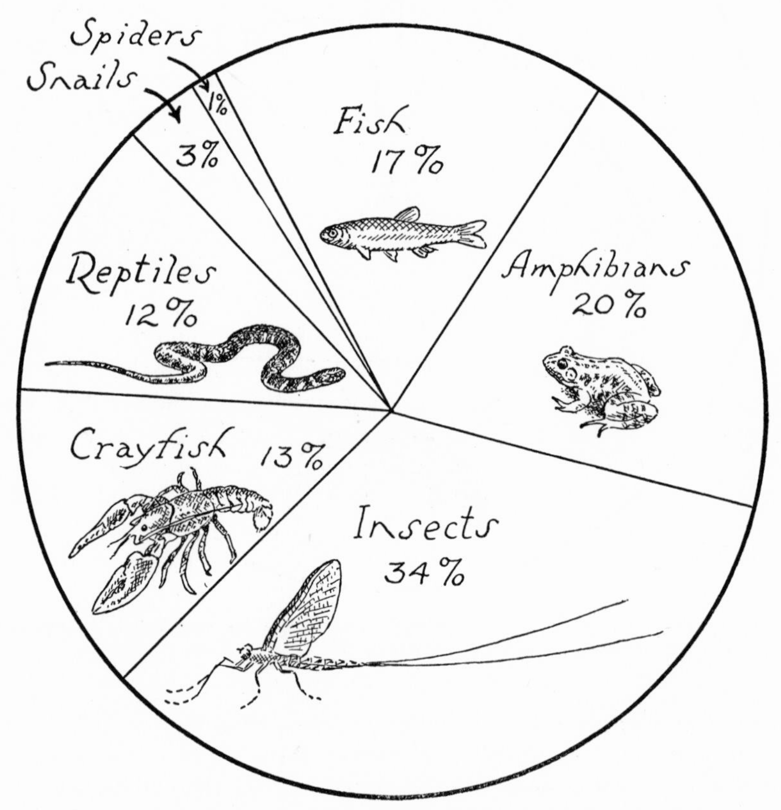

Fig. 30. The food consumed by Amphiuma (*Amphiuma means*) expressed in volume of each type of food. (Data from W. J. Hamilton, Jr.)

the foregoing sections. The sample food study reports are simply a statement of what has been found to have been eaten at a given time in a particular locality. The actual food eaten by the species

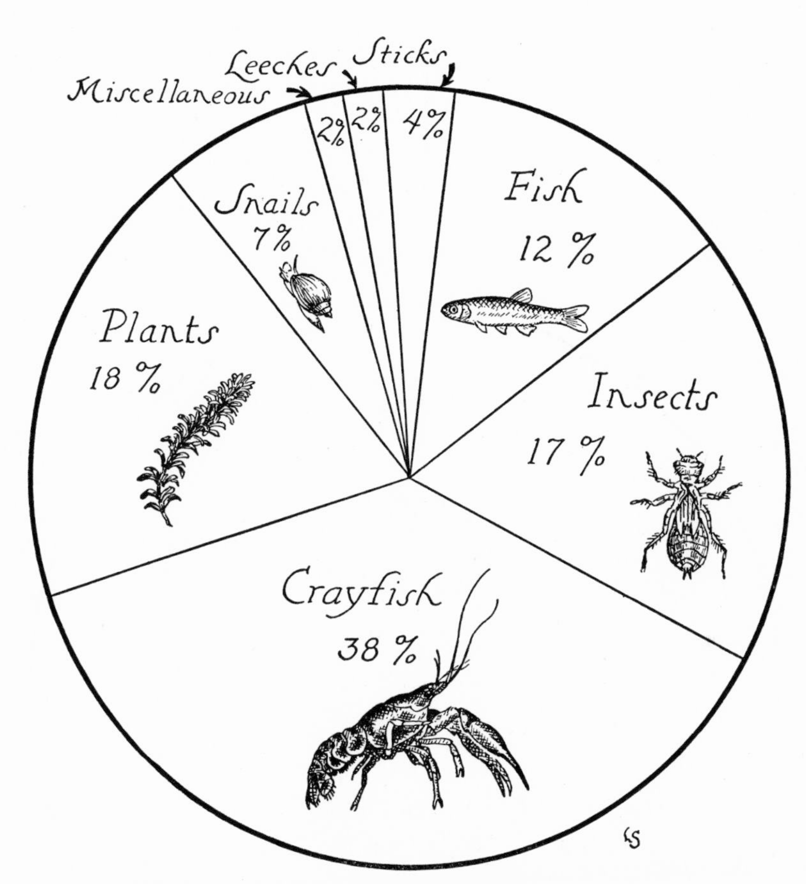

FIG. 31. Food consumed by the Mudpuppy (*Necturus maculosus*) expressed in volume of each type of food. (Data from A. S. Pearse)

may vary considerably from place to place, from time to time, and from individual to individual. However, these studies do give some indication of the general food habits known for the various species. These specific studies are all based on the careful examination of the stomach contents of captured specimens. Not all the studies, however, are strictly comparable. In the recording of the observed food materials, three different methods may be employed to give a qualitative and quantitative record: (1) Each separate food item is

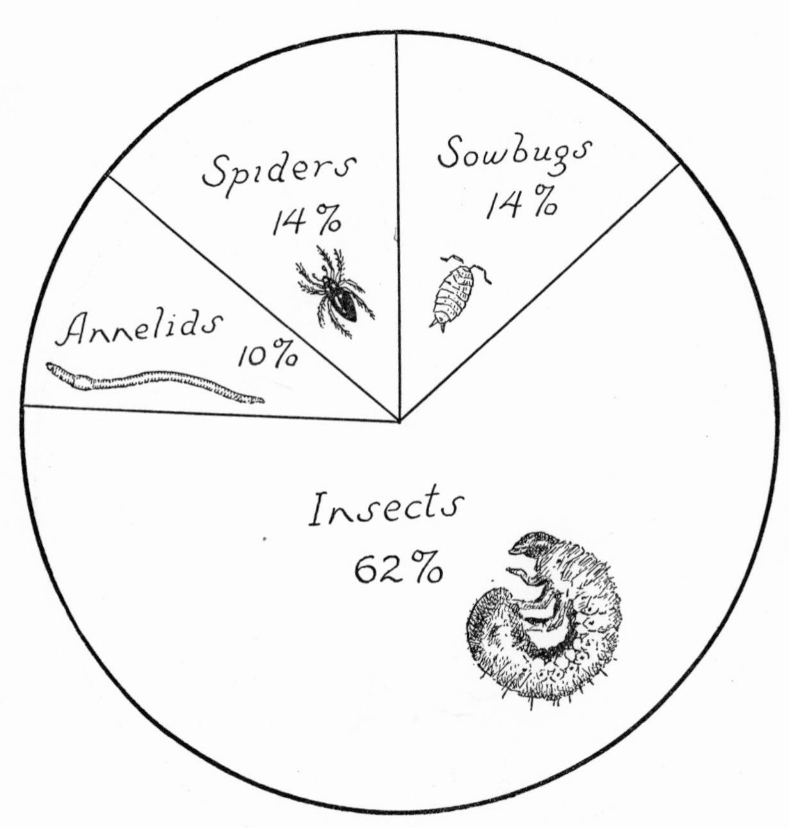

FIG. 32. Food consumed by the Northern Two-lined Salamander (*Eurycea bislineata bislineata*) expressed in volume of each type of food. (Data from W. J. Hamilton, Jr.)

tabulated for all the stomachs, and the total numbers are indicated for each item consumed. (2) Instead of recording the totals for each food item consumed, the total volume of each type of food is measured by determining the amount of water it displaces. (3) The number of stomachs in which a given food item occurs is recorded. Each of the three methods is of value in indicating some aspect of the food habits. The first two methods give a better indication of the relative importance of the different foods, but the second method provides a more accurate measure of relative food

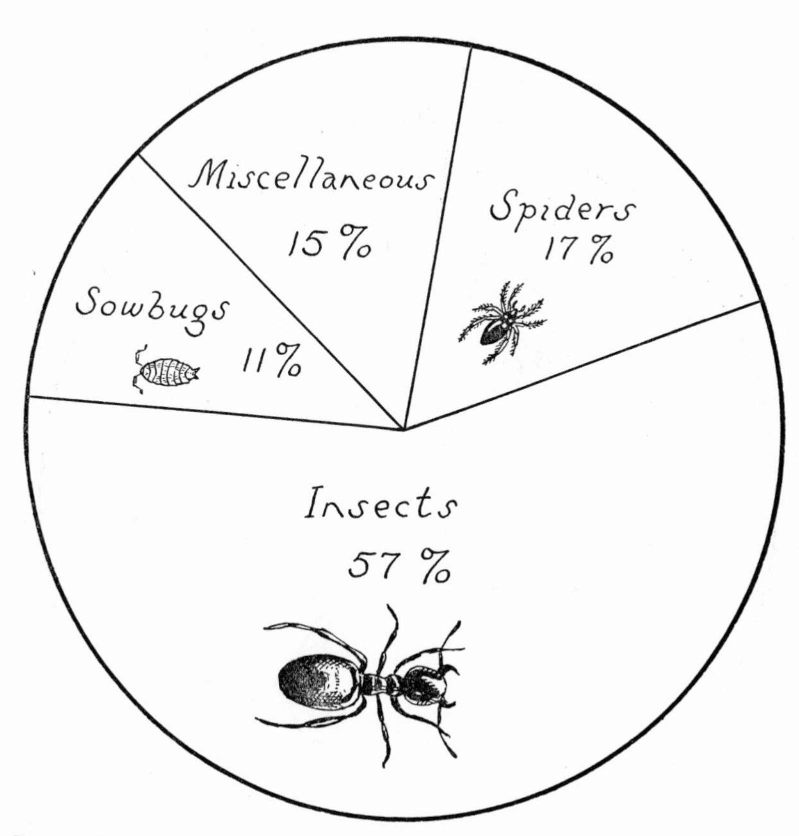

FIG. 33. Food consumed by the Red-backed Salamander (*Plethodon cinereus cinereus*) expressed in volume of each type of food. (Data from W. J. Hamilton, Jr.)

consumption for the separate items. In the paragraphs that follow, some of the food studies are based on item frequency, whereas others record the volume.

Salamanders. There are relatively few detailed studies on the food habits of salamanders. Most of those that have been recorded are for aquatic species. All salamanders appear to be meat eaters or scavengers. Where vegetable food has been found, it usually appears to have been ingested accidentally. The diagrams show the food consumed by two strictly aquatic species (Figures 30-31),

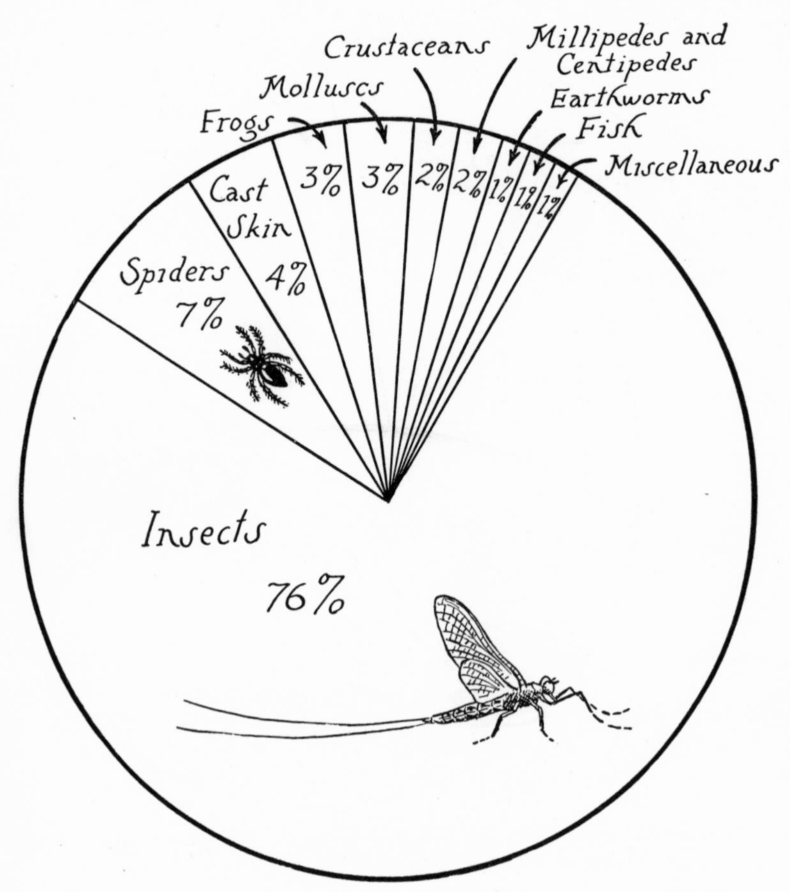

FIG. 34. Food consumed by the Green Frog (*Rana clamitans*) expressed in volume of each type of food. (Data from W. J. Hamilton, Jr.)

one semiaquatic species (Figure 32), and one terrestrial species (Figure 33). Figure 18 shows the food habits of two western salamanders that live in the same habitat but eat different kinds of food organisms. In all the salamander diets, insects form an important item. The two aquatic species augment this with crustaceans, fish, earthworms, amphibians, and reptiles. The semiaquatic and terrestrial species are too small to utilize any vertebrate food; they fill out their diet with invertebrates, such as spiders, sowbugs, and earthworms.

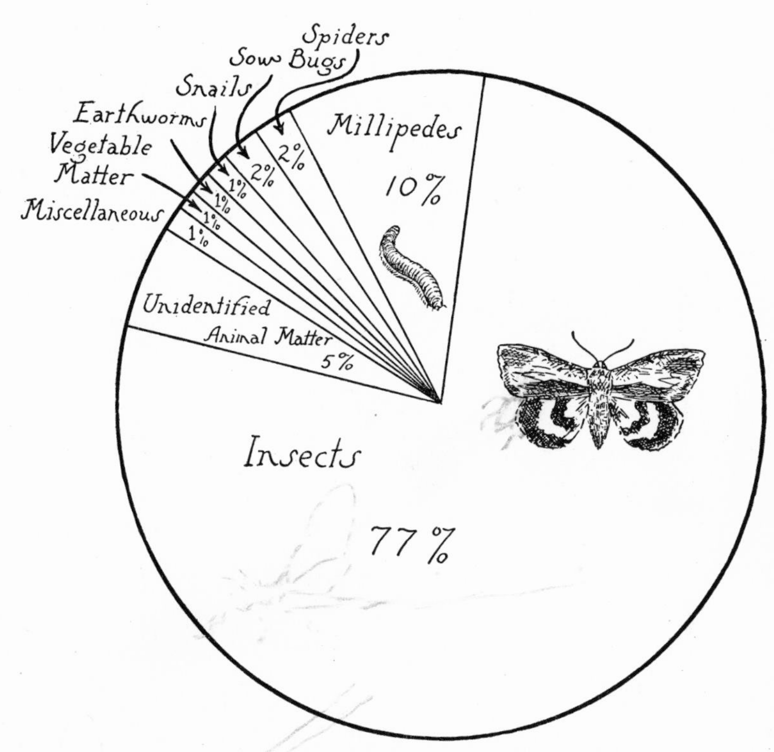

FIG. 35. Food consumed by the American Toad (*Bufo americanus*) expressed in volume of each type of food. (Data from A. H. Kirkland)

Frogs. These are carnivorous, feeding primarily on living, moving prey. They occasionally unintentionally ingest vegetable matter along with animal food and in rare instances may snap up falling plant matter. William J. Hamilton, Jr., found two Green Frogs (*Rana clamitans*) with their stomachs largely distended with elm seeds. These were collected in New York State in May, when elm seeds were showering down from the trees. A similar observation, with more interesting results, was made by Harold Lyon in the Hawaiian Islands, where he found a seasonally fatal epidemic occurring among the Marine Toads (*Bufo marinus*) of the Foster

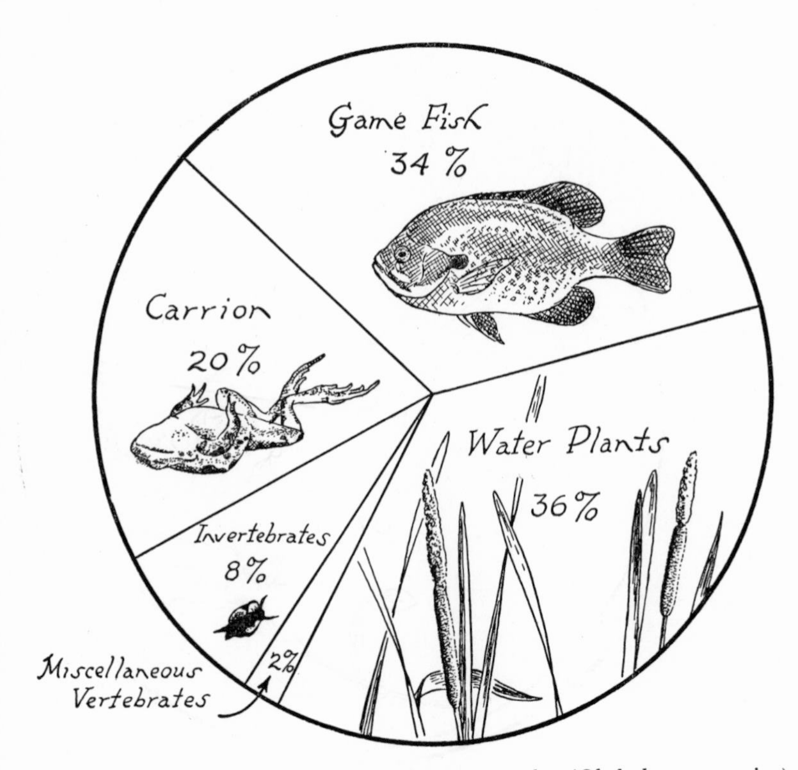

FIG. 36. Food consumed by the Snapping Turtle (*Chelydra serpentina*) expressed in volume of each type of food. (Data from Karl F. Lagler)

Gardens when the blossoms fall from the Strychnine Trees. The toads, attracted by the movement, ingest the falling blossoms and are killed by the strychnine. Except for such unusual occurrences, frogs are strictly carnivorous. The diagrams shown here indicate the food of one representative frog (Figure 34) and one Toad (Figure 35). Frogs are among the most voracious feeders to be found among amphibians and reptiles. They literally feed on anything that moves and can be swallowed. For this reason, only the two examples are shown here; they are sufficient to suggest the variations that result from differences in habitat, abundance of food, and size

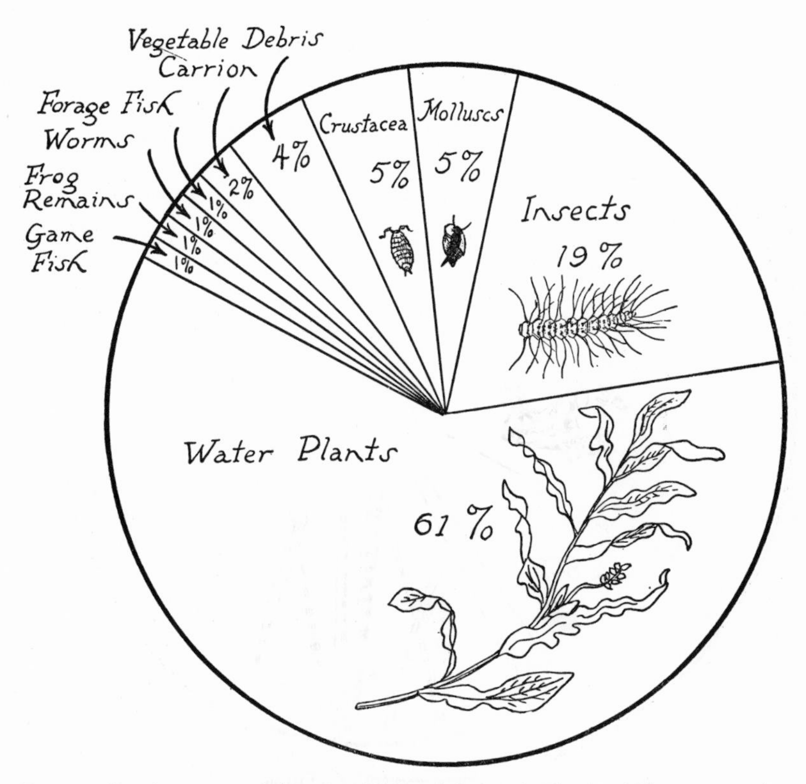

FIG. 37. Food consumed by the Midland Painted Turtle (*Chrysemys picta marginata*) expressed in volume of each type of food. (Data from Karl F. Lagler)

of the predators. Large toads have even been known to pursue and try to swallow ping-pong balls that were bounced toward them. In general, the bulk of the food is always made up of insects.

Crocodilians. All crocodilians are meat eaters or scavengers. No detailed data are available for the food habits of the American

Crocodile. Information for the Alligator shows the foods reported for a series of specimens collected in a short period of time and of varying sizes. Table 9 compares the food habits reported for

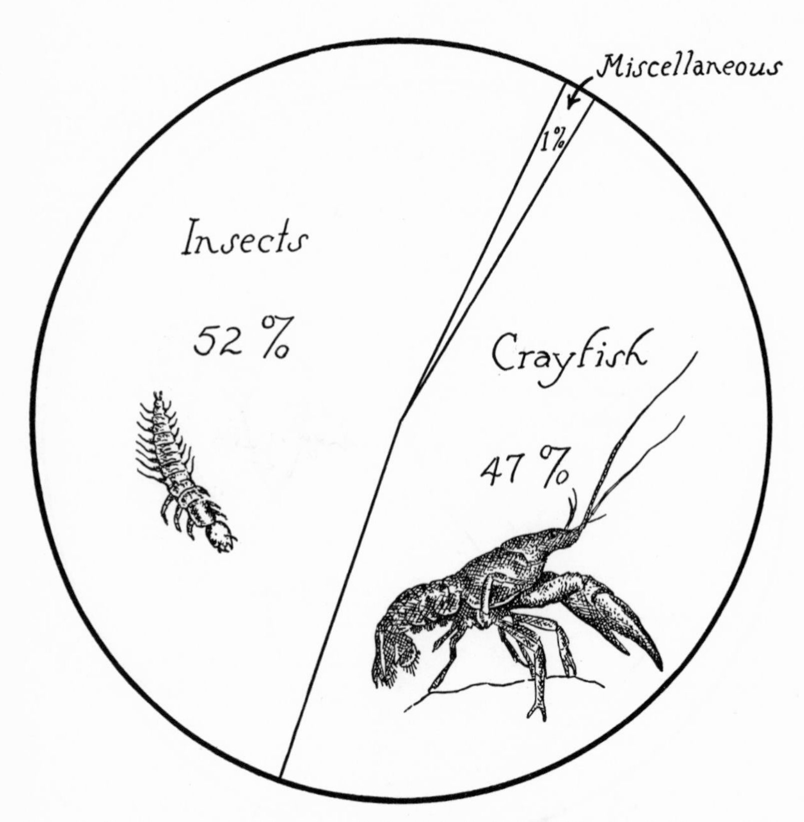

FIG. 38. Food consumed by the Midland Soft-shelled Turtle (*Trionyx ferox spinifera*) expressed in volume of each type of food. (Data from Karl F. Lagler)

the Alligator from two different sources. The variation in observed food is partly due to differences in the ages of the animals studied and possibly to seasonal differences in food available. E. A. McIlhenny examined the stomach contents of 24 adult Alligators and found 70 per cent of all food items were birds, mostly herons; 14 per cent, turtles; 11 per cent, garfish; 4 per cent, snakes; and 1 per cent, mammals. These adults were collected in a bird sanctuary where aquatic birds were unusually numerous.

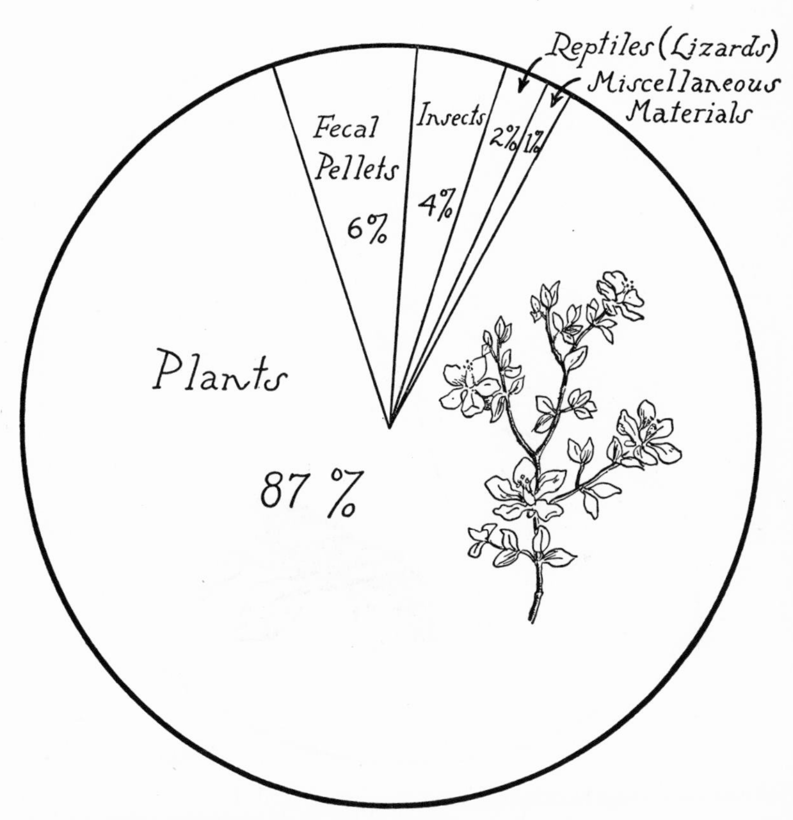

Fig. 39. Food consumed by the Desert Iguana (*Dipsosaurus dorsalis dorsalis*) expressed in volume of each type of food. (Data from Kenneth Norris)

Turtles. Turtles have the most varied food habits of any of the amphibians and reptiles. Some species are mostly herbivorous, others are omnivorous, and still others are nearly entirely carnivorous. Virtually all aquatic species are believed by fishermen to feed exclusively on fish. The several diagrams show that this is not so. Moreover, some maligned turtles are shown to perform a real service as scavengers. The diagrams of the three species selected give

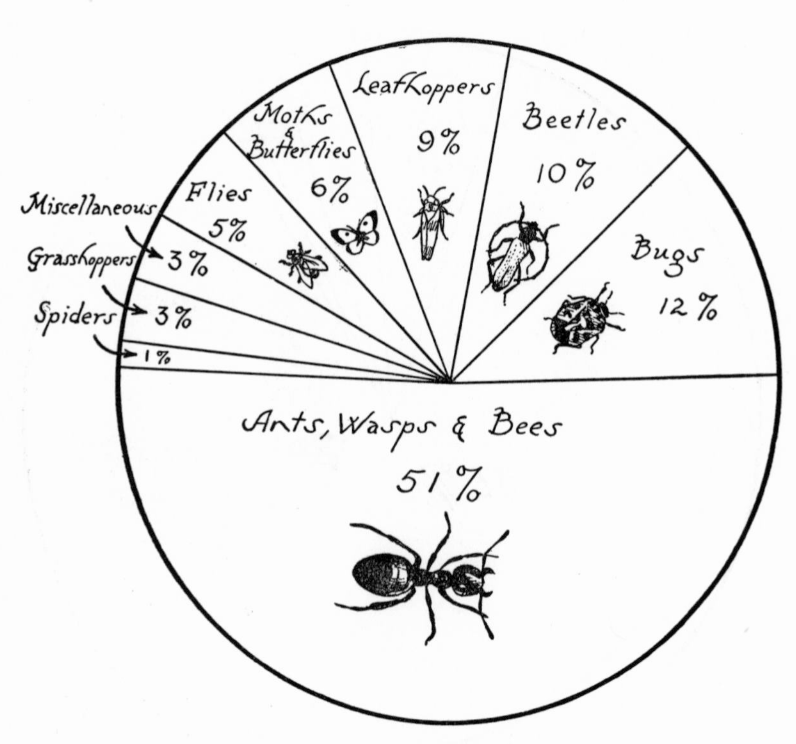

FIG. 40. Food consumed by the Sagebrush Lizard (*Sceloporus graciosus graciosus*) expressed in the number of items of food. (Data from George F. Knowlton)

an indication of the variety of food habits found among our fresh-water turtles (Figures 36, 37 and 38). No terrestrial species is shown because of a scarcity of data for such species, which are primarily vegetarian in diet.

Lizards. Most lizards are carnivorous; a few are herbivorous or omnivorous. The majority are insectivorous, feeding on different kinds of insects. The several food-habit studies shown here indicate

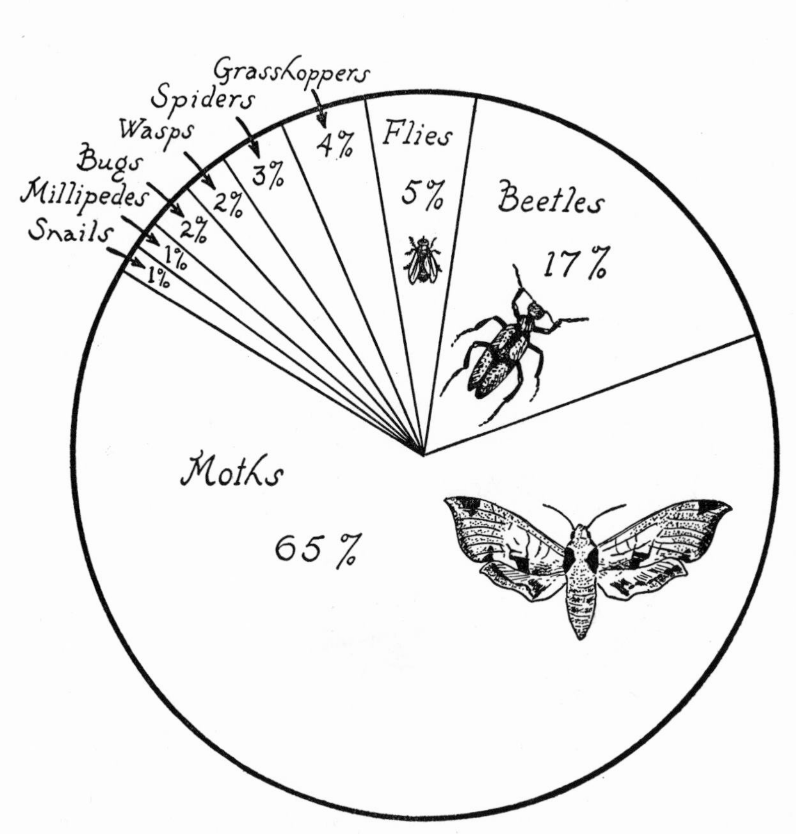

FIG. 41. Food consumed by the Shasta Alligator Lizard (*Gerrhonotus coeruleus shastensis*) expressed in the number of items of food. (Data from Henry S. Fitch)

to what extent the various species feed on different groups of insects (Figures 39, 40, 41 and 42). The variations are partly the result of dietary preferences, and partly the result of abundance of food organisms.

Snakes. Snakes are meat eaters, egg eaters, or scavengers. Snakes do not eat vegetable food except accidentally when swallowing animal prey or by mistake. The diagrams indicate the foods reported

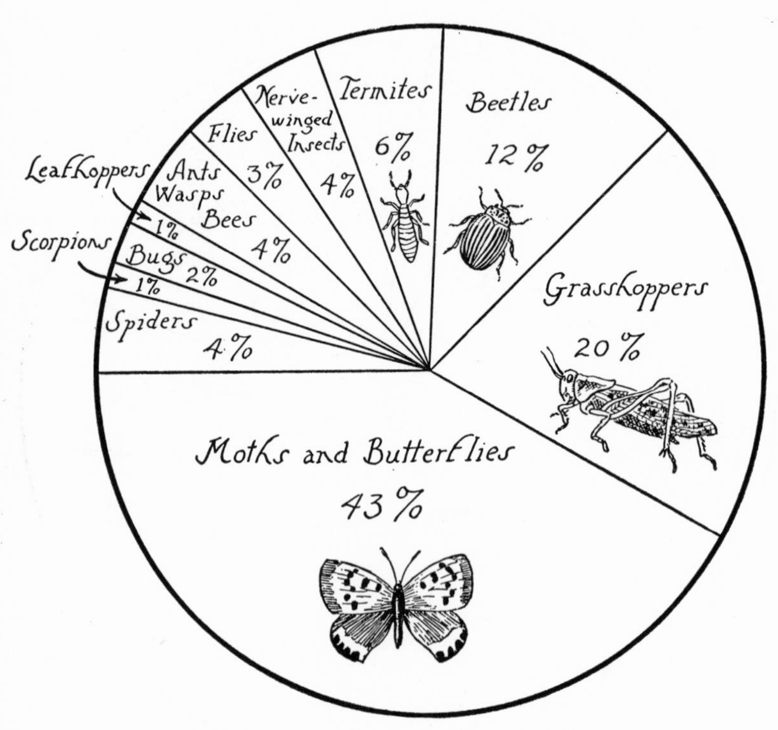

Fig. 42. Food consumed by the Tessellated Race Runner (*Cnemidophorus tigris tigris*) expressed in the number of items of food. (Data from George F. Knowlton)

for four representative species (Figures 26, 43, 44, 45). Figure 19 shows the differences in diet in three species of Garter Snakes (*Thamnophis*) in Southern Michigan. The food diagrams shown here were selected to show variation in food habits. Some species are highly selective and will feed only on a single type of food.

The Eastern Hognose Snake (*Heterodon p. playtyrhinos*) typically eats only Toads (*Bufo*), but an occasional individual will accept a True Frog (*Rana*). The Scarlet Snake (*Cemophora coccinea*) feeds

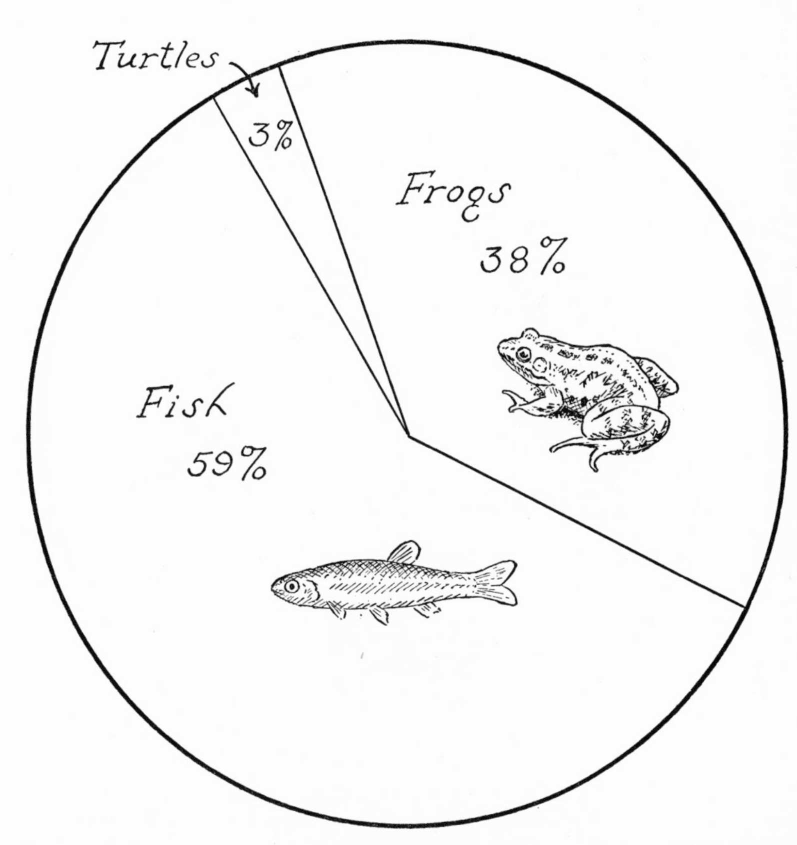

Fig. 43. Food consumed by the Diamondback Water Snake (*Natrix rhombifera rhombifera*) expressed in the number of items of food. (Data from Fred R. Cagle)

primarily on reptile eggs, augmenting this diet with occasional insect larvae. This species is a notorious raider of turtle nests and has been found consuming contents of eggs before the turtle covered its nest.

Snakes of the genus *Lampropeltis* are notorious for their habits of eating other snakes. This is true of only some species, however, others may feed primarily on rodents or lizards. The King Snakes

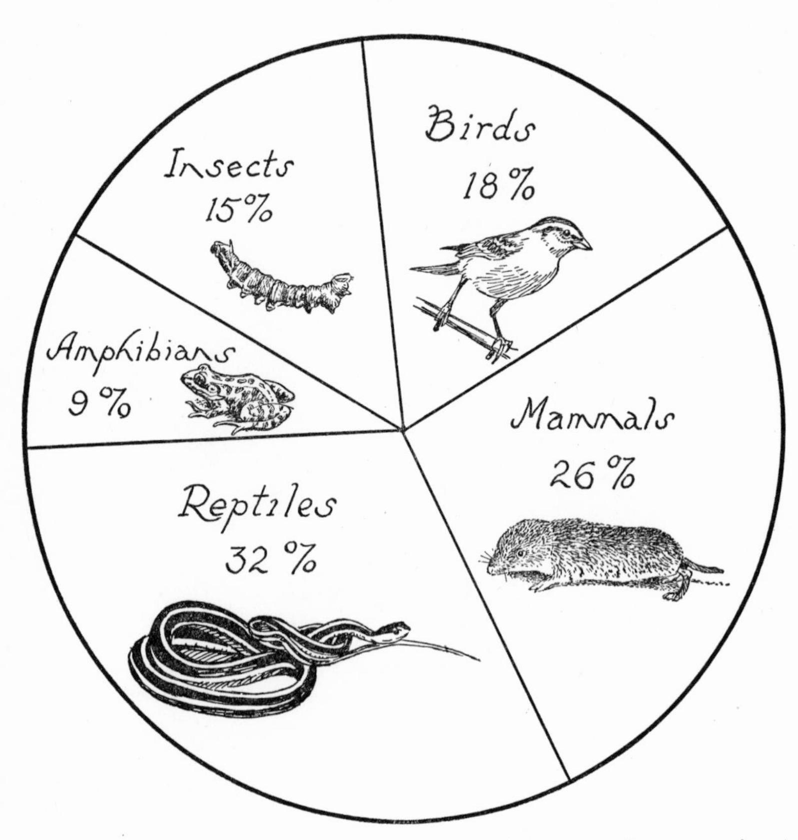

FIG. 44. Food consumed by the Black Racer (*Coluber constrictor constrictor*) expressed in volume of each type of food. (Data from F. M. Uhler, C. Cottam and T. E. Clarke)

(*Lampropeltis getulus*) are true to their reputation and do consume large numbers of snakes. Robert F. Clark examined the stomach contents of 301 King Snakes collected in one year in Louisiana. In the same locality 27 other species of snakes were collected by

Clark. In the stomachs of the King Snakes he found 169 snakes belonging to 11 species, four of which were venomous. The numbers of individuals of different species collected by Clark do not

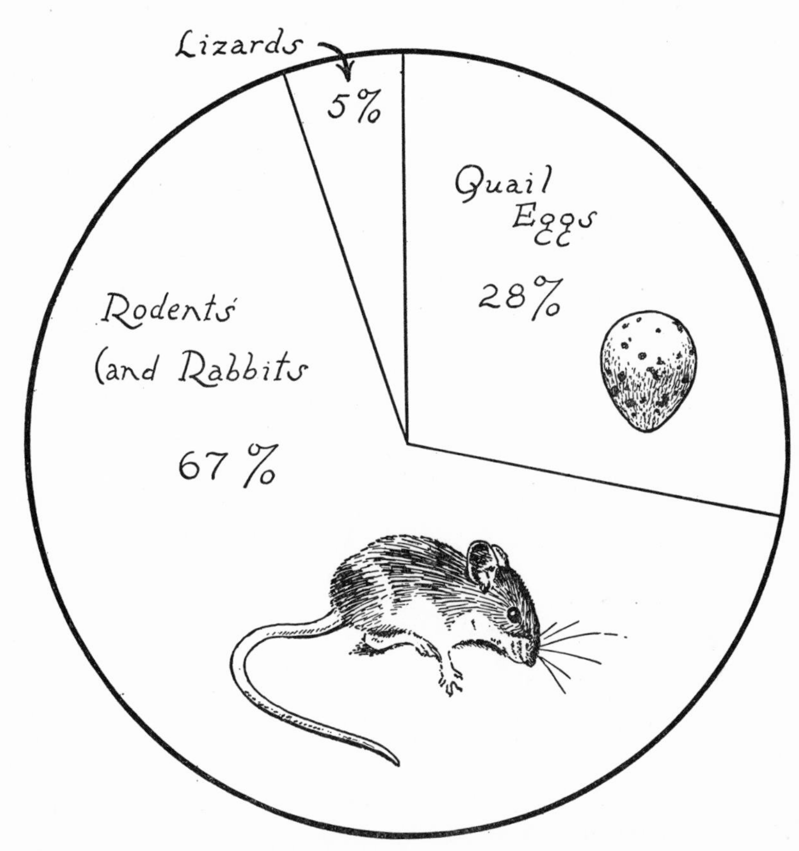

FIG. 45. Food consumed by the Pacific Gopher Snake (*Pituophis catenifer catenifer*) expressed in number of items of food. (Data from Henry S. Fitch)

correspond closely with the frequencies of individuals of the different species eaten by the King Snakes, indicating a quite different collecting ability or selectivity on the part of man and snake. Clark's study demonstrates the fallacy of the popular notion that

King Snakes are primarily enemies of venomous snakes. The venomous individuals totaled only approximately one-fourth of the food items consumed.

TABLE 9

ALLIGATOR FOOD

Items	157 Individuals Examined by Remington Kellogg		318 Individuals Examined by Giles and Childs	
	Number of Items	Per Cent of Total Items	Number of Items	Per Cent of Total Items
Insects	2,638	66	566	32
Spiders	253	6	—	—
Crustaceans	451	12	824	46
Fishes	580	15	193	11
Amphibians	1	—	3	—
Reptiles	26 }		94	5
Birds	15 }	1	35	2
Mammals	12 }		67	4
Total	3,976	100	1,782	100

CHAPTER 11

Reproduction

THROUGHOUT MANY PARTS OF THE country choruses of calling frogs are among the most familiar signs of spring. Some species begin their calls long before the arrival of the first bird migrant from warmer regions or before the first spring flower has pushed its head above unfrozen soil. The Spring Peeper (*Hyla crucifer*) gets its vernacular name from the fact that in most of the eastern United States its high-pitched call heralds the coming of spring. Other species join or replace this little frog in announcing the season in other parts of the country and as the season warms into summer.

The frog choruses, like most of the bird songs of spring, are related to the process of reproduction. As with many animals and plants, the reproductive functions of frogs are typically attuned to the spring and early summer months—but there are a few exceptions. In the spring of the year, males and females come together to mate, resulting in the fertilization of the eggs to start the development of the next generation. Amphibians characteristically lay their eggs in water; the young hatch as aquatic larvae and undergo a metamorphosis to acquire the adult body form. All reptiles on the other hand, lay their eggs on land or give birth to their young. They have no larval stage, and the young appear as small replicas of the adults, except for differences in color and proportions.

Reproduction is, of course, vital to the existence of a species and must be successful enough to produce a sufficiently large number of young to maintain the species population despite the natural losses that occur.

Bisexual Reproduction

In all species of American amphibians and reptiles reproduction is a bisexual performance, involving the fertilization of the female's eggs by the sperm of the male. Normally it is performed only by individuals that have attained sexual maturity. This stage of development is typically associated with the adult body form. However, in some species of salamanders individuals may acquire sexual maturity while still possessing the larval body form. In fact, some species may never change from the larval morphological stage but are able to reproduce because their reproductive organs have matured. Reproduction by individuals that retain the larval body form is spoken of as neoteny. The famed Axolotls (*Siredon, Rhyacosiredon, Bathysiredon*) of Mexico are perhaps the best-known species in which neoteny is the rule rather than the exception. In the closely related Tiger Salamander (*Ambystoma tigrinum*), which is found throughout the United States, neoteny may occur sporadically but is more frequent in some races or in some geographical regions than in others. The San Marcos Neotenic Salamander (*Eurycea neotenes nana*), the Bexar County Neotenic Salamander (*Eurycea n. neotenes*), and the Oklahoma Neotenic Salamander (*Eurycea tynerensis*) are other examples of species that do not undergo metamorphosis prior to attaining reproductive maturity. It should be emphasized that neoteny is not reproduction by newly hatched larvae, but rather by older individuals that fail to undergo metamorphosis or to change to the adult body form.

In amphibians fertilization of the eggs may take place outside the female's body—external fertilization. Or it may occur within the body of the female—internal fertilization. External fertilization is a less efficient method than is internal fertilization; it requires water as a medium in which eggs and sperm can unite. It is the rule among all the frogs and two genera of aquatic salamanders in this country. The only frog in the United States in which internal fertilization takes place is the Tailed Frog (*Ascaphus truei*). In this species the cloaca is elongated in the male and is used in mating to introduce the sperm into the female's body. Among our salamanders, only in the Hellbenders of the genus *Cryptobranchus* and in the Sirens (*Siren*) is fertilization external; in all other salamanders of the United States internal fertilization is the rule, whether mating occurs in or out of water. In reptiles fertilization is always internal, regardless of whether mating occurs in water or on land.

Since reproduction is a bisexual function, the two sexes must come together at the exact time that both are ready for the fertilization process. Each sex is generally in the reproductive state for only a brief period of each year. Thus they must come together at just the right time if they are to contribute offspring to the species population. How is this accomplished when the two sexes normally do not live in family groups?

With the advent of suitable weather conditions, salamanders usually congregate in suitable situations, sometimes in large numbers, literally by the hundreds, and other times in smaller groups. In aquatic species this may take place in a weedy shoal area of a pond or lake, or in a quiet pool of a stream. In species that are terrestrial throughout most of the year but return to water to breed, groups may congregate in woodland ponds or swamps. In the case of the strictly terrestrial species, the aggregations may consist simply of a small colony of individuals in one small area. Regardless of the spot, however, the individuals have been directed to that particular location by specific humidity, temperature, and chemical, geological, or physical characteristics, effective singly or in combination.

The reproductive organs have been undergoing enlargement in preparation for the breeding season. These changes have been stimulated by changing length of daylight and dark and by temperature. As the reproductive organs mature, chemical agents known as hormones are released into the blood of the animal, readying it for the performance of the reproductive function. Sometimes these hormones produce certain changes in external form or color. When the animal's body is in full readiness, it responds to the rising temperatures of spring, the soaking rains that wet the earth, and the periods of increasingly longer light—and it moves to the breeding site of its species, to meet individuals of the opposite sex belonging to its own species.

Sexually activated aquatic Red-spotted Newts (*Triturus v. viridescens*) move toward shallow weedy areas where there is an increased amount of oxygen. Here they breed and lay their eggs. Mudpuppies (*Necturus maculosus*) living in lakes move into flowing streams to carry out their reproduction. The usually terrestrial

Spotted Salamander (*Ambystoma maculata*), following a moisture gradient, moves down hill on the first rainy nights after the ground has thawed out. Thus these three species of salamanders are brought together in breeding aggregation—by chemical stimulus in the case of the Newt, by chemical and current stimulus in the case of the Mudpuppy, and by gravity and moisture gradient stimuli in the case of the Spotted Salamander. Salamanders are essentially voiceless and cannot be attracted or directed by the calling of other individuals. In many frogs, on the other hand, the calls of the males may serve to bring females, and other males, to the ponds and streams where mating takes place. This has been shown to be true for at least most Toads (*Bufo*) and Tree Frogs (*Hyla*), but does not appear to be true in some frogs (*Rana*). The males move to the breeding sites first, being guided by gravity and moisture, and possibly by light and "muscular memory." Charles M. Bogert has found that toads can apparently hear the calls for distances of more than half a mile. Differences in the calls of the different species are important in keeping the various species in a given area separate.

When more than one species is breeding in a given region at the same time, the call may be of considerable importance in keeping the species from attempting to crossbreed. Other factors that are important as "isolating mechanisms" in frogs are the warning croak; species differences in size, structure, and behavior; and differences in time of mating. Albert P. Blair has shown that the different species of toads may have quite distinctive warning croaks. For example, the Colorado River Toad (*Bufo alvarius*) has a warning croak that consists of five vibrations per second, whereas in Woodhouse's Toad (*Bufo w. woodhousei*) this sound consists of 84 to 104 vibrations per second. The differences in the warning croak appear to be effective in preventing crossbreeding between some forms, but fail to influence others.

Arthur Bragg, in his studies on the amphibians of Oklahoma, has found that where related species are to be found breeding in the same area, one species usually occupies one niche and the other breeds in a different niche.

In reptiles, voice may be a factor in bringing the sexes together, especially in the crocodilians. The bellowing of bull Alligators (*Alligator mississippiensis*) is a well-known sound to the inhabitants of the Gulf States. This sound, which is heard in spring and early summer, appears to serve both as an attraction for the females and

PLATE IX. A female Dusky Salamander (*Desmognathus f. fuscus*) guarding her clutch of eggs. Note the newly hatched young in the upper left hand corner. (Photograph by Dr. Charles Stine, Jr.)

PLATE X. Two male Red Diamond Rattlesnakes (*Crotalus r. ruber*) in a "combat dance." In this performance each contestant strives to push the other over and to bring its head above that of its opponent. (Zoological Society of San Diego photograph)

as a territorial indicator to other males. Alligators may be stimulated to roar by the roaring of other males, by thunder, by blasting, and by gunfire, or, as Frank Beach has demonstrated, by the sound of B flat two octaves below middle G (57 vibrations per second) on a French horn. The Crocodile has a lower, less audible bellow, which is more like a low rumble or growl, and is not so pronounced nor so well known as the roaring bellow of the Alligator.

In fresh-water turtles the sexes appear to locate one another simply by sight and juxtaposition in a circumscribed habitat. Here appearance, color, or courtship behavior seem to be the primary bases for keeping species from cross-mating. In these species mating usually takes place in spring or early summer, well before the eggs are laid. In the marine turtles, since they move about over greater distances, which might cause the sexes to encounter greater uncertainty in finding each other at the proper time, mating takes place as the females return to the water immediately after the completion of egg-laying. The males congregate off shore in water along the beaches where the eggs are laid. The female is in a state of readiness for mating immediately after she has laid her eggs. This is an important difference between fresh-water and marine turtles in the relative times of mating.

In land or semiaquatic turtles, odor may play an important part in bringing the sexes together, although this is not known with certainty. During the spring the males appear to move about more and cover greater distances than at other times. Locating a receptive female may be purely a matter of chance and good eyesight.

In some turtles the females have the remarkable ability to retain live spermatozoa within the body for several years, producing clutches of fertile eggs each year during the reproductive season. This means that in these species a single mating may enable the female to lay fertile eggs for several years *without* subsequent matings, thereby reducing the necessity of annual meetings between the sexes. After the first year the number of fertile eggs produced decreases progressively each year, until the female can no longer lay fertile eggs without another mating. This phenomenon is spoken of as *Amphigonia Retardata.* This was first reported by Samuel Hildebrand in the Diamondback Terrapin (*Malaclemys terrapin*). He found that after a single mating a female might lay fertile eggs for as long as four years.

Most lizards tend to occur in more or less well-marked groups or colonies. In some species—for example, the Green Anolis (*Anolis c. carolinensis*), the Banded Gecko (*Coleonyx variegatus*), and the Scaly Lizards (*Sceloporus*)—social hierarchy and clear-cut territoriality may be established. In such groupings the meeting of the sexes is no longer a matter of finding receptive partners, but rather one of unreceptive females avoiding overaggressive males in whose territories they occur. The territory of the adult male usually includes the territories of several females with which he mates and for which he competes with adjacent males. In the few more or less solitary lizards and among the burrowing species, odor or suitable physical stimuli may be the primary means of bringing the sexes together.

In snakes, odor appears to be the most important cue that enables the sexes to come together for mating. During the reproductive season, females secrete a strong odor from the skin and from glands in the base of the tail. This leaves a trail that males can follow readily. G. K. Noble and H. J. Clausen demonstrated that this was the primary sensory mechanism used by males of DeKay's Snake (*Storeria dekayi*) in locating receptive females.

An important factor in bringing receptive individuals of the two sexes of snakes together during the mating period in many parts of the country is the congregation of snakes at a common hibernating site. On emerging in the spring of the year, the snakes remain in the vicinity of the "dens" for a time, and mating usually occurs before they move away. The habit of hibernating in large groups is most notable in snakes, but also occurs in lizards and turtles to a lesser degree. It is primarily a retreat from inclement weather, but also functions to the advantage of the species in increasing the probability of successful mating.

Another factor that is important in virtually all species of amphibians and reptiles is that the males are more active during the breeding period. They are actively seeking receptive mates, and in moving about over a larger area they increase the probability of a successful encounter. An individual male may mate with more than one female in one mating season. In some species there is a greater number of males than females. In most amphibian breeding aggregations the males arrive before the females, so that in the early part of the mating period only males may be found. However, even at the height of the breeding season the males may still outnumber the females to a marked degree. In northeastern Oklahoma, Albert

P. Blair found many more males than females in breeding populations of the American Toad (*Bufo terrestris americanus*) from March to May. Collections of nonbreeding toads at other times of the year more nearly approached an equal sex ratio. This has caused some students to suggest that the females do not breed every year. From the standpoint of species welfare the high proportion of males in relation to females increases the likelihood that every breeding female will find a mate and produce fertile eggs. In Jefferson's Salamander (*Ambystoma jeffersonianum*) a quite different sex ratio may exist in some, but not all, localities. In the vicinity of Albany, New York, Sherman C. Bishop observed that females outnumbered males approximately eight to one, and during the breeding season the females appeared to bid actively for the attention of the males. On one occasion each male was found attended by three or four females. In Michigan, Wesley Clanton found two types of adults in this species: (1) a dark type in which the sexes were approximately even in number; and (2) a light type composed almost entirely of females. Charles E. Mohr observed this species in Pennsylvania; of 62 specimens collected, 40 were males and 22 were females.

Sex Recognition

When we catch a frog, turtle, lizard, or snake and want to know whether it is a male or female, we may be unable to ascertain this by simple examination. If it is difficult for us to identify the sex of these animals when we hold them in our hand, how is sex recognition accomplished by the animals themselves? It is of interest to us to learn that sometimes the animals, too, have the same difficulty, although in most forms it is a simple matter. In amphibians, sex recognition depends on one or more of the following: voice, behavior, odor, tactile stimuli, size, or body resistance. Recognition of sex in these forms is rarely or never accomplished at any distance. Sexually aroused males characteristically court or clasp any individual that is of the right size and continue to do so if the individual proves to be a female. In salamanders, odor and behavior appear to furnish the primary methods of sex recognition. The head-prodding, nosing, and rubbing involved in salamander courtship result partly in sex recognition. The presence of special glands—the hedonic glands—in some salamanders may assist in this recognition.

In frogs, sex recognition seems to be accomplished only after the male has clasped a moving individual. Males of most species clasp any individual frog in their vicinity. Males of the Wood Frog (*Rana sylvatica*) and the Tailed Frog (*Ascaphus truei*) appear to rely primarily on difference in size and resistance to pressure in bodies of the two sexes before egg laying. If a male of these species is clasped by another male, he is released shortly. If a female that is full of eggs is clasped, she is held until her eggs have been laid. If a female that has already laid is clasped, she will be released quickly just as though she were a male. In the Wood Frog the warning croak of a clasped male acts as a secondary factor that assists recognition.

In other frogs the warning croak appears to be the most important aid to recognition. In various species of toads of the genus *Bufo*, Albert P. Blair has shown that the warning croak results in quick release. A clasped male gives the warning croak, but a gravid female does not. The same is true for the Leopard Frog (*Rana pipiens*).

Little is known about sex recognition in crocodilians except for the function of the deep voice of the male. The chin and cloacal gland secretions may provide additional clues.

In turtles, size, behavior, and odor all play a part. Angus M. Woodbury and Ross Hardy observed that the Desert Tortoise (*Gopherus agassizi*) engages in head-bobbing when tortoises encounter one another in the wild and that if the individuals are of the opposite sex courtship may follow. This head-bobbing may serve as a means of sex recognition, as it does in some lizards.

In the nocturnal Banded Gecko (*Coleonyx variegatus*), Bernard Greenberg found that sex recognition depended primarily on behavior and that in the laboratory anesthetized males were treated as females. This is in strong contrast to the condition in the diurnal Fence Lizards (*Sceloporus undulatus*), where color is one of the primary signs of sex. Whenever G. K. Noble painted out the blue patches of a male, it was treated as a female by other males. In some diurnal lizards, such as the Green Anolis (*Anolis c. carolinensis*), behavior and color appear to be of equal importance as aids to sex recognition.

In snakes, sex recognition seems to be essentially a matter of chemical odors, although visual cues and behavior also play a part. G. K. Noble found that the odor of the skin was of greatest importance in DeKay's Snake (*Storeria dekayi*) and the Eastern

Garter Snake (*Thamnophis s. sirtalis*). Rattlesnakes (*Crotalus*) and Moccasins (*Ancistrodon*) are widely noted for the strength of the odors of the cloacal glands, but these appear to play little part in sex recognition. Movements and motion may be important as aids to sex recognition in the case of some of the agile diurnal colubrids, such as the Racers (*Coluber*) and Whip Snakes (*Masticophis*), but this has not been analyzed sufficiently as yet. C. B. Perkins and Charles E. Shaw have noted that captive male Pine Snakes (*Pituophis m. melanoleucas*) take no part in courtship activities when their eyes are occluded prior to the shedding of skin. This indicates some reliance on visual cues during the process, even though the males appear to locate females by following a scent trail. It is probable that size is of importance in some snakes where the sexes differ markedly in this respect. Also, the head-bobbing habit observed in many snakes may serve some function in this connection. The importance of size and behavior in sex recognition are still a matter of conjecture.

Male Combat "Dance"

A phenomenon that may have some relation to sex recognition or at least have a part in precourtship activity is the male combat "dance" that has been observed in snakes on a number of occasions. Its exact significance is still uncertain. In this behavior, two or more individuals come in contact with their bodies parallel and partially entwined. A struggle then ensues, with each trying to tighten the loops around the other's body. In American colubrid snakes in which this phenomenon has been observed, a horizontal position is maintained throughout the performance, but in the American Pit Vipers the anterior parts of the bodies are reared to a vertical position. Since European Colubrids, including members of the genus *Coluber*, raise the anterior part of the body in a vertical position, some American species may be found to do likewise.

The individuals usually have the posterior parts of the body and tail tightly entwined. The heads and necks are loosely looped in a short striking position and are moved up and down or around in the struggle to bring the bodies into tighter loops. The heads may push against each other, but there is rarely any attempt to bite an adversary in this struggle. In the Pit Vipers, with their vertical stance, there is an apparent straining to bring the head above that of the opponent. In all cases observed, the behavior is distinctly different from the typical courtship behavior for the species. Some captive individuals, however, have changed from combat to courtship behavior and attempted to mate with the vanquished individual.

Several of the first observers of this behavior erroneously interpreted it to be a courtship performance between members of opposite sexes. However, in every case where the sex of the individuals has been verified, all have been males. Thus the behavior is entirely limited to the males and is different from courtship behavior. Some herpetologists have suggested that the combat "dance" is a manifestation of territoriality similar to the fighting of males in some species of lizards. Others have suggested that the behavior is related to sex recognition or the assertion of social or sexual domination. Charles E. Shaw has recently augmented and summarized our knowledge of this type of activity in snakes. He points out that the rarity of the phenomenon would indicate that it is not related to territoriality and that the length of time, sometimes as long as an hour, spent in such behavior suggests that it is not related to sex recognition. The fact that no definite territorial tendency is known in snakes also weakens the argument that the "dance" is a manifestation of territoriality, except possibly in an incipient fashion. Shaw points out that most observations of the combat "dance" have been made in spring and early summer, either during a period of breeding activity or during or immediately after feeding. Further observations are needed to reveal the true significance of this behavior and its relation to the snake's life activities. Perhaps it is an incipient expression of social dominance that may precede courtship and mating when another male is present. Whatever the true significance of this behavior, it appears to be related in part to the sexual state of the male.

Courtship

The term courtship is used for the premating behavior that stimulates one or both individuals and initiates the mating performance. Although it is considered separately from the act of mating, to which it serves as a prelude, it may be difficult to designate the point at which courtship ends and mating begins.

Courtship may be of importance not only as a stimulus to reproduction, but also as a method of preventing crossbreeding between closely related species. The type of courtship activities, or the pattern of courtship, varies considerably from one species to another. In some amphibians and reptiles there appears to be little or no courtship involved in the process of reproduction, whereas in others a rather elaborate courtship is an important preliminary phase of the mating behavior.

The studies of G. K. Noble and others have revealed pronounced differences in courtship behavior in salamanders. The aquatic Hellbenders (*Cryptobranchus*), for example, have no definite courtship behavior; the male is simply stimulated to emit sperm by the presence of the string of eggs deposited by the female. In the Ambystomids there are distinct courtship patterns that involve elaborate rubbing and prodding movements with the head, tail waving, and occasional grasping with the hind legs. The male emits a cloacal secretion that attracts the female. Here the courtship appears to be directed to stimulate the female to pick up the sperm clusters or spermatophores that the male deposits.

In the American Salamandrids the courtship behavior typically includes seizure of the female by the male with either the forelimbs or with both pairs of limbs, and rubbing of the female by the male. The male possesses hedonic or "pleasure" glands for stimulating or attracting the females. These glands are usually located on the chin or cheeks of the male and produce an odorous secretion that is rubbed on the female during courtship. After the courtship play, the male moves off a short distance and deposits the spermatophore. The female follows and picks it up with her cloaca.

The Plethodontids possess large numbers of hedonic glands on the cheeks, body, and tail of the male. The basic courtship pattern is illustrated by the Two-lined Salamander (*Eurycea b. bislineata*). The male of this species rubs and prods the female, who is stimulated to straddle the male's tail and press her chin against the glands at the base of his tail. The pair then walk about in this position, with the male bending his tail sharply at the base. Other species of Plethodontids exhibit variation in the details of this type of courtship, but the basic performance is essentially the same and may be performed by either aquatic or terrestrial species. The preliminary rubbing and prodding may be of considerable importance in

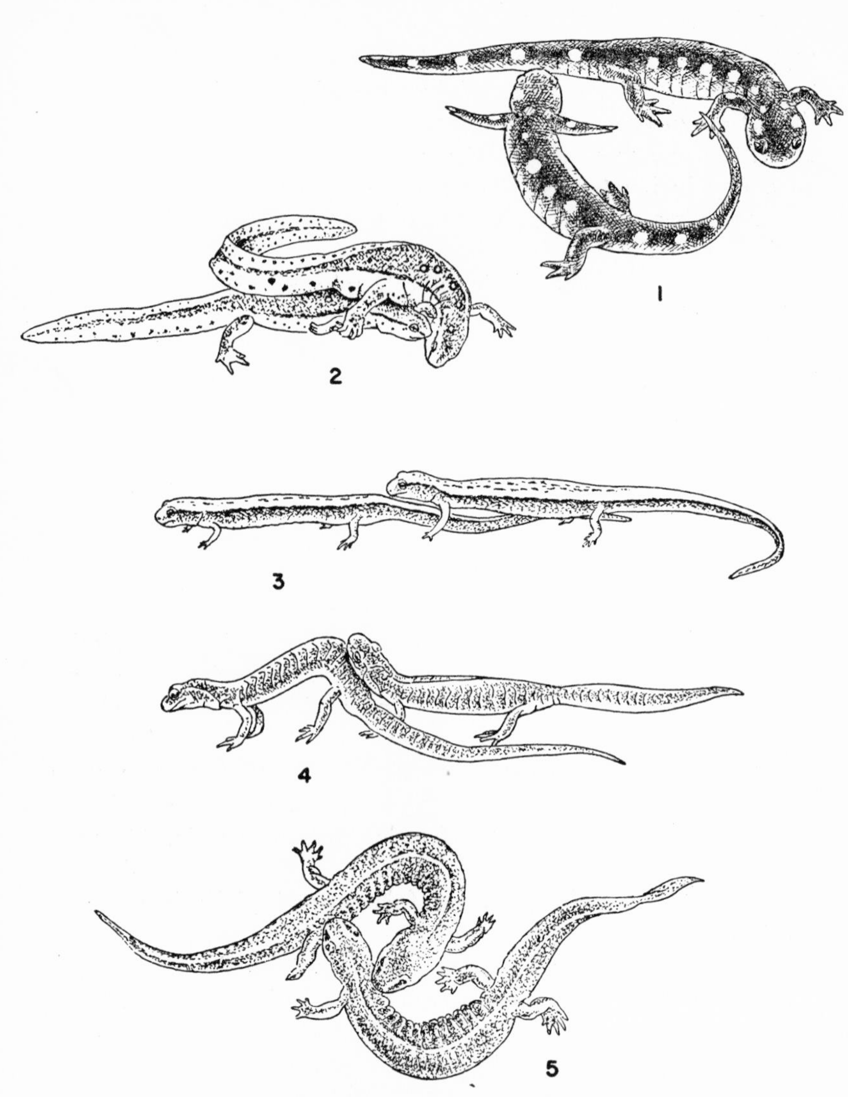

Fig. 46. Representative courtship positions of several species of salamander. 1. Spotted Salamander (*Ambystoma maculatum*); drawn after Ruth B. Breder. 2. Red-spotted Newt (*Diemictylus viridescens viridescens*); after Sherman C. Bishop. 3. Northern Two-lined Salamander (*Eurycea bislineata bislineata*); after G. K. Noble. 4. Yellow-eyed Salamander (*Ensatina eschscholtzi xanthoptica*); after Robert C. Stebbins. 5. Northern Red Salamander (*Pseudotriton ruber ruber*); after Sherman C. Bishop.

Fig. 47. Courtship position in two species of Slider Turtles, showing different method used by male in "titillating" female. Upper, Red-eared Turtle (*Pseudemys scripta elegans*). Lower, Florida Terrapin (*Pseudemys floridana floridana*). (Modified from Fred R. Cagle)

preventing crossbreeding, since differences in secretions are undoubtedly perceived in this process. This was suggested in the experimental studies of G. K. Noble and M. K. Brady on the courtship of the Two-lined Salamander and the Margined Salamander (*Stereochilus marginatus*). Individuals of one species would not court individuals of the other species, although the males did rub and nose the females before rejecting them. Representative courtship positions in several species of salamanders are shown in Figure 46.

In frogs the courtship behavior is limited to the posturing and calling of the male. This behavior attracts receptive females, who are clasped as soon as sighted without any further overtures. So ardent is the reproductive male that he will clasp almost any object of suitable size that moves into his sight. This frequently results in some peculiar temporary distractions. In some species the males have horny excrescences on the body or limbs that may function to stimulate the female but which appear primarily to be aids in clasping.

Courtship in crocodilians consists of the bellowing or roaring of the male, with characteristic posturing in which the neck is arched and the tail may be waved from side to side. This is followed by a lunge at the female, who is seized by the back of the neck in the jaws of the male.

Among turtles, courtship may be developed to a fairly high degree. Among aquatic species, the Painted (*Chrysemys*) and Slider Turtles (*Pseudemys*) have been most fully studied in this regard. The sexually mature males of these turtles have very long claws on the forefeet, and they are vibrated rapidly beside the cheeks of the female. This is called "titillating." Fred Cagle has pointed out that in the Painted Turtles and in many Slider Turtles the male faces the female, and, swimming backward (Figure 47, upper), titillates her from in front. In contrast to this, the Florida Terrapin (*Pseudemys floridana*) males swim up behind the females and titillate them from the rear (Figure 47, lower). In land turtles the males and females indulge in head-bobbing, and the males frequently bite or nudge the females in courtship (Figure 48). This biting and nudging are also characteristic of some of the aquatic species of turtles.

In lizards, courtship behavior may involve considerable biting and nudging, at least during some stages. Because of this, the courtship behavior is somewhat similar to fighting behavior and

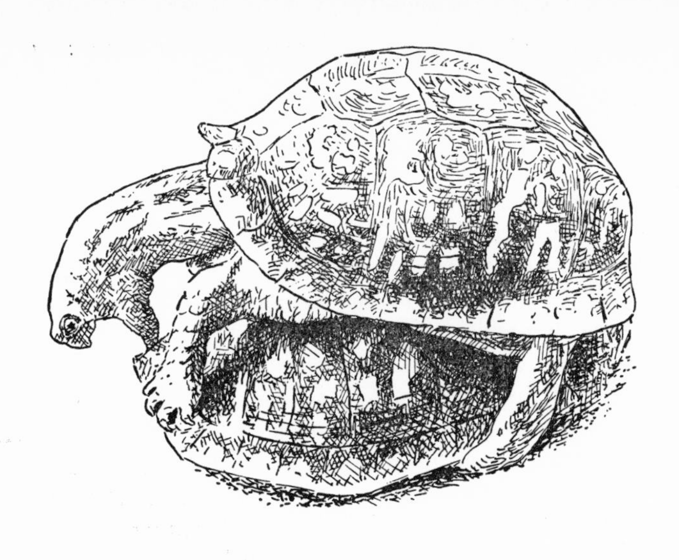

Fig. 48. Courtship positions of Eastern Box Turtle (*Terrapene carolina carolina*). Upper, male mounted on female and biting at her head. Lower, male resting on ground with his hind feet gripped in shell of female. (Modified from L. T. Evans)

has been mistaken for it. In nocturnal lizards, such as the geckos, the courtship usually consists of contact stimuli that may or may not be augmented by voice or chemical secretions. Courtship in diurnal lizards usually involves posturing, strutting, display of brightly colored areas of the body, and head-bobbing or push-ups.

Bernard Greenberg noted that the Banded Gecko (*Coleonyx variegatus*) male invariably begins his courtship by an investigation of the female with his nose to the ground, his body low and his tail waving. He usually pokes her with his snout, or licks her with his tongue, and then bites her on the tail, leg, flank, shoulder, or neck. Retaining his hold, he pushes her jerkily forward in a strutting walk. If she does not resist, he releases his initial grip and moves forward with jerky movements toward her neck, frequently nipping her flank or shoulder. Mating usually follows his biting the female on the neck; he retains this grip until the end of the mating. Under laboratory conditions Greenberg observed twelve times as many courtships as successful matings.

Among diurnal lizards the Iguanids appear to have the most elaborate courtship behavior. Courtship in the diurnal species involves visual cues more than contact stimulation. Actually, in some forms it includes very active chases, feints, and some biting, but the female has ample opportunity to terminate the activity simply by fleeing out of sight of the male. However, the receptive female seldom moves far enough away to discourage the male, and may even return to his side if he is slow in pursuing her.

G. K. Noble studied the courtship and mating behavior of a number of species of lizards, both in the laboratory and in the field. Two of the species studied by him will serve to illustrate courtship in diurnal lizards. The male Northern Fence Lizard (*Sceloporus undulatus hyacinthinus*) quickly recognizes a female of his species by her coloration, and rushes toward her by means of a jerky, stiff-legged gait, with his head and shoulders held high. He pauses several times to bob up and down in the characteristic "push-ups" that are an integral part of Iguanid courtship and threatening behavior. The female usually moves away a short distance, proceeding in short jerky hops with her back arched. The male follows jerkily, pausing to bob, and finally bites her on the neck or shoulders. This grip is usually retained unless the female struggles violently. Mating ensues.

In the Green Anolis (*Anolis c. carolinensis*) the adult male typically displays at a distance when he sights a female. The display here includes flaring his striking ruby-red dewlap out from under the throat and bobbing his head. He then struts toward the female in short spurts, stopping to bob in the push-up fashion. In courtship behavior, the dewlap is generally not flared after the original series of displays. The female usually hops about, much like the female Fence Lizard, and does not get too far away from the male if she is in a receptive condition. The courtship ends when the male grips the female by the neck in his jaws and proceeds to mate with her.

In snakes, courtship behavior involves contact in the form of nudging and rubbing. Therefore the tactile stimuli are exceedingly important in the courtship behavior of these reptiles. Vision plays an important part, in that moving objects attract the reproductive males and movement stimulates some males to continue courtship. Chemical perception is important in exciting males and in enabling them to locate or follow the females. The important chemical stimulus in courtship is primarily that of the dorsal skin, although in some species the cloacal gland secretions may be involved.

The basic courtship pattern in Colubrid snakes frequently begins with the male slowly twitching the end of his tail from side to side. He then approaches the female from the rear and attempts to run his chin along her back, flicking his tongue out rapidly, investigating first one side and then the other of her back. The female habitually moves away from this first approach, and the male endeavors to follow along beside her so that the bodies of the two are parallel. The male continues the chin contact and moves it along the female's back until he reaches her neck. When he reaches this position, the anterior part of his body lies on top of that of the female. Now he attempts to partially encircle her body with the posterior part of his body, getting a firm grip on her tail by twisting his tail around hers. In this position the cloacal region of his body is brought under that of the female, lifting it up, and the male's body begins to writhe in a series of waves that move from the posterior part of the body to the anterior part. These are termed caudocephalic waves, and they may begin at any part of the body and move forward. The male keeps his chin on the female's neck throughout this courtship. The lateral body movements and the caudocephalic waves result in the male tapping many parts of the female's body. Mating may follow this stage of courtship, although the courtship behavior has been

observed many times without mating taking place. Several observers have erroneously mistaken this courtship for actual mating.

Variations of this pattern are found in many of our snakes, with omission or modification of various phases of the behavior. In the Black Racer (*Coluber c. constrictor*) a series of rushes precedes the courtship, and there is less entwining of the two individuals. In the Pilot Black Snake (*Elaphe o. obsoleta*) the female stimulates the male by twitching her body during courtship. In the King Snake (*Lampropeltis getulus*) and the Bull Snake (*Pituophis catenifer sayi*) the male usually bites the female on the back and neck during courtship and sometimes there is no entwining of the bodies and no series of caudocephalic waves. In the Water Moccasin (*Ancistrodon piscivorous*) the courting snakes partially entwine the posterior part of the body, raise the anterior part slightly, and push and rub the heads vigorously—a performance that is somewhat similar to the male combat "dance." In the Prairie Rattlesnake (*Crotalus v. viridis*) the male moves forward on the female with his chin rubbing her back and with his tongue flicking rapidly. His body performs a series of short forward jerks or brief twitches. His body lies on or beside, but not looped around, the body of the female, but his tail may hold that of the female in a single bend.

Mating

The term "mating" means the uniting of a pair. It thus can be used broadly to include both courtship and the sexual embrace. In many species these two activities are so continuous that it is difficult to tell where one stops and the other begins. It may seem unnecessarily pedantic to treat them separately, but the two types of behavior are distinctly different and differ in relative importance in various species. No mating embrace takes place in some Amphibia, and courtship may take place many times without any mating resulting. In this section, the term "mating" is used for the sexual union during which the sperm is transferred to the female—either in internal fertilization or as the spermatozoa are spewed on the eggs in external fertilization. It is readily apparent that a generous definition of the word is needed to cover all the conditions found in amphibians and reptiles.

Fertilization of the eggs by the spermatozoa does not necessarily occur simultaneously with mating. It may take place immediately after mating, as in the case of external fertilization, or it may not take place until a later time in the case of the species with internal fertilization.

Male amphibians lack a copulatory organ for the transmission of the sperm into the body of the female. The single exception in America is the Tailed Frog (*Ascaphus truei*), in which the male has a short tail-like extension of the cloaca that serves in this capacity. Despite this lack of an intromittent organ, fertilization is internal in all of our salamanders except the Hellbenders (*Cryptobranchus*) and Sirens (*Siren*). The sperm is transferred to the female by means of sperm-capped gelatinous structures called spermatophores. These are deposited by the male before or during courtship and are picked up by the female by the lips of her cloaca. The spermatozoa are then stored in sperm receptacles in the female's cloaca until the eggs are fertilized.

In some salamanders the reproductive activity is so poorly defined that it scarcely merits the designation of mating, even under a broad usage of the term. For example, in the Hellbenders, which have no courtship and in which the fertilization is external, the males appear to have no contact whatever with the females and are stimulated to emit sperm at the sight of the eggs. In salamanders in which a well-developed courtship takes place, the spermatophores are deposited and picked up as the finale of the courtship.

In frogs there is little or no courtship, and a gravid female may be clasped by a male as soon as she arrives at the breeding pond. The male in most species mounts the female's back and grips her with his front legs around her body just behind her front legs (Figure 49). In frogs this clasping of the female by the male is called "amplexus." When a male clasps a ripe female, amplexus is maintained until the female deposits her eggs. Actually the grip of the male stimulates, and possibly assists, the deposition of the eggs by the female. The egg-laying movements of the female stimulate the male to eject sperm onto the eggs. Following this the male releases the female. It is not known with certainty what causes the male to release the female following fertilization of the eggs. Lester R. Aronson suggests that reduction in girth of the female, the termi-

FIG. 49. Mating position of the Northern Leopard Frog (*Rana pipiens pipiens*). Upper, normal amplexus. Lower, position near the end of egg-laying process. (Modified from G. K. Noble and Lester R. Aronson)

nation of her egg-laying movements, the termination of the male sperm ejecting movements, or the movement of the female from the egg-laying posture may all be of importance in this connection. If clasping individuals are interrupted or the proper conditions are not present for egg-laying, the pair may remain in amplexus for more than a month.

The mating clasp of the male Tailed Frog (*Ascaphus truei*) differs sufficiently from that found in other frogs to warrant description. This is the only American frog in which the male possesses a copulatory organ and in which fertilization is internal. James R. Slater has presented a detailed account of the mating behavior of this frog. Slater noted that the male clasped the female with the fore limbs, as do all frogs, but instead of surrounding the body just behind the front legs he held her just in front of the hind legs. The female then straightened her hind legs posteriorly in a narrow inverted-V position. Whereupon the male flexed the pelvic portion of his body so that it took a position at right angles to the fore part of his body. By muscular manipulation the male then moved the extended cloacal structure downward so that it was in a position at right angles to the pelvis and in a position to contact the female's cloaca for the transfer of sperm.

In crocodilians and turtles the males possess a single median copulatory organ. In mating, the male alligator seizes the female in his mouth by her neck or the rear of her head. He takes a position above and to her side, with one hind leg holding the base of her tail and with his tail bent down under and to one side of hers. In this position the sperm or seminal fluid is transferred.

In turtles the male always approaches the female from her rear and mounts the dorsal side of her shell, holding the female with his fore feet gripping the front of her shell and sometimes biting her on the neck. The rear of his body is pushed down below the rear of her carapace. Aquatic turtles mate in the water, whereas land turtles mate on land. The concave lower shell, or plastron, of the male land turtles, such as the Box Turtles (*Terrapene*) and the Gopher Tortoises (*Gopherus*), enables the male to mount the high shell of the female without losing his balance—although this occurs occasionally.

Lizards and snakes differ from all other reptiles in having paired male copulatory organs, with an organ on each side of the anal opening. These are called the hemipenes (singular, hemipenis). Either organ may be used, but only one is employed in mating at any one time—the one that is on the side in contact with the female's cloacal region. Actually the two organs are used with approximately equal frequency, unless one is injured or damaged.

In mating, the male lizard usually approaches the female from the rear and grasps her neck or head in his mouth. His body is above and to one side of hers. The legs on the side next to the female are usually over or on her back, and his cloacal region is bent down beside or under hers. The hemipenis next to the female is everted and inserted into her cloaca. The female if receptive remains passive or cooperates by lifting her cloacal area. Mating may last from five to thirty minutes.

At the height of courtship in snakes, the posterior part of the bodies of the male and female are entwined and in contact. By moving his body and tail, the male lifts or turns up the female's cloaca and inserts his hemipenis on the side next to hers. Once the hemipenis is inserted, the male usually slides from the back of the female and remains quite passive; rarely he may continue courtship activity during actual mating. The female remains passive or may crawl slowly along, dragging the male. The caudocephalic waves of courtship are no longer seen. The mating attachment may last from five to thirty minutes—or even hours. Frank N. and Frieda Cobb Blanchard noted in the Eastern Garter Snake (*Thamnophis s. sirtalis*) that if the attachment lasted less than ten minutes it did not result in young. Males may mate with more than a single female following a previous mating, but a mated female normally does not mate again.

Eggs and Young

Amphibians characteristically lay their eggs in water, during or shortly after mating (Figure 50). The aquatic eggs develop only in water and are killed by drying out if taken from the water. In contrast, the eggs of the Marbled Salamander (*Ambystoma opacum*) are laid on land where they will be flooded by fall rains and do not hatch until they are washed into water. In a dry fall the eggs may not hatch until the arrival of spring rains. Most amphibian eggs consist of an inner spherical area that is usually pigmented. This is the vitellus, or true egg with its yolk. It is surrounded by a membrane, the vitelline membrane, and usually by a thick noncellular

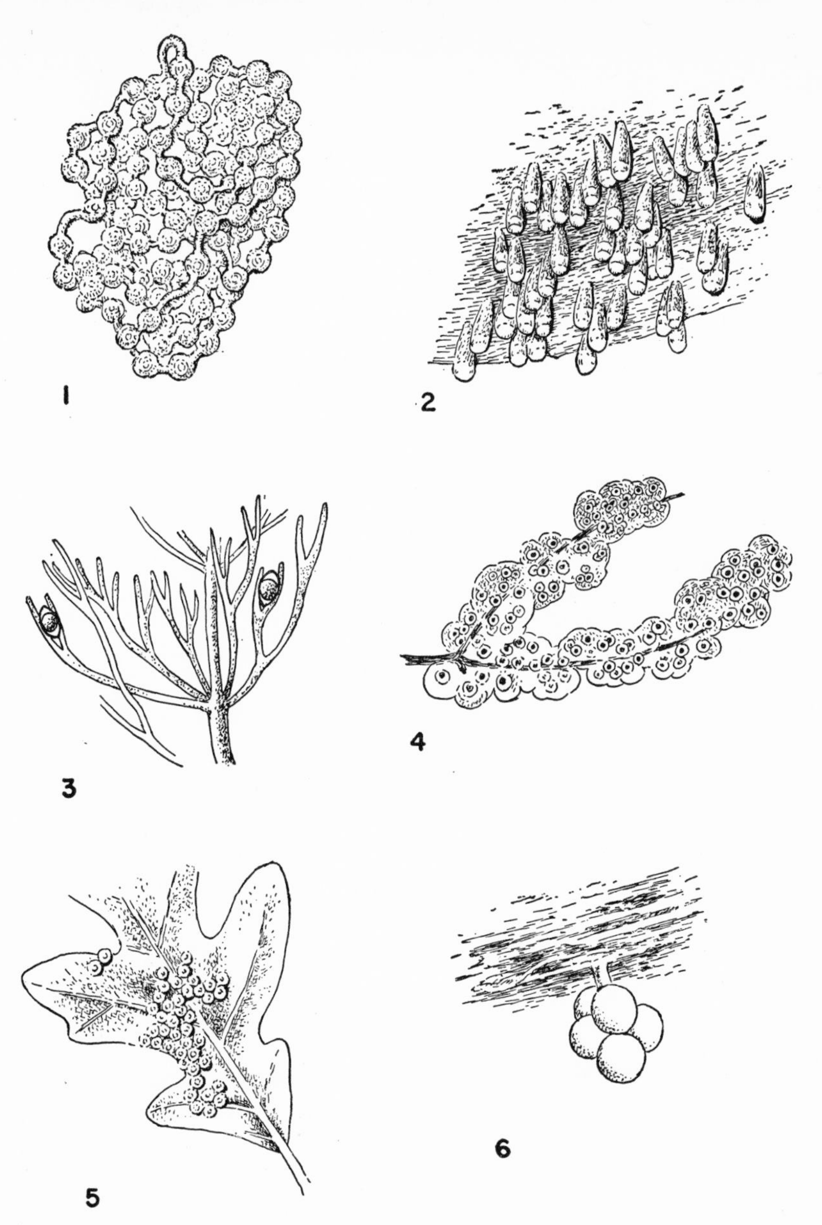

FIG. 50. Representative types of egg clusters of salamanders. 1. Hellbender (*Cryptobranchus alleganiensis alleganiensis*). 2. Mudpuppy (*Necturus maculosus maculosus*). 3. Red-spotted Newt (*Diemictylus viridescens viridescens*). 4. (Jefferson's Salamander (*Ambystoma jeffersonianum*). 5. Northern Two-lined Salamander (*Eurycea bislineata bislineata*). 6. Red-backed Salamander (*Plethodon cinereus cinereus*). (Drawings 1, 2, 3, 4 and 6 are modified from Sherman C. Bishop; number 5 was drawn after John T. Wood.)

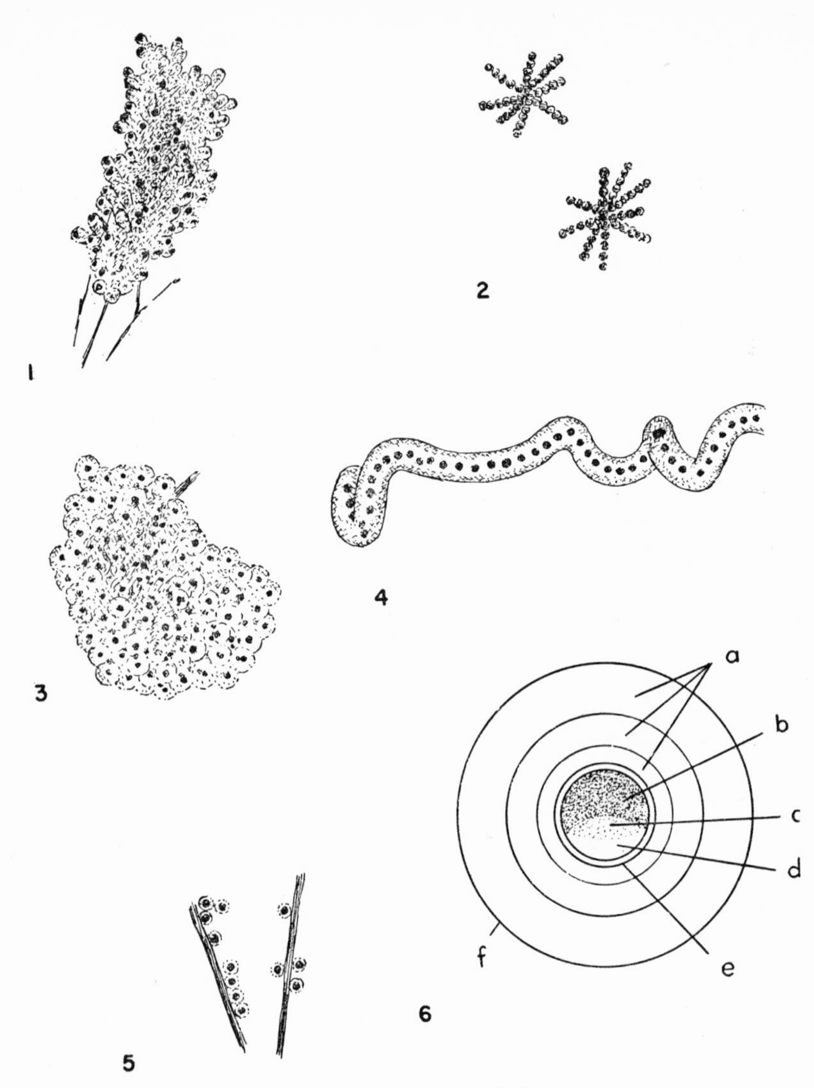

Fig. 51. Representative types of egg clusters of frogs. 1. Western Spadefoot (*Scaphiopus hammondi hammondi*). 2. Oak Toad (*Bufo quercicus*). 3. Eastern Wood Frog (*Rana sylvatica sylvatica*). 4. American Toad (*Bufo americanus*). 5. Spring Peeper (*Hyla crucifer*). All modified from A. H. and A. A. Wright. 6. Detail sketch of amphibian egg, showing (a) non-cellular, gelatinous envelopes or coats, (b) the pigmented hemisphere of the egg, (c) the true egg or vitellus, (d) the non-pigmented hemisphere of the egg, (e) the vitelline membrane and (f) the outer egg membrane. (Drawn after G. K. Noble)

area of clear gelatinous material that protects the egg (Figure 51, no. 6). The over-all appearance of the egg is somewhat similar to that of cooked tapioca. When the egg is first laid, the gelatinous area is thin, but it quickly swells as water is absorbed.

In salamanders the eggs are of two general types: those with a pigmented vitellus and a small, clear, gelatinous outer area; and those without a pigmented vitellus but with a large gelatinous outer area. In general, the more primitive species appear to lay the former type of eggs, whereas the more advanced species usually deposit the latter type. The pigmented type of egg is more often found in open, exposed situations in the water, while the nonpigmented type is more often found in secluded situations and is often attended by one of the parents. The number of eggs laid is usually higher in those species that lay pigmented eggs than in those that lay non-pigmented eggs.

Some salamanders and a few of our frogs constitute an exception to the general rule that amphibians lay their eggs in water. These species deposit their eggs on land in protected, moist situations, and the female usually remains with the eggs. In most of these species there is no aquatic larval stage, and the young hatch as tiny but short-tailed replicas of their parents. From species that are completely aquatic throughout all stages of their life history to the strictly terrestrial forms, there are all degrees of intermediate adaptations. Species such as the Hellbender (*Cryptobranchus*), the Mud-puppy (*Necturus*), the Sirens (*Siren*), and others live their entire lives in the water, laying their eggs in water and having aquatic larval forms. Other species, such as most Ambystomids and some Plethodontids, lay their eggs in water and have an aquatic larval stage, but the adult is adapted to life on land to some degree. At the other extreme are the entirely terrestrial Plethodontids, like the Red-backed Salamander (*Plethodon c. cinereus*), the Shasta Salamander (*Aneides flavipunctatus*), the Worm Salamander (*Batrachoseps attenuatus*), and others.

Table 10 gives data on the egg-laying habits of representatives of each of the families occurring in the United States. Where several species are present in a single family and where the information is available, the maximum and minimum numbers of eggs for the family are given. For most of our species this information is woefully fragmentary. Amphibians usually produce far greater numbers of eggs per female than do reptiles or any of the other land vertebrates.

TABLE 10

SAMPLE SALAMANDER REPRODUCTION DATA

Family and Species	Time of Laying	Number of Eggs	Where Laid	How Laid	Incubation Period	Guarded by Parent
Cryptobranchidae						
Hellbender (*Cryptobranchus a. allegeniensis*)	Aug.–Sept.	300-450	In water; under stones	Long strands in tangled mass	68-84 days	Yes—male
Proteidae						
Mudpuppy (*Necturus m. maculosus*)	May–June	18-180	In water; beneath objects	Attached singly to bottom of object	38-63 days	Yes—female
Sirenidae						
Netting's Dwarf Siren (*Siren intermedia nettingi*)	April	Up to 555	In water; in mud	A mass in excavation in bottom	?	?
Ambystomidae						
Mountain Salamander (*Rhyacotriton olympicus*)	May–June	3-15	In water	Singly on lower surface of stone	?	No
Northwestern Salamander (*Ambystoma gracile*)	Jan.–July	30-270	In water; on sticks or plants	In clusters of 25-270 eggs	14-35 days	No
Marbled Salamander (*Ambystoma opacum*)	Sept.–Dec.	50-232	On land; beneath debris at edge of pond	Singly in simple depression	15-207 days	Yes—female
Jefferson's Salamander (*Ambystoma jeffersonianum*)	Mar.–Apr.	107-286	In water; on sticks or plants	In small cylindrical masses of 1-40 eggs	13-45 days	No
Salamandridae						
Red-spotted Newt (*Diemictylus v. viridescens*)	Feb.–May	200-375	In water; attached to leaves or stems of plants	Singly	20-35 days	No
California Newt (*Taricha torosa*)	Sept.–May	7-29	In water; on sticks, plants, and other objects	In clusters of 7-29 eggs	18-52 days	No
Amphiumidae						
Three-toed Amphiuma (*Amphiuma means tridactylum*)	May–Oct.	42-150	On land; beneath logs near water	Long strings in ball-like mass	30-70 days	Yes—female
Plethodontidae						
Red-backed Salamander (*Plethodon c. cinereus*)	June–July	3-13	On land; in and under rotting logs	In small clusters attached to roof of small chamber	30-60 days	Yes—female
Eastern Four-toed Salamander (*Hemidactylium scutatum*)	July–Sept.	30	On land; in and under sphagnum moss or logs near water	Singly, adhering to nest material	38-60 days	Yes—female
Northern Purple Salamander (*Gyrinophilus p. porphyriticus*)	Apr.–Aug.	44-132	In water; under logs and stones	Attached singly but usually in groups	?	No
Arboreal Salamander (*Aneides l. lugubris*)	July–Sept.	12-19	On land; in cavities in trees or under objects on ground	Singly and attached by stalk to roof of cavity on bottom of object	30-60 days	Yes—female

Salamanders as a group produce fewer eggs than some frogs. This is partly related to the salamander's more efficient internal fertilization and frequent parental care of the eggs, as compared with our native frogs in which fertilization is usually external and in which there is little or no parental care of the eggs. The maximum number of eggs recorded for an American salamander is 555 in the case of the Netting's Dwarf Siren (*Siren intermedia nettingi*). This number may seem like a lot when compared with the number of eggs produced by female mammals or birds, but it is small beside the figure of 25,644 eggs counted for one female Woodhouse's Toad (*Bufo w. woodhousei*). Higher egg counts have been reported for some frogs, but these extreme figures are in need of confirmation.

In virtually all amphibians and reptiles the number of eggs laid by a female varies proportionately with age and size. This is usually true of comparisons between the females of one species. It is also true of comparisons between closely related species that differ in size. However, it is not true of comparisons between distantly related species. John T. Wood's study of the Eastern Four-toed Salamander (*Hemidactylium scutatum*) in Virginia shows this correlation between size of the female and the number of eggs laid. He found the number of eggs per female to vary from 29 to 80. No female with a snout-vent length of 34.5 mm. or less laid more than 45 eggs, whereas all the clutches of 50 or more eggs were laid by females with a snout-vent length of 35 to 40 mm. Among the Tree Frogs, the tiny Least Tree Frog (*Hyla ocularis*) may lay as many as 100 eggs, whereas its larger congener, the Barking Tree Frog (*Hyla gratiosa*), may lay up to 2,000 eggs per female. This relationship between size and number of eggs is frequently simply a matter of difference in carrying capacity, but in some species it may involve different size and structure of eggs. Hobart M. Smith has pointed out that in proportion to body size the toads of the genus *Bufo* are more productive of eggs than any other amphibian.

Table 11 presents information on the egg-laying habits of representative species of frogs. It will be noted that the number of eggs is usually quite large, being the highest for any known land-dwelling vertebrate. It is also apparent that there is no parental protection of the eggs by any of our native frogs, with the possible exception of the Robber Frogs (*Eleutherodactylus*). A few foreign species of frogs have developed quite striking types of parental care of eggs and young.

TABLE 11

SAMPLE FROG REPRODUCTION DATA

Family and Species	Time of Laying	Number of Eggs	Where Laid	How Laid	Length of Incubation
Ascaphidae					
Tailed Frog (*Ascaphus truei*)	May–Sept.	28-50	In running water	In strings attached to underside of stones	30 days
Pelobatidae					
Eastern Spadefoot (*Scaphiopus h. holbrooki*)	Mar.–Sept.	1,000-2,500	In water; temporary pools and ponds	In irregular bands on or around plants	5-15 days
Western Spadefoot (*Scaphiopus h. hammondi*)	Feb.–Aug.	1,000-2,000	In water; temporary pools and ponds	in cylindrical masses on plants	2-7 days
Leptodactylidae					
Mexican White-lipped Frog (*Leptodactylus labialis*)	Apr.–June	86	On land; near edge of pond or stream	In frothy mass in small depression on bank	40 hours
Greenhouse Frog (*Eleutherodactylus ricordi planirostris*)	Apr.–Aug.	19-25	On land	Singly beneath vegetable debris	10-11 days
Bufonidae					
American Toad (*Bufo terrestris americanus*)	Apr.–July	4,000-8,000	In water; in ponds and streams	In one row in long string	3-12 days
Red-spotted Toad (*Bufo punctatus*)	Apr.–Sept.	?	In water; in ponds and streams	Singly to form small film on bottom	1½-3 days
Oak Toad (*Bufo quercicus*)	Apr.–Sept.	610-766	In water; in shallow, grassy, or woodland ponds	In bars of 2-6 eggs on bottom	?
Woodhouse's Toad (*Bufo w. woodhousei*)	Mar.–July	Up to 25,650	In water; in almost any pond or stream	One or two rows in long string	2-4 days
Hylidae					
Northern Spring Peeper (*Hyla c. crucifer*)	Jan.–June	800-1,000	In water; in shallow weedy ponds	Singly on submerged plants near the bottom	?
Pacific Tree Frog (*Hyla regilla*)	Jan.–May	500-1,500	In water; in quiet streams or ponds	Small, loose masses of 5-70 eggs	7-14 days
Gray Tree Frog (*Hyla v. versicolor*)	Apr.–Aug.	Up to 1,800	In water; in swamps, bogs, and woodland ponds or weedy lakes	Small scattered masses of 30-40 eggs	4-5 days
Microhylidae					
Narrow-mouthed Toad (*Microhyla c. carolinensis*)	May–Sept.	Up to 869	In water; in temporary pools and ponds	Surface mass of 10-125 eggs	?

TABLE 11 (Continued)

Family and Species	Time of Laying	Number of Eggs	Where Laid	How Laid	Length of Incubation
Ranidae					
California Yellow-legged Frog (*Rana b. boyli*)	Mar.–May	900-1,050	In water; in shallow streams	In clusters attached to stones	?
Bullfrog (*Rana catesbeiana*)	Feb.–July	10,000-20,000	In water; in ponds, lakes, and quiet streams	In large surface films	5-20 days
Pickerel Frog (*Rana palustris*)	Apr.–May	2,000-3,000	In water; in bogs and woodland ponds	Globular mass on submerged plants	?
Eastern Wood Frog (*Rana s. sylvatica*)	Mar.–Apr.	2,000-3,000	In water; in woodland ponds and quiet streams	Globose masses in shallow water	10-30 days

There is a considerable amount of variation in the way frog eggs are laid, and these differences are characteristic of different species. Albert H. Wright, his wife Anna A. Wright, and his students, especially Robert Livezey, have devoted a great deal of attention to the study of frog egg masses and the way the eggs are laid. From their studies they have worked out methods for identifying the eggs of virtually all of our frog species. Figure 51 shows several different types of egg masses laid by American frogs.

The eggs of reptiles, like those of birds, are adapted for development on land and will not develop if surrounded by water. These eggs have an outer shell and three internal membranous structures that permit the egg to develop out of water. The shell may be soft and leathery as in snakes, some lizards, and some turtles; or hard and calcareous as in crocodilians, some lizards, and some turtles. Representative reptile eggs are shown in Figure 52.

A few lizards and snakes have developed a method of retaining the eggs inside the body of the female until they are ready to hatch. Such eggs lack an outer shell, and the young emerge from the egg membrane shortly after the egg is laid. Species that reproduce in this manner are said to be viviparous, meaning that they bring forth living young. Several published works on reptiles refer to this type of reproduction as ovoviviparous, differentiating it from the viviparous reproduction of mammals. However, the differences involved in the two methods are so completely bridged by some species of

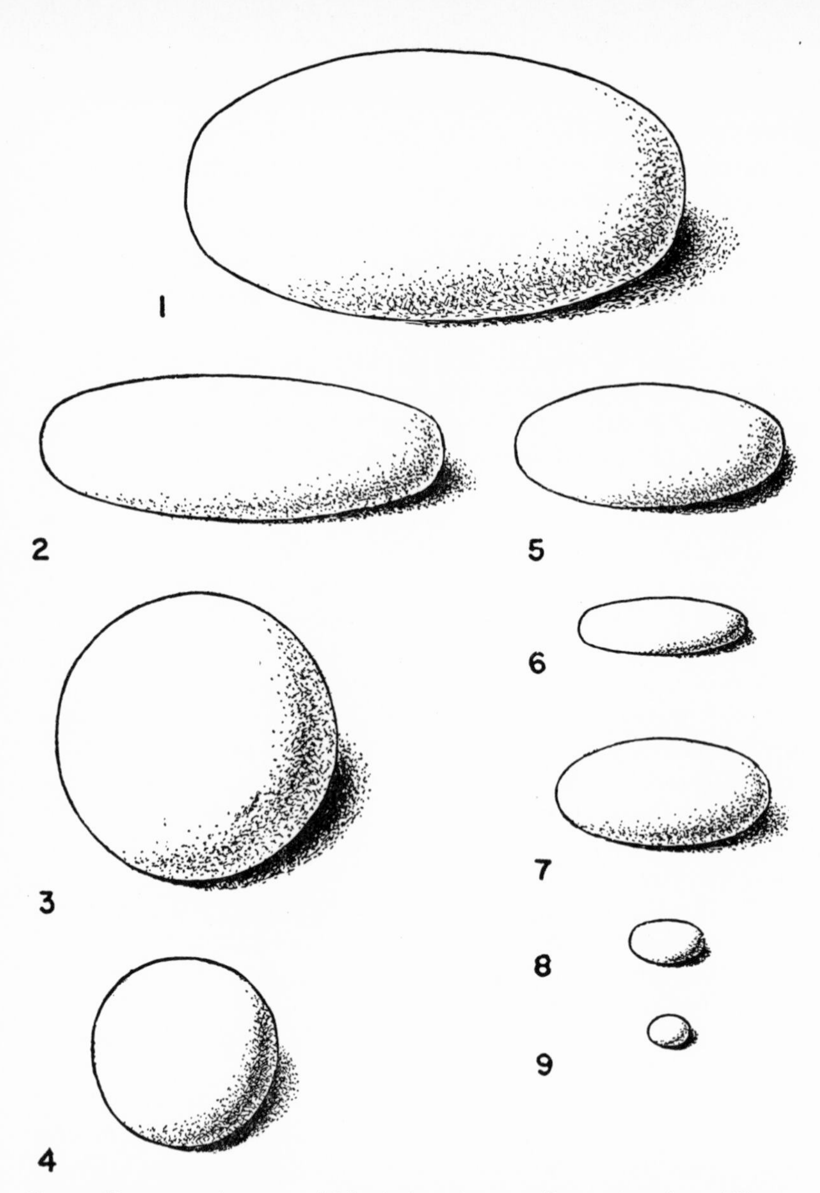

Fig. 52. Representative eggs of North American reptiles. 1. American Alligator (*Alligator mississippiensis*). 2. Pilot Black Snake (*Elaphe obsoleta obsoleta*). 3. Atlantic Loggerhead Turtle (*Caretta caretta caretta*). 4. Snapping Turtle (*Chelydra serpentina serpentina*). 5. Eastern Milk Snake (*Lampropeltis doliata triangulum*). 6. Eastern Ring-necked Snake (*Diadophis punctatus edwardsi*). 7. Eastern Painted Turtle (*Chrysemys picta picta*). 8. Texas Horned Lizard (*Phrynosoma cornutum*). 9. Reef Gecko (*Sphaerodactylus notatus*).

reptiles that the distinction becomes academic and is meaningless except to the specialist in embryology.

Species that deposit eggs for development outside the female are referred to as oviparous. All crocodilians are oviparous, as are all turtles and many snakes and lizards. In these species the eggs are deposited in sheltered situations that are somewhat moist and protected from the direct rays of the sun. Commonly the female digs a hole in the earth, beneath leaf litter or under a log or stone, then lays her eggs and departs. She has met her responsibilities as a mother; she does not protect the eggs during the incubation period and shows no concern for her young. This is the story for virtually all turtles and most of our snakes and lizards. A few species do exhibit some degree of parental care. This starts with the exercise of care concerning the location in which the eggs are laid, the female retaining them until a suitable location is found. Virtually all turtles dig a nest in the ground or in vegetable debris. In the aquatic species the nest is usually located on a sunny slope not far from the water, but generally high enough to avoid being flooded.

Many aquatic turtles have favorite areas where numerous females congregate to lay their eggs. In the case of the marine turtles, certain sandy beaches are the laying grounds for many females. Similarly, large numbers of female Slider Turtles (*Pseudemys*) in the southern United States may be found laying their eggs on a particular sandbar or bank. And several musk turtles may select the same muskrat house in which to put their eggs.

The female Alligator (*Alligator mississippiensis*) is exceptional among our reptiles in building a sizable nest in which to lay her eggs. The nesting habits of this reptile have been studied and described by a number of herpetologists, including Ross Allen, Wilfred Neill, and the late E. A. McIlhenny. They found that the nest is made of a variety of vegetable trash—leaves, leaf litter, roots, stalks and stems—all scraped together in a large mound 6 or 7 feet in diameter and 2 to 3 feet in height. A female may use the same nest year after year, merely piling a little more material on top each year. After the mound is built, she scoops out a hole in the top and lays her eggs inside the mound. When she has finished laying, she covers the eggs with some of the material, packs it down, sometimes puts mud on top, and may crawl back and forth over the top to complete the packing.

Unlike her relative, the Alligator, the female American Crocodile (*Crocodylus a. acutus*) does not build up a large mound of vegetation. Joseph C. Moore, who has recently studied the habits of this species in Florida, has described the nest as a large, low mound of sand in which the eggs are buried and allowed to incubate, usually unprotected by the mother. One nest that Moore measured was 11 feet in diameter and 16½ inches high. There is some suggestion that the mother revisits the nest once or twice during the incubation period, but the purpose of these visits is not known.

The generalization that larger females and larger species produce more eggs or young than their smaller counterparts holds fairly well in the reptiles, as it does in the amphibians. Among lizards, the geckos represent an exception to this condition, never laying more than two eggs; in fact, two is the usual number laid in the family in all but a few instances. In the Red-eared Turtle (*Pseudemys scripta elegans*), Fred Cagle found that larger females tend to lay more eggs than the smaller ones. Among lizards, Charles E. Shaw reported that larger specimens of the Desert Spiny Lizard (*Sceloporus magister*) laid more eggs than did the smaller females. The smallest number of eggs laid was seven, which were by a female 3¾ inches in snout-vent length, whereas the largest number was eighteen, which were laid by a female 4⅛ inches in snout-vent length. The late Frank N. Blanchard demonstrated the same relationship in several oviparous and viviparous snakes. In the Eastern Ringneck Snake (*Diadophis punctatus edwardsi*) he found that the larger females, up to a size of about 15¾ inches, lay more eggs. Beyond this size there was a tendency to lay fewer eggs. Laurence M. Klauber showed that small female Prairie Rattlesnakes (*Crotalus v. viridis*) have fewer young than do larger ones. Sixty-four females less than 28¾ inches in length produced an average of 9.6 young per female, while eighty-four longer females had an average of 13.6 young per female.

Tables 12a-c present data on egg-laying in the various reptile groups. To save space, the data for the Alligator are presented in the table for the turtles. The tables show that no lizard lays as many eggs as does the most fecund snake, and that snakes are outdone by the maximum of 150 eggs laid by the Atlantic Loggerhead (*Caretta c. caretta*). Actually even this number is reportedly exceeded by a record 200 in the case of the Green Turtle (*Chelonia mydas*). It is interesting to note that in some species in each of the major groups the minimum number of eggs deposited by a female may consist of but a single egg. In snakes, where some species produce living young, the greater reproductive potential is found among the live-bearing species. The greatest number of young produced by any American lizard is 30 for the Mountain Short-horned Lizard (*Phrynosoma douglassi hernandesi*), and the greatest number of

TABLE 12a

SAMPLE TURTLE AND CROCODILIAN REPRODUCTION DATA

Family and Species	Time of Laying	Number of Eggs	Where Laid	Kind of Eggs	Incubation Period
Chelydridae					
Snapping Turtle (*Chelydra s. serpentina*)	May–Oct.	8-80	In earth 4-6 inches down	Hard but pliable; spherical	12-16 weeks
Kinosternidae					
Common Musk Turtle (*Sternotherus odoratus*)	Apr.–June	1-5	In stumps, muskrat houses, or other high locations	Hard, brittle; elliptically oval	8-12 weeks
Emydidae					
Eastern Box Turtle (*Terrapene c. carolina*)	June–July	2-7	In earth 2-4 inches down	Soft; elliptically oval	10-16 weeks
Western Painted Turtle (*Chrysemys picta belli*)	May–June	6-20	In earth 2-5 inches down	Soft; oval	9-12 weeks (occasionally over winter)
Peninsular Turtle (*Pseudemys floridana peninsularis*)	Nov.–June	12-29 (appear to lay twice a year)	In earth 4-6 inches down	Soft; oval	11-20 weeks
Red-eared Turtle (*Pseudemys scripta elegans*)	Apr.–June	5-22	In earth 4-8 inches down	Soft; oblong or oval	8-12 weeks
Testudinidae					
Desert Tortoise (*Gopherus agassizi*)	June	2-6	In earth 3-6 inches down	Hard and brittle; spherical or slightly oval	17 weeks
Chelonidae					
Atlantic Loggerhead Turtle (*Caretta c. caretta*)	Apr.–Aug. (in U. S.)	70-150 (lays several times per year)	In sand 8-18 inches down	Soft; spherical	4-12 weeks
Trionychidae					
Midland Soft-shelled Turtle (*Trionyx ferox spinifera*)	June–July	10-25	In sand or earth 2-4 inches down	Brittle; spherical	8-10 weeks
Dermochelidae					
Leatherback Turtle (*Dermochelys c. coriacea*)	June–July (in U. S.)	90-130	In sand 12-20 inches down	Soft; spherical	8-10 weeks
Crocodilidae					
Alligator (*Alligator mississippiensis*)	May–July	15-88	In large nest made of vegetable debris	Hard, brittle; oblong	9-10 weeks

TABLE 12b

Sample Lizard Reproduction Data

Family and Species	Time of Laying or Birth	Number of Eggs or Young	If Eggs, Where Laid	Kind of Eggs	Incubation or Gestation Period
Gekkonidae					
Reef Gecko (*Sphaerodactylus notatus*)	June–Aug.	1-2 eggs	Under debris or rocks	Hard and brittle; oval	?
Iguanidae					
Green Anolis (*Anolis c. carolinensis*)	May–Sept.	1-2 eggs	Under debris, logs, or rocks	Soft; oval	6-7 weeks
Western Collared Lizard (*Crotaphytus collaris baileyi*)	June–Aug.	4-21 eggs	In sand, under rocks, or in burrows	Soft; oval	9-10 weeks
Mesquite Lizard (*Sceloporus grammicus disparilis*)	April	3-12 young	...	...	5-6 months
Northern Fence Lizard (*Sceloporus undulatus hyacinthinus*)	May–Aug.	4-17 eggs	In earth 1-4 inches down; in rotten logs or under bark	Soft; oval	8-10 weeks
Texas Horned Lizard (*Phrynosoma cornutum*)	May–June	13-37 eggs	In sand 2-7 inches down	Soft; oval	5-9 weeks
Mountain Short-horned Lizard (*Phrynosoma douglassi hernandesi*)	July–Aug.	8-30 young	...	...	?
Anguidae					
San Francisco Alligator Lizard (*Gerrhonotus c. coeruleus*)	Aug.–Sept.	2-15 young	...	...	?
San Diego Alligator Lizard (*Gerrhonotus multicarinatus webbi*)	June–July	8-20 eggs	In earth; in diurnal burrows	Soft; oval	8-10 weeks
Helodermatidae					
Gila Monster (*Heloderma suspectum*)	June–July	3-7 eggs	In sand or earth	Soft; oval	?
Anniellidae					
Silvery Footless Lizard (*Anniella p. pulchra*)	Sept.–Nov.	1-4 young	...	...	?
Xantusidae					
Island Night Lizard (*Xantusia riversiana*)	July	6-9 young	...	...	?
Yucca Night Lizard (*Xantusia vigilis*)	June–Aug.	1-2 young	...	...	?
Teidae					
Six-lined Race Runner (*Cnemidophorus sexlineatus*)	June–July	4-6 eggs	In earth, 4-12 inches down, or under rocks	Soft; oval	5-8 weeks
Scincidae					
Little Brown Skink (*Lygosoma laterale*)	June–Aug.	1-5 eggs	In earth; in humus; in or under rotten logs	Hard and brittle; oval	8-10 weeks
Western Skink (*Eumeces skiltonianus*)	June–July	2-5 eggs	In excavations under logs and rocks	Soft; oval	5-6 weeks
Amphisbaenidae					
Florida Worm Lizard (*Rhineura floridana*)	Early summer	2 eggs	In earth 8-20 inches down	Soft; very long and thin	?

TABLE 12c

SAMPLE SNAKE REPRODUCTION DATA

Family and Species	Time of Laying or Birth	Number of Eggs or Young	If Eggs, Where Laid and Kind	Incubation or Gestation Period
Leptotyphlopidae				
Dwarf Blind Snake (*Leptotyphlops humilis*)	Late summer	2-6 eggs	Soft, long, and thin	?
Boidae				
Rubber Boa (*Charina bottae*)	Sept.	1-8 young	. . .	?
Colubridae				
Kirtland's Water Snake (*Natrix kirtlandi*)	Aug.–Sept.	5-11 young	. . .	?
Northern Water Snake (*Natrix s. sipedon*)	Aug.–Oct.	16-99 young	. . .	?
Red-bellied Snake (*Storeria o. occipitomaculata*)	July–Sept.	1-18 young	. . .	?
Wandering Garter Snake (*Thamnophis elegans vagrans*)	Aug.–Sept.	8-12 young	. . .	?
Eastern Garter Snake (*Thamnophis s. sirtalis*)	July–Sept.	14-85 young	. . .	3-4 months
Eastern Hog-nosed Snake (*Heterodon p. platyrhinos*)	June–July	8-61 eggs	In earth; under or in rotten logs; soft; oval	6-8 weeks
Pilot Black Snake (*Elaphe o. obsoleta*)	June–July	10-22 eggs	In earth; under or in logs; soft; oblong	8-12 weeks
California King Snake (*Lampropeltis getulus californiae*)	July	4-9 eggs	In sand; under rocks or litter; soft; oblong	7-12 weeks
Elapidae				
Coral Snake (*Micrurus f. fulvius*)	May–June	2-4 eggs	In earth or humus; in or under logs; soft; elongate	?
Crotalidae				
Northern Copperhead (*Ancistrodon contortrix mokeson*)	Aug.–Sept.	3-14 young	. . .	?
Northern Pacific Rattlesnake (*Crotalus viridis oreganus*)	Sept.–Oct.	4-25 young	. . .	3-4 months

young produced by any American snake is 101 for the Florida Green Water Snake (*Natrix cyclopion floridana*), both of which species are live-bearers.

In studying the annual reproductive potential of a species, we are concerned not only with the number of eggs or young that a female produces at one time, but also the number of times that she reproduces each year. In most species any given female regularly produces young once a year. In others—for example, the Green Turtle (*Chelonia mydas*)—the female may deposit several clutches of eggs at different times during a prolonged breeding season. Females of certain species may regularly produce several clutches of eggs per year in the warmer part of the range, but only reproduce once a year in the cooler regions. This is true of some species that occur over a wide latitudinal range. John D. Dickson III found that female Florida Box Turtles (*Terrapene carolina bauri*) may lay as many as four clutches per year, but in New York the northern race of this species normally lays only once a year. In Florida the Green Anolis (*Anolis c. carolinensis*) normally lays two eggs per clutch and the female appears to lay more than one clutch throughout the long breeding season. George W. D. Hamlett has reported quite a different condition of reproduction for this lizard in Louisiana. Here he found that the female lays one egg at a time, but she lays an egg at regular biweekly intervals throughout the prolonged breeding season. This cyclical reproductive pattern has not been reported for any other North American reptile. Some species at the northern extreme of their range appear to reproduce only in alternate years. Hermann Rahn found that Prairie Rattlesnakes (*Crotalus v. viridis*) in Wyoming produce litters every other year, whereas farther south in Colorado and Utah an annual reproductive cycle seems to be the rule. In southern Michigan the Eastern Garter Snake (*Thamnophis s. sirtalis*) generally reproduces annually, but in northern Michigan and other areas of the north many females reproduce only in alternate years.

Because of the particular environmental requirements for the breeding of some amphibian inhabitants of the drier regions of the country, it is probable that in an occasional year they do not breed at all. Arthur Bragg has found that the Great Plains Toad (*Bufo cognatus*) may go for two or three years without a successful breeding season in Central Oklahoma. This toad breeds in shallow, temporary ponds. In dry years, or when the early spring rains are cold —conditions that force the toads to breed later in the year—the tadpoles do not complete the larval period before the pools dry up. This has the effect of reducing the number of offspring produced.

Whether or not the species that reproduce less frequently compensate for this by producing a larger number of eggs or young at a time is not known. Perhaps they produce the same number of offspring in a lifetime as their more active relatives, simply by living over a greater span of years. Thus a Florida Box Turtle that lays three eggs twice a year for twenty years lays no greater total number of eggs than her New York relative who lays three eggs per year for forty years. There is some indication that northern members of a species do live more years than their southern relatives. There is

PLATE XI. Hatchling Eastern Box Turtles (*Terrapene c. carolina*) just emerging from the egg. Note the light spot at the end of the snout. This is the caruncle that slits the egg shell. (New York Zoological Society photograph)

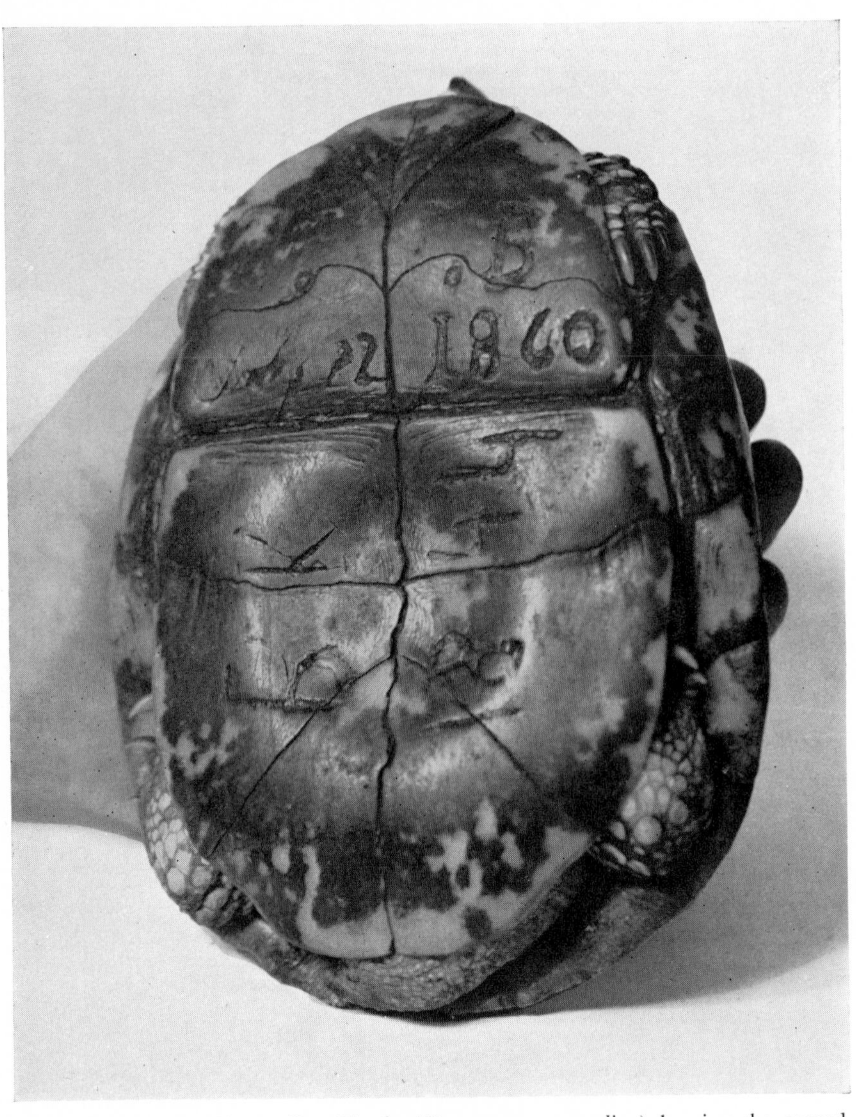

PLATE XII. An old Eastern Box Turtle (*Terrapene c. carolina*) bearing the carved dates 1844 and 1860 on the lower shell. This turtle was collected in Rhode Island in 1953 and appears to be an authentic centenarian. (New York Zoological Society photograph)

also an indication in some species that the number of eggs per clutch may increase toward the northern part of the range. For example, the Common Snapping Turtle (*Chelydra s. serpentina*) appears to lay more eggs at a time in the North than in the South. A great deal more information is needed on the interesting question of comparative reproductive potential.

Incubation and Embryonic Development

The period of incubation in an oviparous species is the time between the deposition of the eggs outside the female's body and the beginning of hatching, which is marked by the rupture of the egg membrane or shell. The period of embryonic development extends from the time of fertilization of the egg to the birth of the young. The two periods are not strictly comparable, and each varies considerably from species to species. In some oviparous forms, such as the frogs, fertilization usually takes place when the eggs are deposited, whereas in other forms—for example, some oviparous lizards and snakes—fertilization may take place quite a while before the eggs are laid. The period of incubation is easier to determine by observation than is the period of embryonic development, because of the difficulty of determining when fertilization of the eggs actually takes place. It was long believed that the eggs of most reptiles were fertilized at the time mating occurred. We now know that this is not necessarily true. Actually there may be a considerable time lapse between mating and fertilization. Despite the difficulty of definition just mentioned, the period of embryonic development is generally considered as the time between mating and birth of young.

In amphibians the incubation period may be quite short, since the embryo usually completes its development in a free-living larval stage rather than within the egg. In some frogs, such as the Spadefoot Toads (*Scaphiopus*), the eggs may hatch in only a day and a half. In large salamanders, particularly those inhabiting cold water like the Hellbenders (*Cryptobranchus*), the incubation period may extend over two and a half months—or fifty times the length of the period required by the Spadefoot. Tables 10-12 indicate some important differences in the length of incubation periods required by the various species.

Eggs of American reptiles may require up to eight months or more to complete incubation, although most of them hatch at the end of two or three months. In oviparous reptiles the eggs are usually laid a short time after fertilization, and most of the embryonic development takes place during incubation. However, a female may retain her eggs until embryonic development is nearly completed. This condition has been interpreted as representing an approach to the viviparous type of reproduction.

Like all other life processes in amphibians and reptiles, the length of time required for incubation and embryonic development is greatly influenced by temperature. Thus, while there are marked differences between various species, there is also considerable variation in relation to differences in temperature. The effect of temperature on the incubation rate of eggs of one species of frog is clearly shown in the experiments of Arthur W. Pollister and John A. Moore on the Wood Frog (*Rana s. sylvatica*). They showed that at a temperature of 50° F. it takes 275 hours for the eggs to hatch; at a temperature of 60° F. it takes 130 hours; and at 68° F. it takes only 87 hours.

Moore also made studies on the temperature responses of various species of True Frogs (*Rana*), particularly in relation to their reproductive habits. He observed a similar acceleration of developmental rate with an increase in higher temperatures. However, he found striking differences among species in relation to their responses to different temperatures. For example, those species characteristic of northern regions that breed early in the year, when the environmental temperatures are low, have eggs and larvae that can tolerate lower temperatures than species of more temperate regions; and at a given temperature they have a more rapid rate of development than their relatives living in the warmer climates. On the other hand, this adaptation to environment of the northern species includes a greater susceptibility of the eggs and larvae to higher temperatures. Detailed data of Moore's findings are shown in Table 13.

Moore has shown that the embryos of northern species tend to remain in the jelly envelopes of the eggs for a longer period than those breeding in warmer environments, and that they hatch at a more advanced stage of development. Eggs exposed to temperatures below the optimum and then raised to a suitable higher temperature have been found to develop faster than those remaining constantly

TABLE 13

RELATIONSHIP BETWEEN TEMPERATURE AND REPRODUCTION

(Data from J. A. Moore)

Species	Breeding Season in New York	Average Temperature of Water When Breeding	Northern Limit of Range (in Latitude)	Temperature Toleration of Embryo	Hours to Hatch at 68° F.
Eastern Wood Frog (*Rana s. sylvatica*)	Mid-March	50° F.	67° 30′	37-75° F.	72
Northern Leopard Frog (*Rana p. pipiens*)	Early April	54° F.	60°	43-82° F.	96
Pickerel Frog (*Rana palustris*)	Mid-April	57-59° F.	55°	45-86° F.	105
Green Frog (*Rana clamitans*)	May	75° F.	50°	54-90° F.	114
Bullfrog (*Rana catesbeiana*)	June	70° F.	47°	59-90° F.	134

in the higher temperature. This phenomenon has been noted in both salamanders and frogs.

The faster rate of embryonic development at higher temperatures is reflected in the different larval periods of frogs that live both in the northern and southern regions of the United States. The best illustration of this is the Bullfrog (*Rana catesbeiana*). Moore found that the *rate* of development was the same for eggs and embryos from Louisiana and New York. However, because of the warmer average temperatures and longer growing season in Louisiana as compared with New York, the larval period lasts for only one year. In New York the period is two years, and in Nova Scotia, still farther north and hence cooler, it may extend over three summers. In his studies on the amphibians and reptiles of Nova Scotia, Sherman Bleakney found all species of True Frogs (*Rana*) wintering over at least one winter in the larval stage.

I know of no work on the effect of temperature on the incubation of reptile eggs so detailed as that of Moore's on the frogs. However, the same phenomena appear to exist, judging from the mass of unrelated observations that have been made.

According to John D. Dickson III, the incubation period of the Florida Box Turtle (*Terrapene carolina bauri*) is between 45 and 120 days, but usually around 60 days. The longer periods were observed in eggs laid in the colder part of the year. In the northern part of the country it has been noted that in cool years, or in the case of eggs deposited late in the season, the young may spend their first winter in the egg or the nest. In some cases the young appear to hatch—break through the egg shell—but do not emerge completely from the egg until the spring. In other cases the eggs do not hatch until the spring. Norman E. Hartweg found Midland Painted Turtles (*Chrysemys p. marginata*) in Michigan hatching but wintering over in the eggs. On the other hand, William J. Hamilton, Jr., found some Common Snapping Turtles (*Chelydra s. serpentina*) in upper New York hatching in the spring.

Frank N. and Frieda Cobb Blanchard found that the period of embryonic development in the Eastern Garter Snake (*Thamnophis s. sirtalis*) varied from 87 to 116 days in southern Michigan. The shortest period occurred during an extremely hot summer, and the longest during an unusually cool one. The difference in average temperature between the two summers was 7.20° F., making a difference in embryonic-development time of about four days per degree of temperature. I have kept Great Plains Garter Snakes (*Thamnophis radix*) in separate rooms at constant temperatures of 80° F. and 70° F., respectively. Females at the higher temperatures produced young in 103 days, whereas at the lower temperatures development of some had not been completed after 172 days.

From the foregoing remarks it is obvious that within limits the eggs and young will develop faster at warmer temperatures. There is an advantage to placing the eggs in a suitably warm location, since amphibian eggs, when laid in shallow water or in floating surface films, hatch more quickly than do those in cooler water or those in deeper water where eggs are below the surface. However, eggs in warmer, shallower water are in danger of drying out. Eggs placed in rotting logs or decaying vegetable matter gain the heat of decomposition and also protective insulation. The eggs must be laid in situations that are not too hot, not too cool, and sufficiently moist to prevent desiccation. Amphibian eggs have the relative stability of water temperatures to protect them from sudden changes, but they still are subject to the detrimental effects of extreme temperatures. Reptiles that bury their eggs give them greater protection than do species that merely lay them under some protective shelter. Perhaps the best incubation medium is obtained by turtles that lay their eggs in muskrat houses and Alligators that build large vegetable mound nests (Figure 54, no. 4).

The effectiveness of the Alligator nest as an incubator was recorded in Louisiana by E. A. McIlhenny. He made daily temperature observations on a large Alligator nest during the incubation period. He found that the daily temperature of the air varied between 5° and 22° F., with an average variation of 15° F., whereas within the nest the variation was only 2° to 8° F., with an average variation of 3° F. Moreover, the temperatures within the nest averaged 5° F. above the minimum air temperature.

Even the nests of reptiles beneath logs and stones provide some protection from extreme temperature variations. For example, W. J. Breckenridge, who studied the life history of the Black-banded Skink (*Eumeces s. septentrionalis*) in Minnesota, found that this lizard invariably lays its eggs in excavated cavities immediately under logs, bark, or stones. Breckenridge recorded the air temperature outside and inside a nest cavity. He obtained the following sample readings:

Aug. 13—3:00 P.M.	Outside	91° F.	Inside	80° F.
" "—7:45 P.M.	"	85° F.	"	80° F.
" 14—7:00 P.M. (rain)	"	74° F.	"	80° F.
" 15—5:30 A.M. (after rain)	"	67° F.	"	75° F.
" 17—5:30 A.M. (cool night)	"	62° F.	"	70° F.

Observations indicate that female snakes carrying developing eggs or young are often abroad, basking in the sun. In summer, females of some species of snakes are more frequently encountered than males, and it has been assumed that they were more frequently found in exposed situations because of this tendency to bask. Captive gravid females have been observed to take a position so as to expose only the rear portion of the body to the direct sunlight. Perhaps the greater bulk of the body of such females simply warms up more slowly than the body of thinner males and nongravid females, and therefore requires more prolonged basking to bring the body temperature up to the modal figure.

Care of Eggs or Young

Amphibians and reptiles are generally noted for their casual relations to their eggs and young. In most species the eggs are simply deposited in a more or less suitable situation and abandoned by both parents. If the resulting young are later encountered by the

parents, there is no apparent recognition of relationship and no interest shown, other than the occasional cannibalistic interest of some species. This is the general rule, but there are many degrees of variation from this basic pattern.

Among salamanders, the primitive Hellbenders (*Cryptobranchus*), while not having developed any courtship activities, do give protection to their eggs. In this case the male remains with the eggs until they hatch. In the Three-toed Amphiuma (*Amphiuma means tridactylum*), the female guards the eggs. There is apparently no instance in American salamanders of females shepherding the young after they hatch, although Robert E. Gordon did note a renewed protective response in the Green Salamander (*Aneides aeneus*) on the part of egg-guarding females upon the hatching of the young. However, this was merely a snapping reaction when wires were introduced into the nest. There was no attempt by the female to keep the young in the nest area. A number of other salamanders, both aquatic and terrestrial, remain with the eggs until they hatch. Here the guardian parent, most often the female, apparently contributes little other than protection against small predators that might destroy the eggs. In his study of reproduction in the Western Four-toed Salamander (*Batrachoseps wrighti*), Robert C. Stebbins observed that the guardian female (Figure 53) crawled about

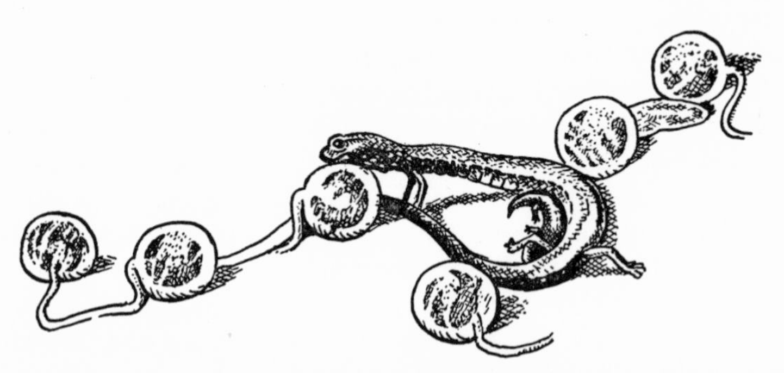

Fig. 53. Female Western Four-toed Salamander (*Batrachoseps wrighti*) guarding her eggs. Note the developing embryo inside the eggs. (Drawn from Robert C. Stebbins)

among the eggs during hatching and twice nosed the emerging young. "Once she nosed a young animal that had only its head protruding, slid her chin along its neck, and pushed the capsule halfway along its back." Stebbins saw this only once and believed that it probably was accidental.

In some species, such as the Eastern Four-toed Salamander (*Hemidactylium scutatum*), several females may deposit their eggs in the same location, and some (but not all) may remain to guard the communal nest. In Michigan and New York the females appear to remain with the eggs until hatching; in Virginia, John T. Wood found that most of the females abandoned their nests halfway through the incubation period. The Mount Lyell Salamander (*Hydromantes platycephalus*) has been thought to be viviparous but is now known to lay eggs like other American species.

No frog of this country appears to provide much in the way of parental care once the eggs are laid. This is in marked contrast to some of the species of frogs found in the New and Old World tropics, where elaborate care of both eggs and tadpoles has been developed. However, even these are exceptions, and the general rule of little or no care applies.

In the Crocodilians, the nest-building and parental care of the female Alligator (*Alligator mississippiensis*) have already been mentioned. She is truly an outstanding mother among reptiles, granting care to both eggs and young. After laying her eggs and carefully covering them, the female packs the nest down by crawling back and forth over it. She is also reported to wet the nest material several times during the incubation period by emptying the contents of her bladder on the mound. She remains around the nest, usually in an adjacent den hole or somewhere nearby, until the incubation period is ended. When the young hatch, they begin to make a high-pitched grunting sound that attracts the female. If the nest is packed too hard for the young to get out by themselves, the female is reported to scrape away the top of the nest and release the young. Once they are out of the nest, she frequently shepherds the young around for from one to three years. She scoops out a wallow pool or cove from 10 to 20 feet in diameter, in which the young remain and near which she stays to protect them from predators.

Unlike the Alligator, the American Crocodile (*Crocodylus a. acutus*) does not appear to give either her eggs or her young any care after covering the nest. Turtles generally appear to give no further attention to parental responsibility once their eggs have been covered. There is considerable difference among turtle species in the time and effort spent covering the nest. The female Common Musk Turtle

(*Sternotherus odoratus*) may lay her eggs scattered about, in shallow excavations or partly concealed in leaf litter and vegetable debris. The Common Mud Turtle (*Kinosternon s. subrubrum*) partly covers the eggs with earth, but makes no attempt to conceal the fairly prominent excavation. In contrast to these desultory habits are those of the Slider Turtles (*Pseudemys*) and some of the Marine Turtles that spend considerable time camouflaging their nest with vegetation.

A curious and so far unconfirmed observation of maternal behavior has been reported by L. A. Hodsdon for the Bahaman Slider Turtle (*Pseudemys malonei*). Several of these turtles were kept in an outdoor enclosure in Miami, Florida. On a number of occasions mating took place and the females laid eggs in May or June. Each laid two or three times at intervals of a week. In August the females were observed to act in an unusual manner, slowly walking about with the snout close to the ground, stopping to scratch a little soil away from different spots, and finally, at a selected spot, digging a small hole about 3 inches across and 1 inch to 1½ inches deep. The females then returned to the water, and in one or two days young turtles emerged from the holes the females had dug. Hodsdon reported that he had "observed this behavior several times during August, and every time it was followed by the emergence of small turtles from the small hole scratched in the ground by the female." He further stated that the ground had become hard-packed over the nest and that the young turtles would have been unable to escape from the nest by themselves. To my knowledge this is the only report of this type of maternal attention in turtles. Does it represent true parental care or was it coincidental behavior observed under crowded conditions of captivity? The fact that Hodsdon observed the action in different years and in more than one female suggests that it is an unusual form of parental care, somewhat similar to that of the Alligator.

In lizards most species give no parental protection to young or offspring, but a few do remain with the incubating eggs to give protection and possibly even enhance incubation. This behavior is best known in skinks of the genus *Eumeces* (Figure 54, no. 5) and in the Glass Lizards (*Ophisaurus*) (Figure 54, no. 2). G. K. Noble and others have studied the brooding behavior of these lizards and found that the female not only protects the eggs from small predators, but also periodically turns them and moves them to keep the clutch together. She also aids incubating the eggs by warming her body at intervals by means of basking. Parental care of the eggs does not extend to the newborn or newly hatched young. The remarkable habit of the mother Night Lizard (*Xantusia*) of assisting the birth of the young is described in the next section.

As in lizards, parental care in American snakes is an unusual phenomenon. Where it occurs, it involves only the brooding of eggs, not the care of young. The exact incidence of brooding behavior in snakes is poorly known. Individuals of several species have been found, in seclusion, coiled around eggs. Whether this was actually a brooding parent or merely a female that had not yet left her newly laid eggs may be difficult to determine. In one or two cases there are fairly authentic observations of brooding behavior in species that are known customarily to abandon their eggs. Such appears to be the case in the reports on the Pilot Blacksnakes (*Elaphe o. obsoleta*) observed by O. P. Medsger. Here both parents were said to sun themselves and then incubate the clutch of eggs deposited in a sawdust pile, supposedly carrying heat absorbed by the body to the buried eggs. On one occasion the male was found actually encircling the eggs.

The studies of George P. Meade on the interesting Mud Snake (*Farancia abacura*) have revealed the fact that this snake frequently remains with its eggs in captivity (Figure 54, no. 1). He reports a number of instances where both wild and captive females were found with their eggs. It is possible that careful field studies will reveal that the brooding of eggs is more common among snakes than we now realize, but at present it is recognized as an exceptional condition in amphibians and reptiles. At present no North American Lizard or snake is known to aid the incubation process by an actual increase in its body temperature—as has been observed in brooding pythons where the snake's body temperature may be raised 5.5° to 7.5° F. From the meager observations available it is suggested that the American lizards and snakes bring warmth to the eggs by alternately sunning themselves and returning to the eggs. However, there are no figures to indicate the effectiveness or actual extent of this behavior.

Hatching and Birth

In the foregoing section the hatching of the egg and the birth of the young were indicated as the end points of incubation and embryonic development. Both involve the emergence of the new

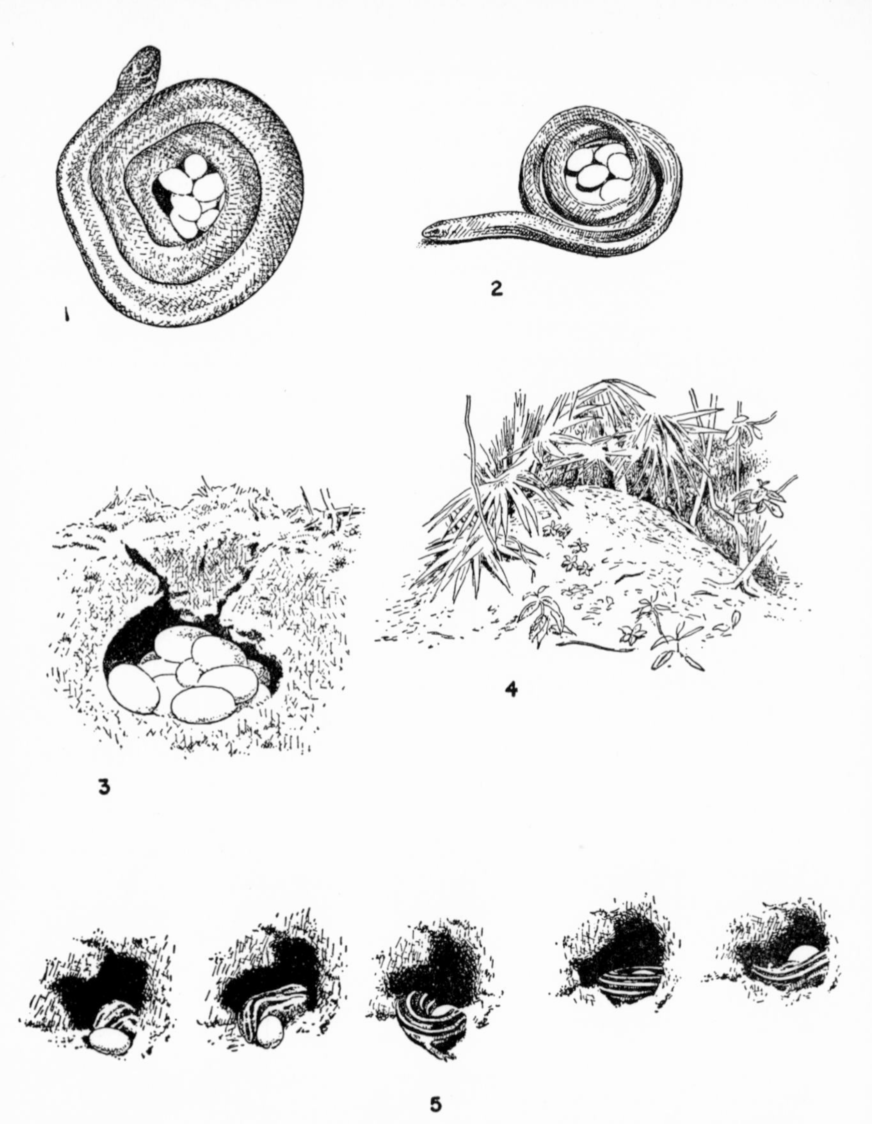

FIG. 54. Various types of parental care of eggs observed in North American reptiles. 1. A female Western Mud Snake (*Farancia abacura reinwardti*) coiled around her eggs. (Modified from George P. Meade). 2. A female Eastern Glass Lizard (*Ophisaurus ventralis*) coiled around her eggs. (Modified from G. K. Noble and E. R. Mason). 3. Eggs and nest of Red-eared Turtle (*Pseudemys scripta elegans*). (Modified from Fred R. Cagle). 4. Nest of American Alligator (*Alligator mississippiensis*). 5. Female Five-lined Skink (*Eumeces fasciatus*) returning egg to nest. (Modified from Fred R. Cagle)

individual from either an egg or the body of its mother; they signal the start of a free-living existence. Most amphibians continue the developmental processes as larval forms. The aquatic amphibian egg is ruptured relatively easily, partly as a result of the internal pressure of imbibed water and partly from a weakening of the egg membrane by chemical secretions produced on the head of the embryo. Shortly before hatching, a series of one-celled glands develops on the snout of many frog and salamander embryos. These glands secrete a substance that digests the egg membrane near the head, freeing the embryo. In the aquatic species and in most terrestrial forms, there are no special structures for tearing the egg membrane in order to permit the escape of the embryo. However, in a few species that lay eggs on land there is an egg tooth that assists the young in escaping from the egg membrane. Coleman J. Goin studied the life history of the Greenhouse Frog (*Eleutherodactylus ricordi planirostris*) in Florida. He observed that the hatchling has a small, single-spined egg tooth on the midline of the front of the upper jaw and that it rips the egg membrane with this structure at hatching. This is a true tooth, located on the premaxillary bone; it is shed shortly after hatching. In amphibians, emergence from the egg occurs as soon as the membrane is ruptured (Figure 55).

The shelled egg of reptiles is more difficult to rupture than the

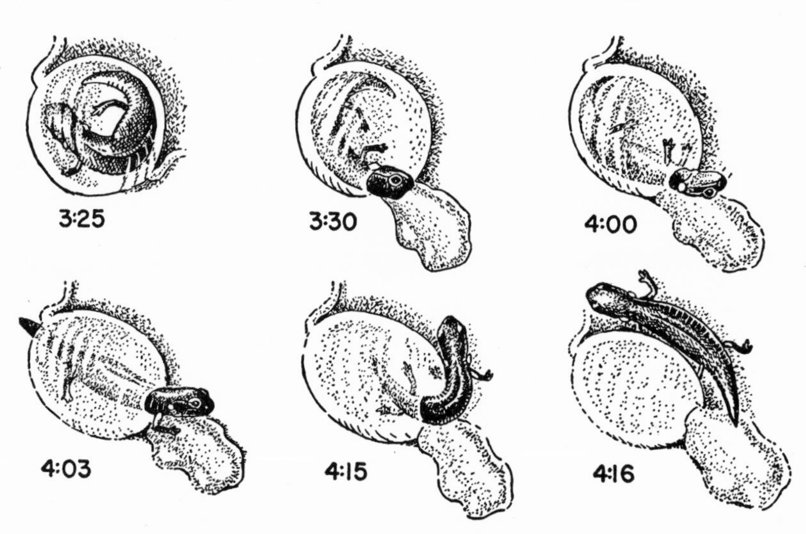

FIG. 55. Stages in the hatching process of the Western Four-toed Salamander (*Batrachoseps wrighti*). The figures beneath each drawing indicate the time (P.M.). (Drawn from Robert C. Stebbins)

amphibian egg, and in all oviparous species there are structures that assist the embryo in making a hole or in tearing the shell. In embryonic turtles and crocodilians there is a horny "caruncle" on the tip of the snout (Figure 56, left), whereas in oviparous lizards and snakes there is an egg tooth protruding from the front of the roof of the mouth (Figure 56, right). This egg tooth is a true tooth

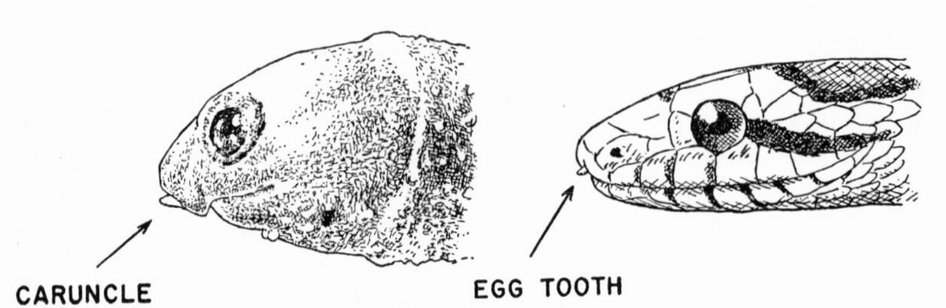

FIG. 56. Horny caruncle of hatchling Snapping Turtle (*Chelydra serpentina serpentina*), left, and egg tooth of Eastern Milk Snake (*Lampropeltis doliata triangulum*). (Drawing of turtle modified from W. J. Hamilton, Jr.)

carried on the premaxillary bone and is quite different from the caruncle of the turtles and crocodilians. It is shed a short time after hatching. In turtles the caruncle may be carried for about 10 days in the Red-eared Turtle (*Pseudemys scripta elegans*), 2 or 3 weeks in Box Turtles (*Terrapene*), and 3 to 4 weeks in Snapping Turtles (*Chelydra*). In lizards and snakes the egg teeth are shed more quickly, usually within a day or two. The geckos differ from all other lizards in having a pair of egg teeth instead of a single tooth. When the embryo nears the end of the incubation period, the caruncle or egg tooth is well developed, and the size of the embryo has increased to the point where it presses against the egg shell. At this time sideward movements of the head bring the shell-pipping structures into play. A single large tear or cut of the shell may enable the hatchling to emerge (Figure 57), but frequently additional opening of the shell is necessary. In some lizards and turtles the sharp claws of the feet may rip the shell open or enlarge the original break made either by the egg tooth or by the caruncle. As the time of hatching approaches, the inner part of the shell of the egg is eroded away by enzyme action from the inside, so that it becomes very thin, particularly near the head of the embryo. This erosion of the shell simplifies the hatching process, but occasional individuals are unable to break through the shell.

Once the original break is made in the shell, hatching has begun. It is usually continued at a leisurely pace, requiring several hours for completion. Some turtles spend the winter in the egg after rupturing the shell. Usually, however, hatching is completed within 24 hours after the original break.

In the live-bearing or viviparous reptiles, birth is a comparable process but simpler than hatching. There is only a thin, transparent membrane for the embryo to rupture and no special structures are required to break through. Viviparous lizards and snakes lack functional egg teeth, although a team of British herpetologists has recently shown that a small, nonfunctional egg tooth may be present in the embryos of some live-bearing snakes, such as the Massasauga Rattlesnake (*Sistrurus catenatus*). Once the young have passed out of the mother's body, it is usually only a matter of minutes before they emerge from their enveloping membranes. Occasionally the membrane is broken as it passes out of the female's body, and the newborn young appears to crawl from its mother's body. In both hatching and birth, the young may venture forth almost immediately, but usually they remain for several hours or a few days in the secluded situation where they first enter the world.

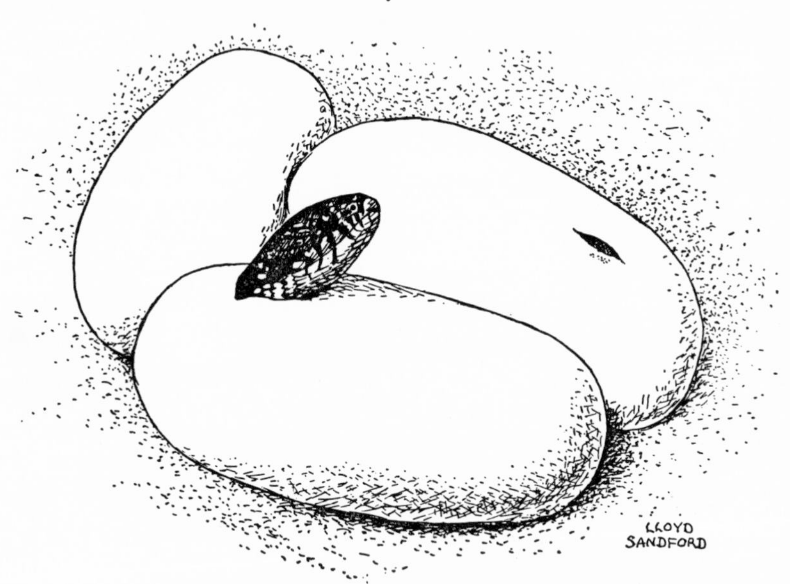

FIG. 57. Hatching eggs of Eastern King Snake (*Lampropeltis getulus getulus*). Note single slit in shell of rear egg on the right.

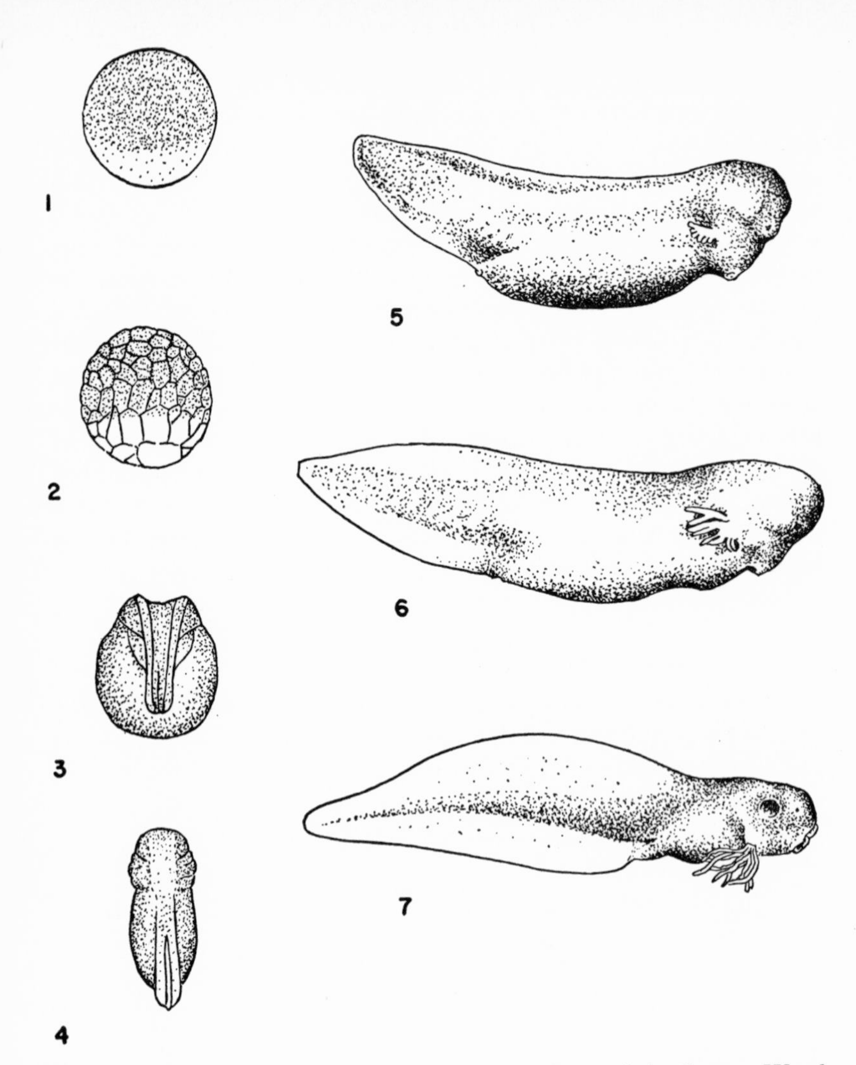

FIG. 58. Developmental stages of the egg and embryo of the Eastern Wood Frog (*Rana sylvatica sylvatica*). Note that in these drawings the outer gelatinous envelopes are not shown since they take no noticeable part in the developmental processes. 1. Undivided egg. 2. Egg showing multiplication of cells six hours after fertilization. 3. Nerve fold stage 40 hours after fertilization. 4. Beginning development of tail bud 58 hours after fertilization. 6. Free-swimming stage 112 hours after fertilization. 7. Free-swimming form with full development of "tadpole" shape 164 hours after fertilization. This stage marks the beginning of the active swimming tadpole stage. The rate of development given here is at a temperature of 65 degrees Fahrenheit. (Drawn from Arthur W. Pallister and John A. Moore)

Raymond B. Cowles and Charles E. Shaw have independently described the birth of young Night Lizards (*Xantusia*) and the interesting behavior of the mother at this time. At the moment of birth when the foetus and its enveloping membrane begin to push out of the vent, the mother's body is fully turned so that her mouth is immediately beside the vent. When the membrane appears, she grasps it in her teeth and rips it open, releasing and activating the young. The partially extruded young lizard comes out tail and hind legs first, sometimes wrapping around or grasping the base of the parent's tail for purchase. At this time the mother may nip the emerging young on the tail or exposed flank, stimulating it to further activity. More remarkable still, the mother may actually seize the exposed tail or legs in her teeth and pull the young free. This is an astounding feat in several ways, not the least of which is pulling the young out by the fragile tail. As in many live-bearing lizards, the mother usually eats the afterbirth.

Larvae

When some amphibian eggs hatch, the emerging organism may show a fairly close similarity to its parents in body form, as in the case of the salamanders (Figure 59, upper), or it may have little or

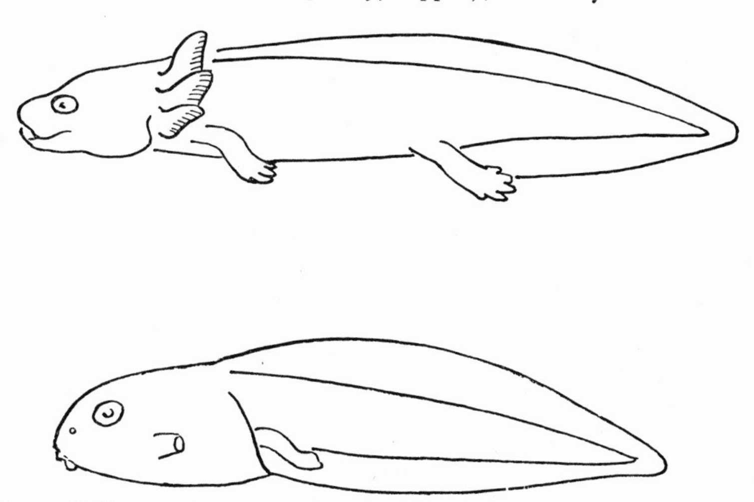

Fig. 59. Differences between larval salamander (above) and larval frogs (below). The latter is the characteristic tadpole larva of frogs. (Drawn from Grace L. Orton)

no resemblance to the parents, as in the case of the frogs (Figure 59, lower). In either event the hatchling is a larva and will continue its development in the larval stage. As a free-living organism it passes through stages of morphological development that are somewhat like those that the reptile embryo passes through within the egg. At the end of the larval period the individual characteristically undergoes a change or metamorphosis and takes on the body form of the adult. The length of the larval period varies in different species and within the same species under different environmental conditions.

Larval salamanders differ from frog tadpoles in a number of respects, the more important of which are the possession of true teeth, the presence of external gills, and an elongated body with four limbs throughout the larval period. Tadpoles lack all of these except that four limbs are present shortly before metamorphosis.

The larval salamander resembles the adult except in several minor details, such as possessing external gills; it is clearly a salamander. Because of this similarity it has no special name or designation other than "larval salamander." The larval frog, however, is so different that it is widely referred to as a tadpole. While the tadpole of one species is sufficiently like that of another species for both to be recognized as tadpoles, there are often vast differences among the tadpoles of different species. Many of these differences are adaptive. Grace L. Orton, our foremost student of tadpoles, has classified these larvae into seven adaptive types: generalized; arboreal; surface-feeding; direct development; mountain-stream; carnivorous; and nektonic, or deep-bodied, high-finned, free-swimming forms (Figure 60). All of these types, except the arboreal and the surface-feeding forms, are found in the species of frogs inhabiting the United States. Examples of the different types are listed in the legend for Figure 60 and were supplied through the kindness of Dr. Orton.

In salamanders a few aquatic species retain the larval body form throughout life. Such species are said to be neotenic. Most salamanders characteristically metamorphose into the adult body form before taking up the reproductive life of the mature stage. Usually the transformation in body form is accompanied by a change in habits and habitat—moving from the water to a partially terrestrial existence. Unlike some frogs, virtually all salamander larvae develop in more or less permanent bodies of water—streams, lakes, and ponds—rarely or never in temporary rain pools. The larval period generally varies from two to four months, being shorter in the warmer areas and longer in the cooler regions. In the Marbled Salamander (*Ambystoma opacum*), which breeds in the fall, the eggs generally hatch late in the fall and the larvae winter over, transforming the following spring after a larval period of five to six months. The longest larval period for any American species that undergoes a definite metamorphosis is that of the Hellbender (*Cryptobranchus alleganiensis*), whose larvae may retain their gills for 18 months.

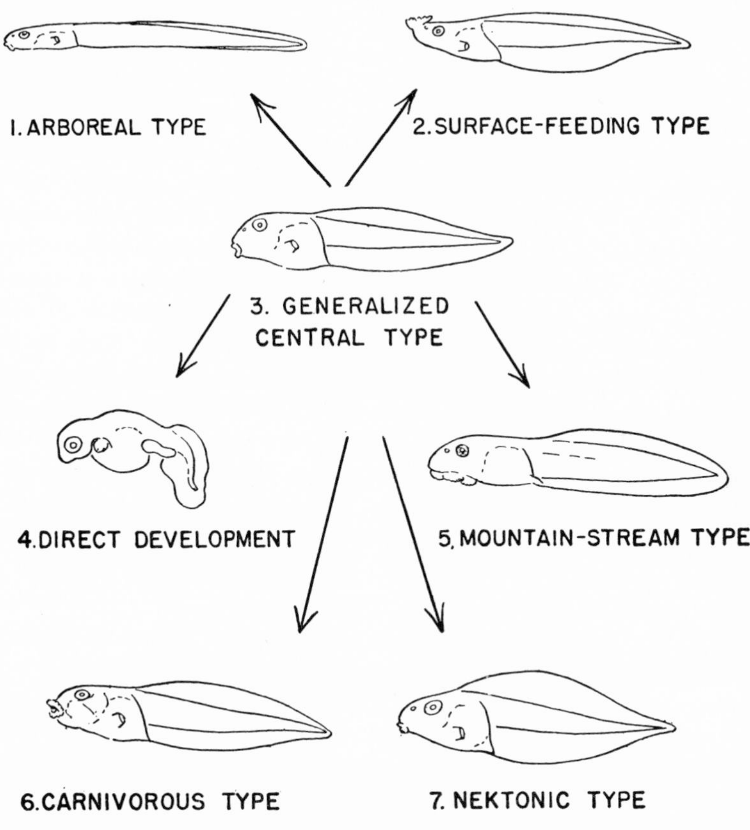

FIG. 60. Adaptive types of frog tadpoles. Types 1 and 2 are not represented among the North American species. Examples of species with the other modifications are: 3. Leopard Frog (*Rana pipiens*). 4. Robber Frog (*Eleutherodactylus latrans*). 5. Tailed Frog (*Ascaphus truei*). 6. Hammond's Spadefoot (*Scaphiopus hammondi*). 7. Barking Tree Frog (*Hyla gratiosa*). (Information and illustrations from Grace L. Orton)

Frogs, which occur in a greater variety of habitats than salamanders, have both longer and shorter larval periods. This statement may be qualified to exclude the neotenic salamanders, since in a sense they are larvae throughout their lives. The briefest larval periods among our American Amphibia are found in the frogs adapted to living in semiarid conditions or breeding in temporary bodies of water. Here short incubation and larval periods frequently mean the difference between success and failure, for these frogs are living under marginal environmental conditions where there is barely enough water to make reproduction possible. The shortest time known to me between the laying of the eggs and the metamorphosis of the young is that of 13 days reported by Arthur N. Bragg for Hurter's Spadefoot Toad (*Scaphiopus holbrooki hurteri*) in Oklahoma. This includes an incubation period that probably lasted at least one day thus the actual larval period was 12 days or less. Bragg states that this is the fastest developmental rate that he has observed; also, that the transformed young in this instance were the smallest North American Frogs that he had ever seen. The usual time required for the combined incubation-larval period of this Spadefoot is 18 to 25 days.

Bragg has made careful observations on the life habits of the frogs of Oklahoma. His studies reveal interesting differences in time of incubation-larval periods in several species of frogs, all of which bred in the same pond in Oklahoma during one spring. The species bred at various times during the season, so that the young did not develop under the same temperature conditions. Bragg's results, shown here, indicate the number of days from the time the eggs were first laid until newly transformed young appeared:

Hurter's Spadefoot (*Scaphiopus holbrooki hurteri*)	21	days
Great Plains Narrow-mouthed Toad (*Microhyla carolinensis olivacea*)	26-28	"
American Toad (*Bufo terrestris americanus*)	18-31	"
Gray Tree Frog (*Hyla v. versicolor*)	39-41	"
Strecker's Chorus Frog (*Pseudacris s. streckeri*)	40-48	"
Southern Leopard Frog (*Rana pipiens sphenocephala*)	53-60	"

In general, the more aquatic frogs, such as those of the genus *Rana*, have a longer larval period than the more terrestrial species. Within a given species the larval period, like the incubation period, is markedly influenced by temperature, being shorter when warmer temperatures prevail. Apparently a slight increase in the concentration of mineral salts in the water may accelerate the developmental rate of the larvae. Thus tadpoles developing in a shallow pool that is drying up will develop more rapidly than tadpoles of the same species in the shallow water of a more permanent pool. Here it is not only the higher temperature of the shallow pool but apparently also the increasing concentration of salt in the evaporating pool that speed up the development of the larvae. Bragg has also shown the importance of an abundant supply of organic food in the development of the tadpoles. He noted that an inadequate food source may prevent the completion of the larval period before the drying up of the pool. In this connection Bragg observed the interesting phenomenon that the loss, through desiccation, of larvae during one breeding season may increase the probability of success for larvae the following season because of the added organic food material present in the pools from the dead bodies. This can be considered a compensatory contribution to the over-all good of the species.

The longest larval period of any American frog is that of the Bullfrog (*Rana catesbeiana*). In the extreme northern part of its range this species may spend three winters as a tadpole, while in the Gulf States it transforms at the end of the first winter. Some species of *Rana*, such as *pipiens*, usually undergo metamorphosis at the end of the summer in which they hatch. All intermediate conditions between these two species may be found in some species of *Rana* or in some geographic area.

CHAPTER 12

Growth, Size, and Longevity

TWO QUESTIONS ABOUT ANIMALS that are asked with great frequency are "How big does it get?" and "How long does it live?" The answers to both questions are matters of considerable factual interest but of little biological importance, since the questions usually refer to extreme conditions of size and age, not to the characteristic average size or average length of life for a species. Nevertheless, it is of interest to know what the maximum recorded size or age of a given animal is. Because we are concerned here with extremes, and because of considerable popular interest, it is often difficult to obtain reliable figures. Frequently hearsay evidence, estimates, and incomplete or faulty observations are offered on the size or age of an animal. Like "the fish that got away," amphibians and reptiles gain stature or years in the telling of tales. It is impossible for the professional herpetologist to examine each case personally, but he must use extreme caution in verifying as far as possible those records that are to be accepted. One difficulty comes from the fact that herpetologists, too, are human beings and differ in their ideas of what constitutes reliability. One leading Curator of Reptiles put it this way: "Maximum size of reptiles is becoming largely a matter of taste." The situation is not so extreme as this, however. There actually is general agreement on most of the published figures.

Both the size and longevity of amphibians and reptiles are intimately related to growth.

GROWTH

Growth is a universal biological phenomenon. It is one characteristic of living matter that distinguishes it from nonliving matter.

In simplest terms, growth is an increase in size. But various parts of the body generally increase at different rates, so that growth is not a simple process. The differential growth that takes place in an animal's body accounts for some of the variations seen between newborn young and adults of a single species. Genetic differences in growth patterns, in duration, and in rate of growth account for many of the differences in size and proportions between species.

In mammals—for instance, dogs and cats—the individual grows at a more or less rapid rate until shortly after it has reached sexual maturity, after which it slows down and soon stops growing altogether. Even if a mammal lives three or four times as long as it took to attain maximum size, it gets no larger. Such growth is said to be *determinate*, since it terminates at a characteristic size for the species. Some amphibians and reptiles exhibit a similar type of determinate growth that ceases after a certain maximum size has been reached. However, many amphibians and reptiles grow throughout their lives, exhibiting *indeterminate*, or continuous, growth.

While such forms may continue to grow throughout their life span, growth is generally intermittent, not going on at all times nor at a constant rate from week to week. There are periods of active growth interspersed with periods of little or no growth. For example, when animals hibernate, growth is greatly reduced or stopped. Mature individuals may stop growing for some time and then renew growth for a time. John T. Nichols cites an example: An Eastern Box Turtle (*Terrapene c. carolina*) in New York grew rapidly to a measurement of 4¾ inches, had no measurable growth during the next three years, and then grew to a length of 5⅜ inches in six years. This phenomenon of intermittent growth has been observed in all major groups of amphibians and reptiles.

The rate of growth is similar in determinate and indeterminate growth, being rapid in the early stages of life and gradually becoming slower. The essential difference is that one type appears to come to a complete stop whereas the other continues, at a decreased rate.

Growth can be studied by measuring various body proportions or body weight. The most frequently used indicator is the largest over-all linear dimension that can be easily recorded with accuracy, such as total length. This measure in a reptile includes the head, the body, and the tail. Since these three parts usually grow at different rates, they should be measured separately for detailed studies of growth, but such precise measurements are not necessary for a general consideration of the primary features of growth. Total length, meaning the greatest over-all length from the tip of the snout to the end of the tail, will be used in referring to the size of salamanders, crocodilians, lizards, and snakes. For frogs, the primary measure is the snout-vent length, from the tip of the snout to the posterior edge of the vent. In turtles, shell length is the midline length of the carapace, or upper shell. This is usually spoken of as the carapace length. The length of the lower shell, or plastron, is also used in studying growth changes in some turtles, such as the Box Turtles (*Terrapene*) and Slider Turtles (*Pseudemys*). All the measurements indicated here are straight-line measurements and *not* over the curve of the body or shell.

Information on growth in animals is acquired in three ways: (1) by repeated measurements of wild individuals that can be identified with certainty over a period; (2) by measuring large numbers of preserved animals that can be placed as to their approximate age groups; or (3) by measuring the growth of captive animals. Each of these methods has its drawbacks and its difficulties. The first method yields the best information for most species; however, it is a long, laborious task and is sometimes impracticable. The third method is the most uncertain of the three and may reveal only the potentialities of growth under specific conditions, but the data obtained by this method frequently represent the only information available or may supplement fragmentary observations on wild animals.

At the present time our knowledge of growth in amphibians and reptiles is very incomplete. For example, in most species we cannot yet say whether growth is determinate or indeterminate. From the state of our knowledge about some species it appears that growth may be determinate in one part of the animal's range, but indeterminate in another. In Florida the Southern Fence Lizard (*Sceloporus u. undulatus*) appears to grow throughout its one- or two-year life span, but in Maryland, where it may live for 8 years, the growth appears to stop after about the fifth or sixth year and is therefore determinate. In another species—for example, the Alligator (*Alligator mississippiensis*)—the rate of growth may be so slight after sexual maturity that it is not known for certain whether it stops completely or continues at a very slow rate. Certainly it takes a long time for any 'gator to reach the maximum size of nearly 20 feet. Probably 'gators reach this size by continuous but very slow growth throughout life. However, because of persecution by man few of them live long enough to reach that length.

A common difficulty involved in the study of growth is the great variation between individuals of the same species—even between individuals of the same brood living under identical conditions. The extent of this individual variation makes the recognition of discreet age groups difficult or impossible in many species as soon as the early stages of life are past. What causes such great differences in growth between different species and between individuals of the same species? We can name some of the factors, but we cannot give a complete answer to this question at the present time. First of all, differences in growth between different species is partly an expression of differences in genetic constitution, which in turn influence the metabolic and physiological processes of the different species. Similar but less extensive genetic differences may be responsible for the differences in growth exhibited by members of the same species or even by brood mates.

Environmental factors that have a marked influence on growth are temperature and light, availability and nature of food, and availability of water. Within limits, a higher temperature speeds up the growth processes and a lower temperature inhibits them. The effects of temperature are not just the simple direct influences relating to a speed-up of the chemical processes involved, but include the indirect effects on the animal's hormone system. Light appears of primary importance in this latter role. Availability of food and water are important in furnishing the building materials for the body increase.

What growth conditions do we find in amphibians and reptiles? Throughout most of the United States there is a marked seasonal influence on their growth, with few species growing throughout the year. Even in those that do continue to grow all year long, there are periods of maximum and minimum growth. Maximum growth generally occurs in times of optimum temperature and abundant food. In the northern part of the country or at high altitudes such conditions frequently occur only during the summer months. In the southern part of the country they may occur in spring and in fall. In more arid regions they may come at the time of maximum rainfall. Thus, for most species, growth is an intermittent or periodic process.

The total growth potential of an individual is also influenced by the maximum size of the species to which it belongs. In general there appears to be a relationship between maximum size and the size at birth, the size at sexual maturity, and rate of growth and longevity. Species of smaller dimensions usually have proportionately larger offspring, attain sexual maturity at a size close to the maximum for the species, grow at a more rapid rate, and have a shorter life span than the larger species. The exact details of these relationships are not clearly understood, and numerous exceptions can be cited.

Sexual Differences in Growth and Size

Many species of amphibians and reptiles show pronounced differences in size between the two sexes. These are genetic differences and are usually associated with differences in the rate of growth. The sex that attains the larger size usually grows at the more rapid rate. This can be seen in Figures 67 and 69, which show the growth rate for the Alligator and the Green Anolis.

In some species the male attains the larger size. This appears to be true among some of the species of lizards in which social organization is best developed, such as the Green Anolis (*Anolis c. carolinensis*). In these species, where the males establish territorial groups of females, the advantages to the species of large robust males is apparent. However, in other Iguanid lizards which have similar social groups, such as the Scaly Lizards (*Sceloporus*), the females usually attain a larger size than the males. There are other species with larger males than females in which the advantages are not so obvious—for example, the Eastern Tiger Salamander (*Ambystoma t. tigrinum*) and the Crater Lake Newt (*Taricha granulosus mazamae*). In most species of amphibians and reptiles where there is a sexual difference in size, it is the female that is the larger. Here a real advantage is apparent because of the correlation between the number of eggs produced and the size of the female. Many salamanders, most frogs, most turtles, some lizards, and many snakes exhibit this sexual difference in size, with females being larger than males.

The matter of size difference between the sexes is not a simple one of an obvious advantage for the species. Often no real reason is apparent, and the difference may appear to be merely a matter of chance or evolutionary whim. For example, in the Black-spotted Newt (*Diemictylus meridionalis*) the males are smaller than the females, whereas the Crater Lake Newt, which is of the same family, has the reverse size relationship between the sexes. What, if any, is the advantage to each species?

As noted in the chapter on food habits, such a difference may enable the species to draw on a greater source of food because individuals of the larger sex can consume large food organisms while the smaller sex can concentrate on smaller ones. This could be an important feature in the economy of a species, and such an advantage may be a prime factor in the appearance of sexual size differences, regardless of which sex is the larger. Often the differences are too small to be of any real significance and many species do not exhibit any difference in size between the two sexes.

Sexual Maturity

Sexual maturity is the growth stage at which the individual acquires the ability to reproduce. It is marked by the maturing of the gonads and may or may not be accompanied by the development of certain secondary sexual characters. In amphibians and reptiles sexual maturity is reached at a size below the average adult size for the species. In fact, the attainment of sexual maturity is a criterion for indicating the beginning of the adult life stage, the reproductive age.

Identification of adults, or sexually mature individuals, is based on studies of the reproductive organs to determine at what sizes functional sex cells are present. These studies may be augmented by investigations on the secondary sexual characters, if any, and on a study of the age at which reproduction begins in animals in the wild. Studies on the reproductive organs can be made in detail only on dead individuals, whereas the other investigations can be made on either wild or captive individuals.

Secondary sexual characters include differences in size, shape and proportions, color, texture of skin, and the presence of special structures. In the discussion of differential growth, examples of differences in size between the sexes have been pointed out. In many species there are pronounced differences in the proportionate size of some parts of the animal. For example, male newts (*Diemictylus* and *Taricha*) have a more prominent tail crest than the females; the male Bullfrog (*Rana catesbeiana*) has a much larger eardrum than the female (Figure 61); the web of the hind foot of the male Woodfrog (*Rana sylvatica*) is larger than that of the female; the claws on the forelegs of some male turtles, such as Painted Turtles (*Chrysemys*) and some Slider Turtles (*Pseudemys*), are greatly elongated; males of land turtles characteristically have concave lower shells as compared with the flat or slightly convex lower

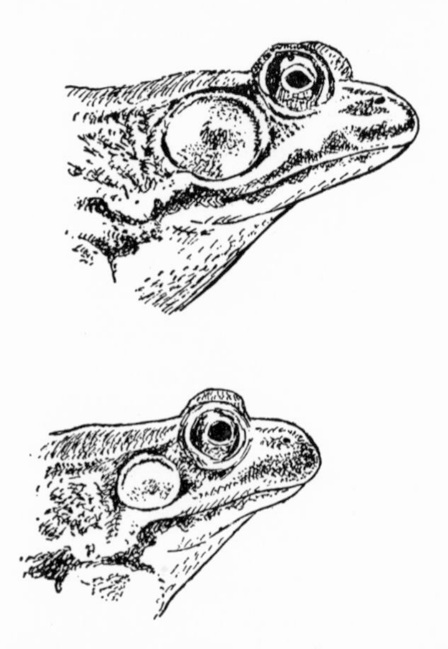

FIG. 61. Heads of male (upper) and female (lower) Bullfrog (*Rana catesbeiana*) showing sexual difference in size of the ear.

shell in females; and in many species the males have a longer tail than the females (Figures 62 and 63). These are a few of the many secondary sexual characters that are involved in differences.

Sexual differences in color are most pronounced among lizards; they are found to a lesser degree among other reptiles and in amphibians. Perhaps the most pronounced sexual difference in color in American amphibia is that found in the Yosemite Toad (*Bufo canorus*). The female is strongly marked with large black spots outlined with white, and there are touches of yellow and rust in the dorsal ground color. The male is virtually a uniform olive green, sometimes with small yellow or white bordered black spots. Other examples of sexual color differences in amphibians are found in the dark throats of many male Toads (*Bufo*), the yellowish throats of male Cricket Frogs (*Acris*) and Green Frogs (*Rana clamitans*), and the dark cloacal band in the male Western Red-bellied Newt (*Taricha rivularis*).

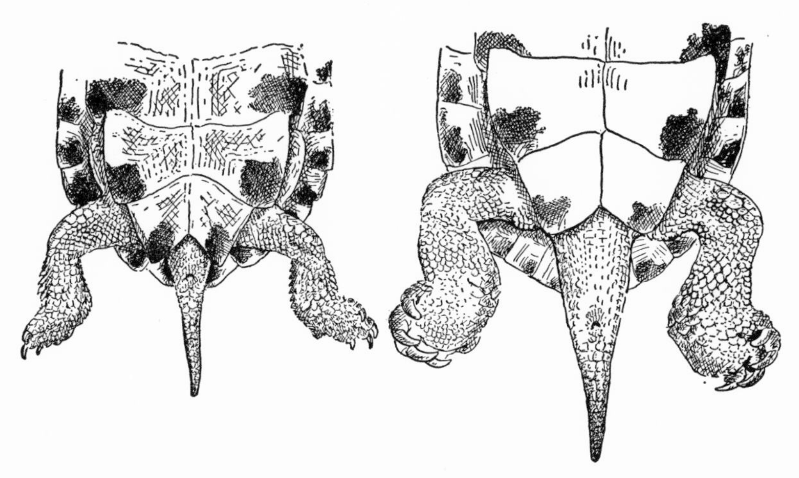

FIG. 62. Sexual differences in tails of female (left) and male (right) Wood Turtles (*Clemmys insculpta*). Note the vent opening in back of the edge of the upper shell in the male and his thicker tail.

Turtles sometimes exhibit slight sexual differences in color in the relative size of some markings. For example, the yellow spots are larger on the female Spotted Turtle (*Clemmys guttata*) than in the male. Another color difference associated with sex is that of the

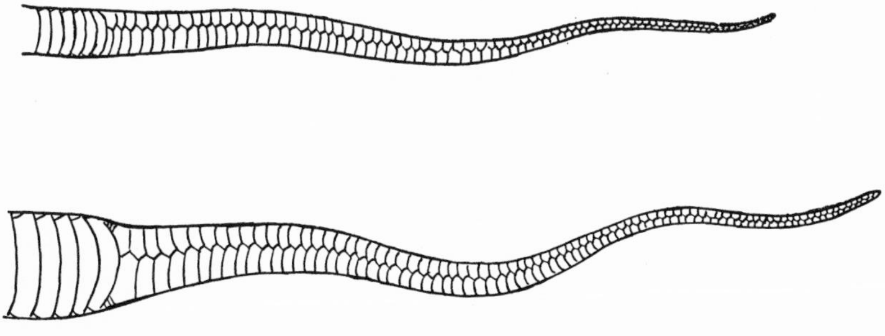

FIG. 63. Sexual differences in tails of male (top) and female (bottom) Diamondback Water Snakes (*Natrix rhombifera rhombifera*). Note the sharply tapering tail of the female and the more nearly parallel base of the male's tail.

iris of the eye in some species. Male Spotted Turtles generally have brown eyes, whereas the female iris is bright orange. Eastern Box Turtle (*Terrapene c. carolina*) males usually have a reddish eye, whereas females generally have dark eyes of a gray or brownish color. The most striking color differences between the sexes in turtles is that found in the *scripta* section of the Slider Turtles (*Pseudemys*), in which males become progressively darker in color with age, finally assuming a nearly uniform black color.

Black, or melanistic, individuals are encountered in several species of snakes; they usually possess a distinct pattern. However, such dark individuals represent both sexes and are not, like the Slider Turtles, examples of a secondary sexual character. Perhaps the most widely quoted example of this is the Timber Rattlesnake (*Crotalus h. horridus*). In this snake two color phases occur as variants from the usual color pattern: (1) a dark-banded yellow phase, in which the ground color is a light sulphur yellow; and (2) the black phase, in which the banded pattern is virtually obliterated by black pigment. There is a widespread belief in the northeastern United States that the light-colored individuals are females and the dark ones males. Howard K. Gloyd, in his extensive studies on these rattlesnakes, found no sexual correlation for the color phases. Actually all degrees of variation from one pattern to the other may be present in either sex. With only one exception I know of no secondary sexual characters in American snakes that involve color alone other than in some of the Central and South American species. The single exception is found in the Rainbow Snake (*Abastor erythrogrammus*) where, as noted by Neil D. Richmond, males and females can be distinguished solely on the basis of the color of the belly and under the tail. The proportionate differences in body and tail length may result in dissimilar proportions in markings on the involved regions—for example, a greater number of dark bands on the longer tail of a male compared with fewer bands on a similarly sized female.

Among many lizards there are striking differences in color between the two sexes. In a number of members of the family Iguanidae, the males possess rich red, blue, or black belly and throat patches. Females lack these colors or show them only faintly. These male colors are present throughout the year, but are brightest during the mating season. In the Common Gridiron-tailed

Lizard (*Callisaurus draconoides gabbi*) males have a blue area on each side of the belly. Each patch encloses two diagonal jet-black marks. These colors are present throughout the year. In addition, during the breeding season the male acquires a metallic greenish-blue color on the sides of the body and a pink color on the light areas of the throat. A quite different situation exists in the Common Leopard Lizard (*Crotaphytus w. wislizeni*). Here the male acquires no special breeding color, but the female during the breeding season following mating develops a salmon-reddish color on the undersurfaces and sides of the body and tail.

Lizards of the genus *Anolis* have an interesting color feature in the dewlap. This is a brightly colored flap of skin surrounding the elongated hyoid bones of the throat. By moving the extension of the hyoid downward, the dewlap can be distended, or "flared," flashing a patch of bright color. The color varies in different species. In the Green Anolis (*Anolis c. carolinensis*) it is raspberry red. The dewlap is well developed only in the males, but females also have a tiny patch of the same color on the throat. The Greater Five-lined Skink (*Eumeces laticeps*) is also called the Red-headed Skink because of the orangish-red color of the head in males. Adult males also differ from females in having a uniform dorsal color of light brown on the body and tail. Females lack red on the head and retain the striped body pattern of the juveniles. Although many other lizards could be mentioned to illustrate the sexual differences in color, not all lizards show such dimorphism.

Differences in texture of skin are sometimes present in amphibians. During the breeding season the male California Newt (*Taricha torosus*) loses the papillae of the skin, so that it takes on a smooth appearance and develops numerous dark-colored papillae around the base of the hind limbs. The cloaca of the male becomes greatly swollen in many species of Salamanders (Figure 64). Male frogs of many species develop horny nuptial pads on the thumb and sometimes other fingers during the breeding season. These pads aid in gripping the female in amplexus. They are present only during the breeding season. All male salamanders of the family Plethodontidae possess hedonic glands to attract the females. These glands are usually located on the chin or cheeks, or on the base of the tail. Male Gopher Turtles (*Gopherus*) have a pair of glands under the chin that may function in a similar fashion. Male Diamondback

Water Snakes (*Natrix r. rhombifera*) possess chin tubercles and minute ridges or supraanal keels that may function to stimulate the female during courtship. The males of many Plethodontid Salaman-

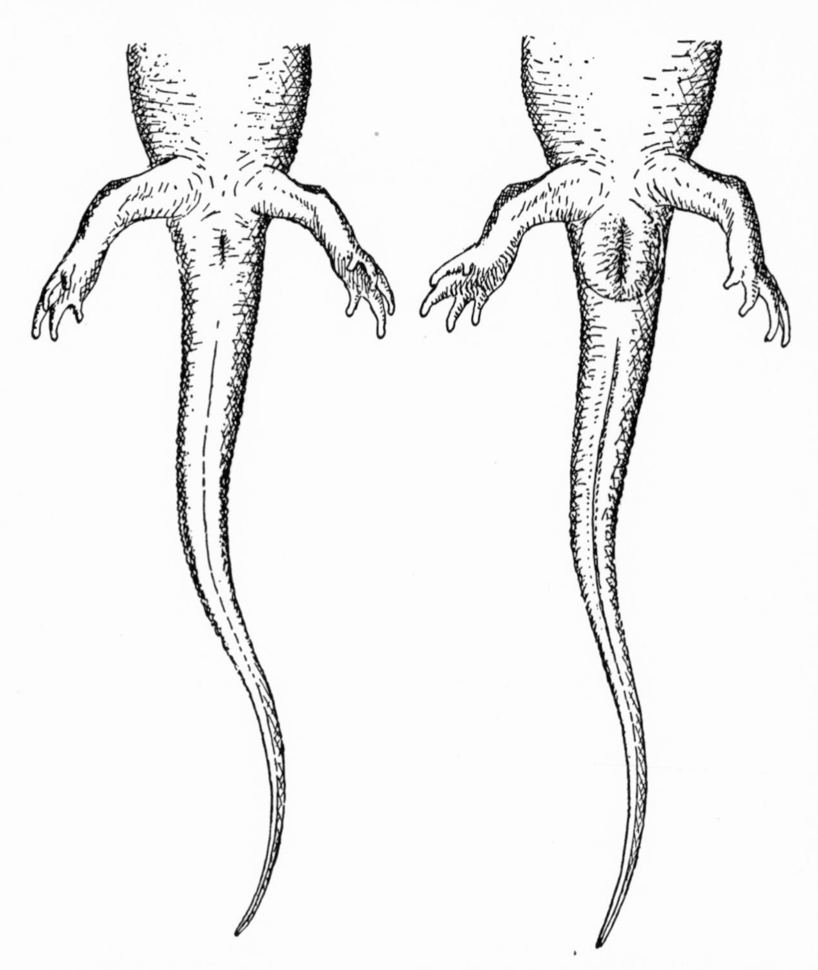

FIG. 64. Sexual differences in vents of female (left) and male (right) Newt (*Taricha granulosa*). Note the greatly enlarged lips of the male's vent.

ders have the premaxillary teeth elongated and directed forward.

The majority of the sexual differences mentioned develop under the control of the sex hormones secreted by the ripened or ripening gonads. These characters therefore make their appearance only when

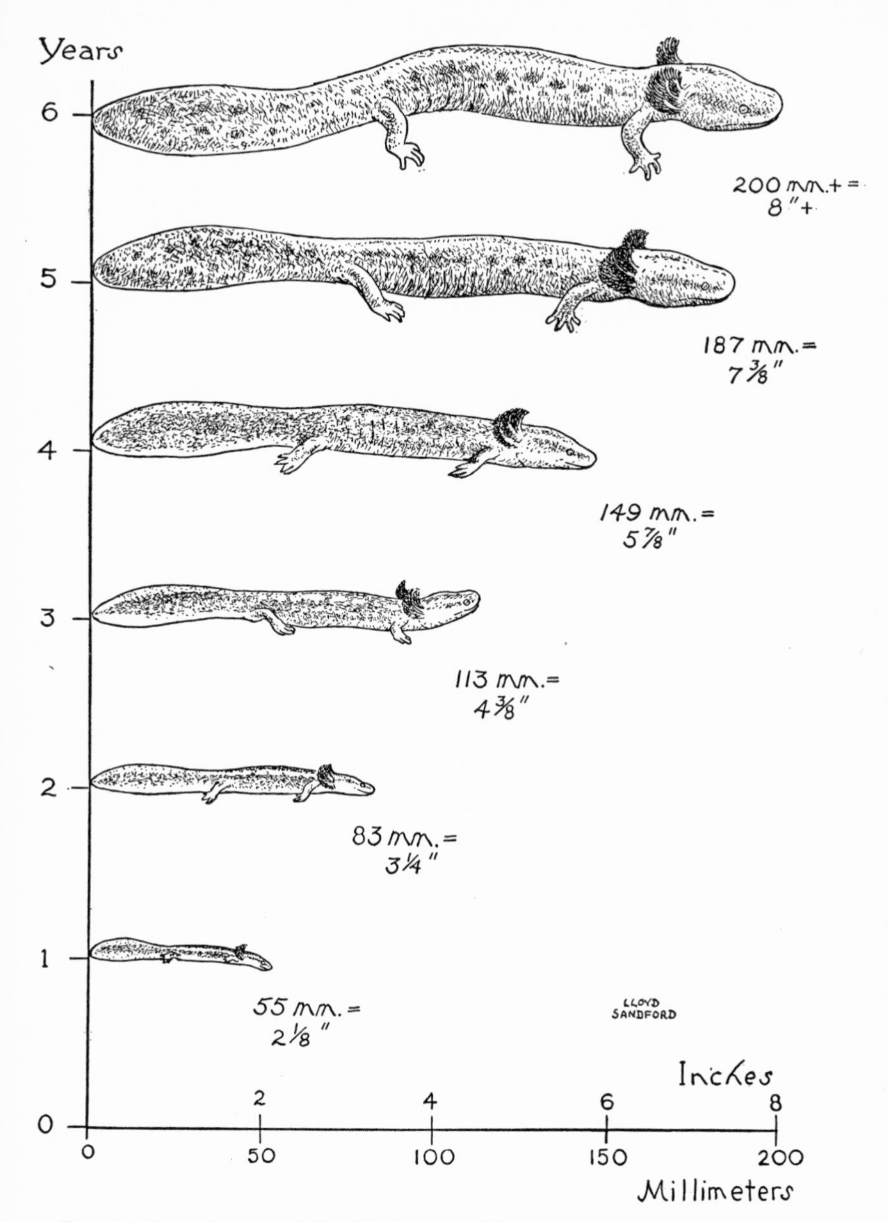

FIG. 65. Growth rate of the Mudpuppy (*Necturus maculosus maculosus*) in New York State. (Data from Sherman C. Bishop)

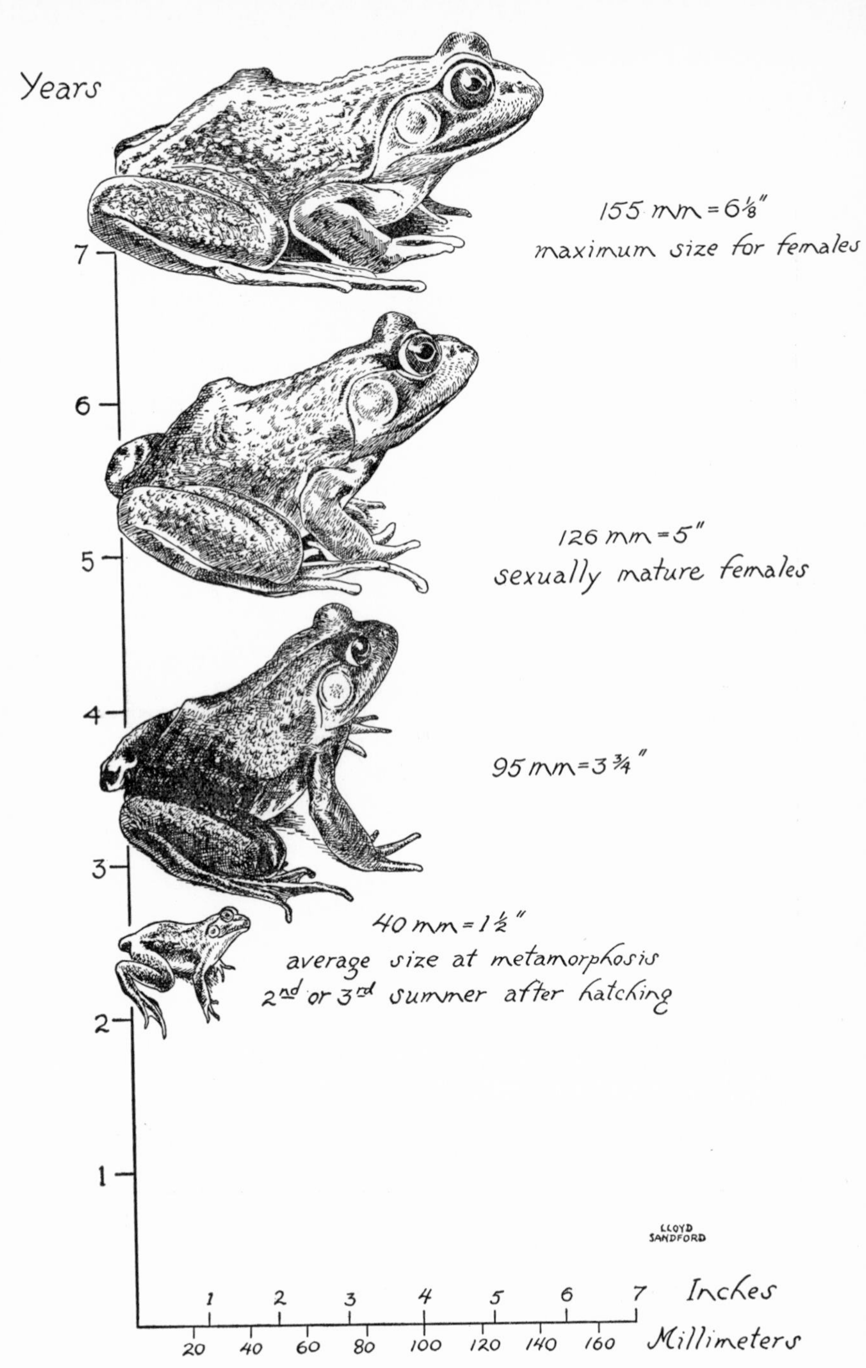

FIG. 66. Growth rate of the Bullfrog (*Rana catesbeiana*) in New York State. (Data from Edward C. Raney and William M. Ingram)

the individual is becoming or has become capable of reproduction, and they furnish valuable clues to the individual's developmental state. Obviously it must be ascertained with certainty that a character is hormonally regulated before it can be used in this type of study. In reptiles, for instance, males frequently have relatively longer tails than females, but this is usually not under hormonal control, for at birth males already have proportionately longer tails. On the other hand, the longer claws of the male Red-eared Turtle (*Pseudemys scripta elegans*) are definitely related to the male sex hormone and do not elongate until the male is sexually mature.

Herpetologists are using various combinations of studies on gonads and on the time of development of secondary sex characters; and field observations on growth and time of reproduction. Thus a considerable amount of information is being accumulated on size and age at sexual maturity for many amphibians and reptiles. Clifford H. and Sarah H. Pope carefully analyzed preserved specimens of the Slimy Salamander (*Plethodon g. glutinosus*) from Virginia and West Virginia. They found that this salamander reached sexual maturity at a snout-vent length of 1⅞ inches for the males and 2¼ inches in the females. Because of the slower growth rate of the males, both sexes reach maturity at the same time, at about three years of age. Sherman C. Bishop studied Jefferson's Salamander (*Ambystoma jeffersonianum*) in New York. He found the larvae transformed at 86 to 170 days after the eggs were laid. At this time they were 1⅞ to 3 inches in total length. They would breed when approximately two years old, at a length of at least 4¼ inches. Frank N. Blanchard found that the strictly terrestrial Red-backed Salamander (*Plethodon c. cinereus*) in Michigan also attained maturity in the second year of life, at a minimum length of 2¼ inches. Bishop observed that in New York the Mudpuppy (*Necturus maculosus*) reached sexual maturity in its fifth year at a size of 8 inches (Figure 65). Clifford H. Pope has stated that the Eastern Tiger Salamander (*Ambystoma t. tigrinum*) may reach sexual maturity in one year's time. Byron P. Glass studied neotenic individuals of the related Yellow-barred Tiger Salamander (*Ambystoma tigrinum mavortium*) and found that they also attained sexual maturity at about one year of age.

Edward C. Raney and William M. Ingram noted that Bullfrogs (*Rana catesbeiana*) in New York reach sexual maturity at an age of four or five years (Figure 66). This involves a larval period of two to three years. The American Toad (*Bufo terrestris ameri-*

canus), studied in the same state by William J. Hamilton, Jr., reached maturity in one or two years. In Central Oklahoma, Arthur N. Bragg found that males of the Plains Toad (*Bufo cognatus*) exhibited secondary sexual characters at the end of their first summer but did not breed until two years old, regardless of size. Females bred a year later than males—that is, at three years of age. The small Ricord's Frog (*Eleutherodactylus planirostris ricordi*) was found by Coleman J. Goin to reach sexual maturity in less than one year.

In his studies of the Alligator (*Alligator mississippiensis*) in Louisiana, E. A. McIlhenny determined that both sexes attain sexual maturity at an age of about six years and a total length of at least six feet (Figure 67). In turtles there is considerable variation in different species. In an excellent series of studies combining the examination of gonads with careful observation of marked wild individuals in Illinois, Tennessee, and Louisiana, Fred R. Cagle worked out the life history of the Red-eared Turtle (*Pseudemys scripta elegans*). He found that males of this species attain sexual maturity upon reaching a size of 3½ to 4 inches in plastron length; this size is reached in 2 to 5 years. Females are mature at a size of 6 to 7¾ inches in plastron length, this size being reached in 3 to 8 years. Thus Cagle concluded that in this turtle sexual maturity was not so much a matter of age as it was of size. In general this is true of most reptiles and amphibians. Paul L. Risley investigated the life cycle of the Common Musk Turtle (*Sternotherus odoratus*) in Michigan. He noted that males become adult at a shell length of 2⅛ to 2½ inches in their third or fourth years of life. Females mature at a much slower rate, being 9 to 11 years old and 3 to 3¼ inches in shell length when adult. On Long Island, John T. Nichols observed that the Eastern Box Turtle (*Terrapene c. carolina*) became mature between 12 and 16 years of age at a plastron length of about 4½ inches (Figure 68).

In Louisiana the Green Anolis (*Anolis c. carolinensis*) was found by Fred R. Cagle to reach sexual maturity in less than one year, and to be breeding the first spring following hatching. He found that both sexes mature at a total length of approximately 5¾ inches. Cagle based his report on the analysis of a large number of preserved specimens. In studying marked individuals in north Florida, I found that young hatched early in the summer (May or June)

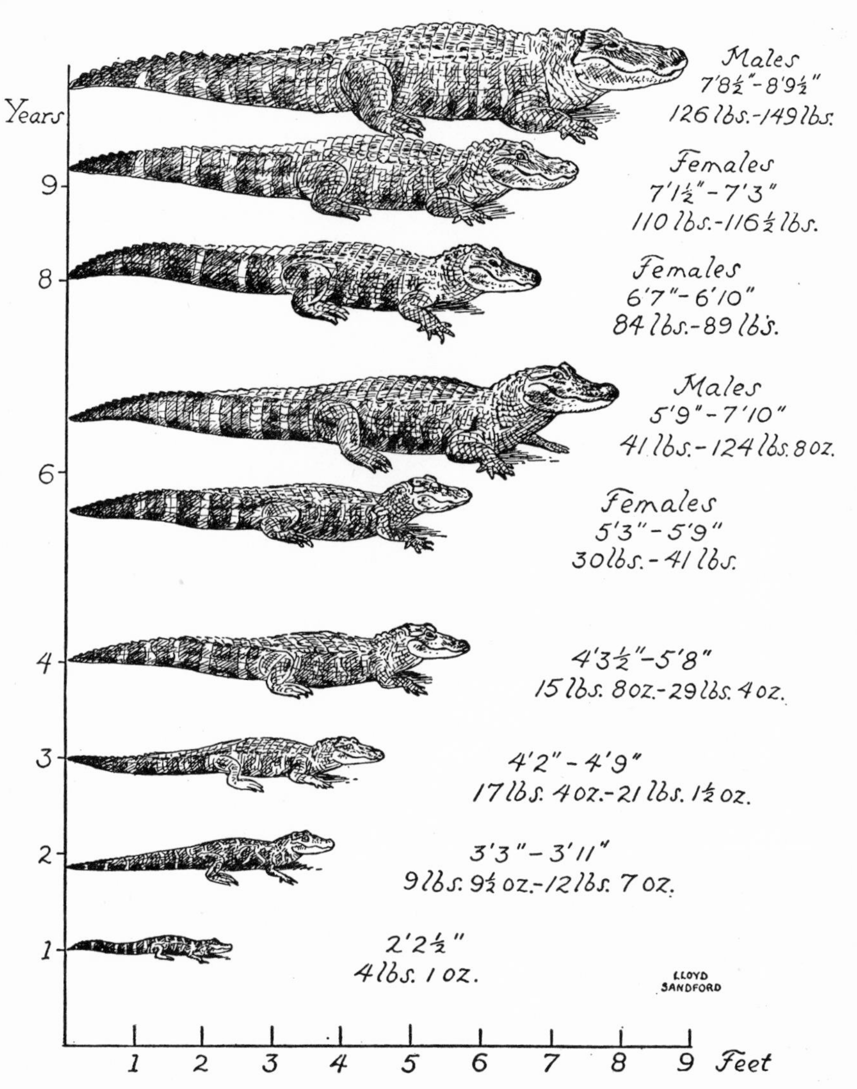

FIG. 67. Growth rate of the Alligator (*Alligator mississippiensis*) in Louisiana. (Data from E. A. McIlhenny)

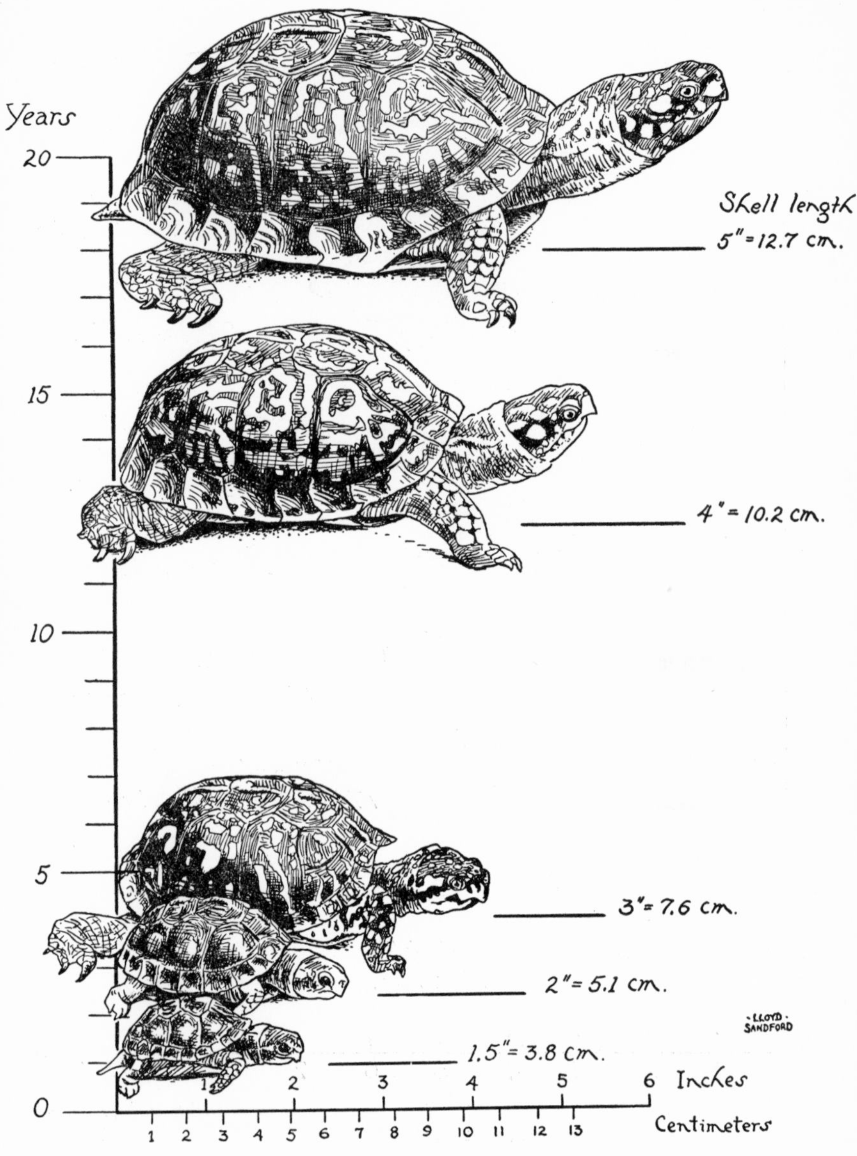

FIG. 68. Growth rate of the Eastern Box Turtle (*Terrapene carolina carolina*) in New York State. (Data from John T. Nichols)

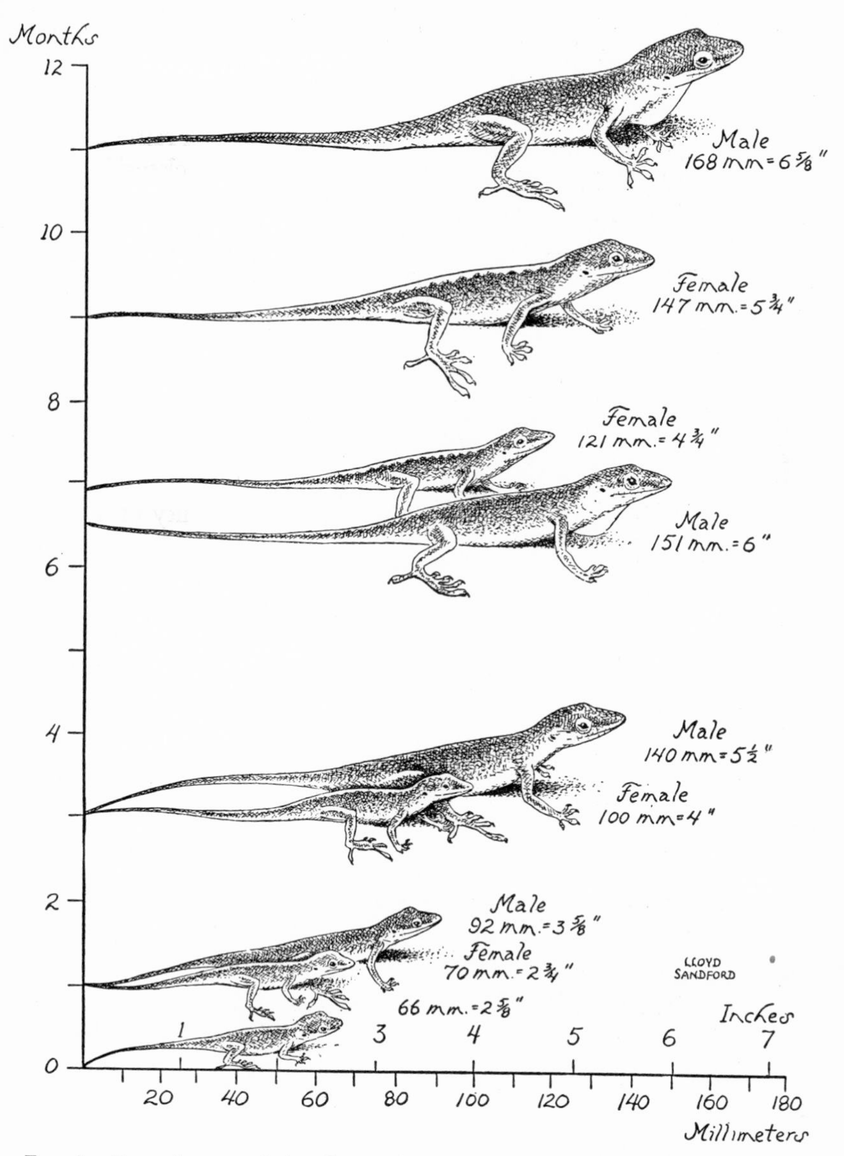

FIG. 69. Growth rate of the Green Anolis (*Anolis carolinensis carolinensis*) in Florida. (Data from James A. Oliver)

could reach sexual maturity and actually mate in the fall, when only four or five months old. This was not a common occurrence, but most males and females hatched before September had reached adult size by the end of the year. For example, one male hatched the end of July had doubled his length by the middle of September and measured 5½ inches in total length by the middle of October. Males usually grow faster than females (Figure 69).

In the Southern Fence Lizard (*Sceloporus u. undulatus*), on the other hand, females appear to grow at a more rapid rate than males. In north Florida the Fence Lizard, like the Green Anolis, normally reaches sexual maturity and mates the first spring of life. In six to eight months they have doubled their length. The small mountain-dwelling Sierra Pine Lizard (*Sceloporus graciosus gracilis*) was found by Robert C. Stebbins to require approximately three years to attain sexual maturity. In Minnesota the Northern Prairie Skink (*Eumeces s. septentrionalis*) was found by W. J. Breckenridge to attain adult status in two years at a length of 6¾ inches or more. Richard M. Johnson observed that the little Brown Skink (*Lygosoma laterale*), if hatched between May and August, reached sexual maturity the spring following hatching. At this time they measure a minimum of about 3½ inches. Charles M. Miller noted that the Silvery Footless Lizard (*Anniella pulchra nigra*) attains a minimum length of seven inches when it becomes adult. It requires at least three years to attain this size.

Frank N. Blanchard and his associates have studied the life histories of a number of snakes. They give the following information on age and size at sexual maturity for two of our smaller snakes:

Line Snake (*Tropidoclonion lineatum*), in the vicinity of Tulsa, Oklahoma, one year and nine months at minimum length of 8¾ inches for males and 9½ inches for females.

Red-bellied Snake (*Storeria o. occipitomaculata*), in northern Michigan, at two years of age and a minimum length of 8¾ inches for both sexes.

Henry S. Fitch studied large numbers of marked Northern Pacific Rattlesnakes (*Crotalus viridis oreganus*) in the Sierra Nevada foothills of Central California and found that they usually reach sexual maturity in their third year of life at an approximate length of 27½ inches (Figure 70). Eastern Cottonmouth Moccasins (*Ancis-*

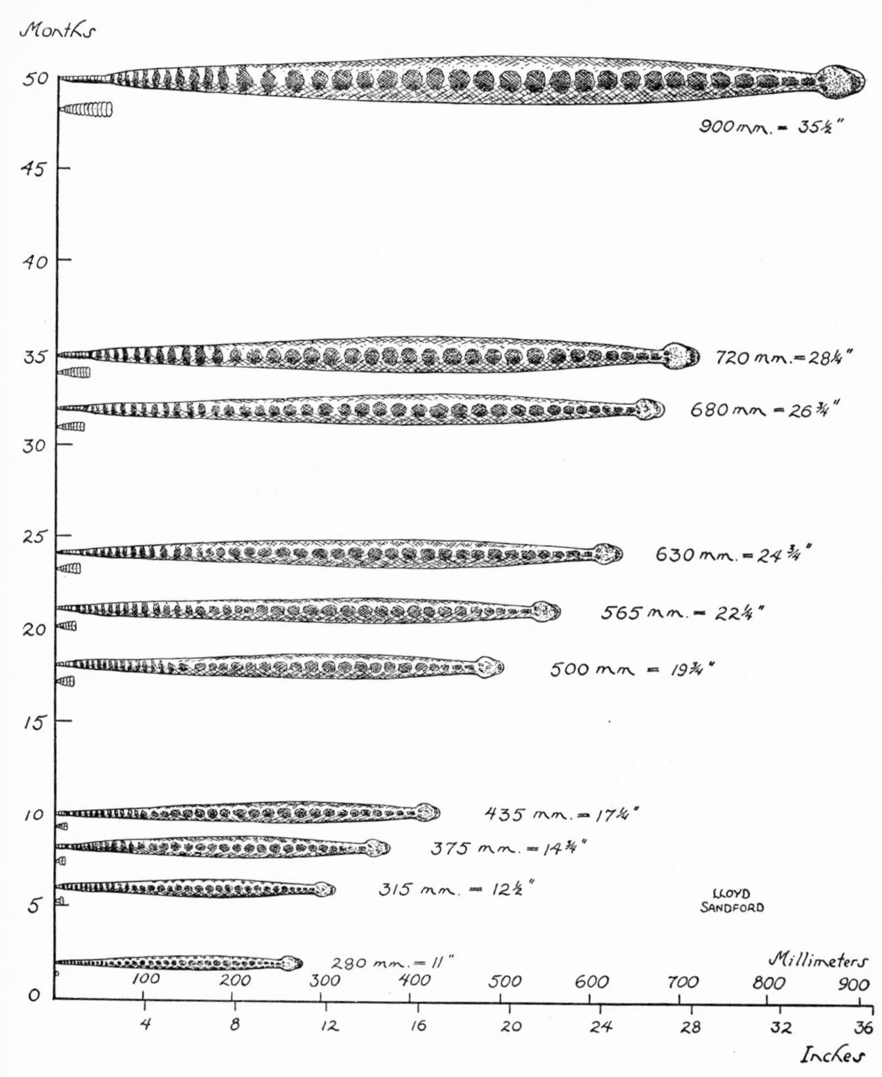

Fig. 70. Growth rate of the Northern Pacific Rattlesnake (*Crotalus viridis oreganus*) in central California. (Data from Henry S. Fitch)

trodon p. piscivorous) born in captivity at the New York Zoological Park attained sexual maturity at two years of age.

Senility

Senility, or physiological aging, can be measured partly by a loss in reproductive capacities. In this respect it is the opposite of sexual maturity. To judge from conditions in other animals, the cessation of reproduction may occur at quite different times in individuals of the same species. Precise information on this topic is difficult to obtain, but we do have a few scattered observations that give us some indication of the duration of individual reproductive activities.

The maximum age known for the California Newt (*Taricha torosus*) is 21 years. At this age the animal was reported still to be able to reproduce. A pair of Alligators (*Alligator mississippiensis*) kept in the Dresden Zoological Gardens were said to be able to breed when they were 40 years old or even older. Two female Eastern Box Turtles (*Terrapene c. carolina*) kept in captivity in outdoor enclosures in New York are known to have laid fertile eggs when 35 and 56 years old, respectively.

Fred R. Cagle estimated that the period of reproduction in the Red-eared Turtle (*Pseudemys scripta elegans*) in the wild lasts from 40 to 50 years. Since this turtle reaches sexual maturity at 2 to 10 years of age, this would mean that it would be capable of reproduction through the sixtieth year of life. He estimated that the average natural longevity may possibly be between 50 and 75 years, with many individuals reaching senility.

Several observers have noted that the number of eggs laid by a female shows a direct relation to her body size, increasing in number as the body increases in bulk—up to a certain point, where the number decreases. Thus in the Eastern Ring-neck Snake (*Diadophis punctatus edwardsi*), Frank N. Blanchard found an increase up to a total length of 15¾ inches, at which point the number of eggs decreased. This decrease is interpreted as indicating a reduction in reproductive capacity and hence senility. A great deal more information is needed on this interesting subject. How is it affected by the environment? Is it directly proportional to longevity or to the age at the attainment of sexual maturity? It has already been pointed out that extremely high temperatures may produce sterility. What is the effect of living in an unusually warm, but not extremely hot, environment for the species?

Shedding the Skin

A common physiological process that has frequently been thought to be associated with growth and age changes in amphibians and reptiles is the shedding of the outer layer of the skin. The exact relationship of this process to growth is not completely understood, although shedding is controlled by the same hormones or chemical agents that regulate growth. In general, actively growing young individuals shed more frequently and more regularly than adults that are growing slowly or have stopped growing. There are also pronounced variations in the method and frequency of shedding among different species. Amphibians shed their skins more frequently than reptiles. The greatest frequency of skin shedding appears to be that reported by John D. Kilby for the Green Tree Frog (*Hyla c. cinerea*) in Florida. Having made studies of this frog in the field and in the laboratory, Kilby reported the almost incredible condition of daily shedding in adults of this species. Toads (*Bufo*) are known to shed their skins every three to ten days. Both amphibians and reptiles may shed their skins in a single piece, as do toads, snakes, and such smooth-scaled lizards as the Alligator Lizards (*Gerrhonotus*), but other species peel piecemeal. Most water turtles—for example, the Painted Turtles (*Chrysemys*) and the Slider Turtles (*Pseudemys*)—shed the outer horny plates of the shell, whereas land species like the Box Turtle (*Terrapene*) do not shed the outer shell plates, but wear them away slowly. Many amphibians and some reptiles, such as the Anolis Lizards (*Anolis*) and probably all geckos, habitually eat the shed skin, tearing it off with the mouth and swallowing it. Most amphibians shed their skin at or soon after metamorphosis, while most reptiles shed their skin very soon after hatching or birth.

That shedding is associated with growth was suggested by experiments which demonstrated the process to be partially under the control of the chemical secretions of the hypophysis and the thyroid. Observations on wild and captive animals showed that young, actively growing individuals usually shed more frequently than older, slower-growing individuals. Robert C. Stebbins and

Harry B. Robinson found that young Sierra Pine Lizards (*Sceloporus graciosus gracilis*) shed two or three times and the adults only once during the summer activity period. The same condition has been reported for many other species, however, and starving Red-spotted Newts (*Diemictylus v. viridescens*), nongrowing Eastern Garter Snakes (*Thamnophis s. sirtalis*), and Red-eared Turtles (*Pseudemys scripta elegans*) have also been observed to shed regularly. In his study of the Red-eared Turtle, Fred R. Cagle found that of 19 individuals which shed their plates, only 11 showed measurable growth, and of 11 turtles that did not shed, 5 exhibited an increase in size. Thus the exact relationship of shedding to growth is still not clear, but there does seem to be some broad relationship between the two.

A number of factors have been reported to influence the frequency of shedding in captive reptiles. It is not clear at the present time which of these affect the actual skin-shedding mechanism directly and which affect the general health of the animal and thus in turn influence the shedding process. Among these influences are temperature, moisture, the presence of ectoparasites, change of environment, change of food, and confined quarters. To illustrate the effect of temperature, I kept four Plains Garter Snakes (*Thamnophis radix*) for a year at a constant temperature of 70° F. Each of these snakes shed two or three times during the year, whereas each of four other individuals of the same species kept at a constant temperature of 80° F. shed five to seven times in the same period. Obviously, the entire metabolism of the snakes at the colder temperature was reduced, and not just the frequency of shedding. However, some individuals at each temperature exhibited similar growth, although those at the higher temperature showed a greater average growth than did those at the lower temperature.

Robert M. Stabler kept careful records of the frequency with which twenty of his captive snakes shed their skins. These snakes were kept under varied temperature conditions, with a cool weather rest period of approximately six months per year. Observations for each individual extended from one to three years. Counting the entire year, the snakes shed once every two to six months, with an average of once every three months. If only the months of activity are considered, however, the snakes shed every one to three months, with an average interval of one and a half months between shedding.

C. B. Perkins, the skillful Curator of Reptiles at the Zoological Park in San Diego, California, points out that different species of snakes often exhibit differences in the frequency of shedding. He also found that the same individual snake may vary in frequency from year to year. He cites a Texas Indigo Snake (*Drymarchon corais erebennus*) that shed 8 times in 1946, 12 times in 1947, and 14 times in 1948 and in 1949. In this and another individual of the same species Perkins found that the longest intervals between sheddings occurred during the first year in captivity. There is no apparent reason for this occurrence, but he suggests that change of environment, different food, irritation by the public, or confined quarters may be contributing factors.

The shedding of the skin in the Rattlesnakes (*Crotalus* and *Sistrurus*) is of particular interest because of its relation to the development of the rattle. The formation of a new segment of the rattle is coordinated with the shedding of the outer layer of the skin to the extent that the skin is shed at the same time that a new segment of the rattle is developed. Henry S. Fitch has studied the development of the rattle in a wild population of the Northern Pacific Rattlesnake (*Crotalus viridis oreganus*) in Central California. Just as in the variation in rate of growth, there was much variation from individual to individual. These snakes have an activity period from March to October. Young born in the fall have a single rattle, the button, and most of those caught soon after emerging from their first hibernation still have but one rattle. Young snakes a little more than a year old and ready to enter their second period of hibernation usually have strings of four rattles. A year later, when they are slightly more than two years old, most have six or seven rattles. Later the frequency of shedding and the addition of segments slows down to an average annual rate of 1.5 for males and 1.1 for females.

It is perhaps unnecessary to point out that the number of segments in the rattle cannot be used to determine the snake's age, despite the fact that adult females among Fitch's rattlesnakes added segments at an approximate rate of one per year. Aside from the variation in number of rattles per year in young snakes, only a few adults have complete sets of rattles because of wear and tear. The maximum number of rattles observed on a snake in the wild by Laurence M. Klauber, our foremost student of these snakes, was sixteen. Sets with larger numbers of segments can be manufactured easily by carefully piecing together several separate sets, and such artificially long sets are sometimes displayed on rattlesnakes in carnivals. The obviously different growth in the various parts of the country also results in a variation in the number of rattles added per year. Klauber has reported on the unusual condition of captive reared Western Diamondback Rattlesnakes (*Crotalus atrox*) 27 months old with strings of rattles of 14 to 16 segments each.

Longevity

The old courthouse in Eastland, Texas, was being razed in 1928 when a former county clerk remembered that he had placed a "Horned Toad" in the cornerstone of the building back in 1897. The clerk was a man of experimental bent who wished to test the popular belief that toads can live for a hundred years or more without food or water. As operations proceeded toward the cornerstone, interest ran high and a large crowd assembled. Finally a worker broke the concrete layer, removed the metal cover of the stone, and stepped aside to allow a minister to check for the imprisoned animal. To the great joy of the assembled throng a living Horned Lizard was allegedly removed and shown around. It was appropriately named "Old Rip" and became famed from coast to coast. In memory of Old Rip, Eastland holds an annual "horned frog derby."

The "toad"—whether involving true toad, Spadefoot Toad, or "Horned Lizard"—story is a rather venerable tale that frequently assigns a far greater age to the buried animal than the mere 31 years accredited to Eastland's Old Rip. Scientists do not credit such tales about animals surviving for long periods without food or water. Certainly some species remain dormant underground for more than a year, and captive North American reptiles are known to have survived for more than two years without food and some of the large Old World constrictors are reputed to have lived for three years without eating, but to last much beyond that span appears to be an impossibility in the light of our present knowledge. Years ago a man by the name of Buckland decided to put the toad tale to test, so he placed a number of American Toads (*Bufo terrestris americanus*) in boxes of limestone and of sandstone and buried them three feet in the ground in his garden. At the end of thirteen months, when the sandstone boxes were opened, the toads were all dead. Those in the limestone boxes lived a little longer, but were dead before the end of two years.

The yarn about the buried toad is representative of the widespread tendency to assign great age to amphibians and reptiles. What are the facts on the maximum ages of these animals, and how is such information acquired? It is more meaningful to answer the last part of this question first. There are three general methods of studying the age and life span of animals: (1) observations on individuals in the wild; (2) records of length of life in captivity; and (3) the study of morphological indicators of age.

Herpetologists try wherever possible to learn how long amphibians and reptiles live by careful studies on wild individuals that can be definitely identified from time to time. This usually involves some type of identification mark placed on a large number of individuals and prolonged subsequent observations on a sufficient number of them to give an adequate indication of the average life span for the species. Such studies are beset with numerous difficulties and require a considerable amount of time, especially in the case of long-lived animals. John T. Nichols, of Mastic, Long Island, has been marking and studying the Eastern Box Turtle (*Terrapene c. carolina*) since 1915. To date he has marked over a thousand individuals and has recaptured a sufficiently large number of them to learn a great deal about this species. However, few of us today remain in one location long enough or have sufficient persistence to carry on such a project for nearly forty years. Even at that, the life span of this turtle is longer than that of a human being! Fortunately, many amphibians and reptiles are short-lived and can be more readily studied in the wild.

At the present time most of our knowledge of the maximum age reached by animals has been gained from individuals living under conditions of captivity. Information on most species in the wild today is too incomplete for adequate comparison with life spans in captivity. In those cases where we have sufficient information, captive animals appear to live longer on the average than do wild individuals of the same species. Several possible reasons readily come to mind: in captivity the animals are no longer exposed to danger from predators, starvation, thirst, or unfavorable environmental changes; and recognized ailments are given attention to reduce their severity. The primary difficulty with data from captive specimens is that the span of life indicated *may not* represent the maximum longevity in the wild. Unless individuals are marked in some fashion so that they can be identified with certainty, there is also the possibility of attributing erroneously long life spans to them.

A few species possess morphological structures that change in a regular fashion, thus indicating growth, the cessation of growth for an interval, or some periodic physiological change. Such indicators exist in very few species and are frequently of value only at certain ages. The most widely known of these are the rattles of the rattlesnakes and the growth rings in turtles. However, the popular belief that each segment on the rattlesnake's rattle indicates a year of life is erroneous.

The growth rings on the horny dermal scutes of many turtles' shells have also been thought to indicate annual growth cycles. These growth rings are grooves resulting from a differential rate of production of the horny material comprising the scutes. The time of groove formation is believed to correspond to a period of reduced or interrupted growth activity. In some species this may occur during hibernation, whereas in others that are more or less active throughout the year it generally occurs during a period of less favorable weather or less abundant food supply. Actually, any major alteration of growth rate, no matter what time of the year it occurs, influences the formation of grooves and therefore may make them unreliable indicators of age. For example, in the Desert Tortoise (*Gopherus agassizi*), which lives under quite changeable weather conditions, Loye Miller found the rings too variable to be of value as age indicators. In the Diamondback Turtle (*Malaclemys terrapin*), the Common Musk Turtle (*Sternotherus odoratus*), and the Eastern Box Turtle (*Terrapene c. carolina*) the growth rings can be used with fair accuracy for the first five to ten years, but they become unreliable with the wearing down of the shell as the turtle matures. In his studies on turtles of the genus *Pseudemys*, Fred R. Cagle utilized a method of measuring the rings on the plastral scutes to determine age and growth. He found that these rings were reliable up to about three years of age, or as long as the original birth plate remained on the scute.

It has been shown in fish and some other vertebrates that the microscopic examination of cross sections of certain bones reveals rings that appear to be correlated with size and age. This technique can be employed only on dead individuals, of course, but may prove of value in checking age at which death occurred. Skinks and

Anguid lizards possess bony platelets, or osteoderms, under the horny scales of the body. The markings on these platelets change regularly with an increase in size and may prove useful as indicators of age after the variation has been correlated with growth in a given region. Aside from these few morphological indicators of age, there are size groups, color changes, the appearance of the secondary sexual characters, and possibly other attributes that can be used in specific instances to assist in studying the ages of individuals, but for the most accurate information on age under natural conditions, the herpetologist must rely on studying marked individuals.

Table 14 presents some of the maximum known life spans for our American amphibians and reptiles. These figures present the known extreme old age for the species listed. They do not, however, show the average life expectancy or the average maximum age for the forms. The majority of the records are from animals in captivity. From an examination of this table certain generalizations are apparent. Turtles live longer than other reptiles or amphibians. In fact, the only vertebrates that live much beyond sixty years of age are man and some of the turtles, with the latter claiming the record of more than 150 years. Among the reptiles, the crocodilians are next to the turtles, followed by the snakes and lizards. In the amphibians, the maximum life span appears to be about the same for frogs and salamanders, but more salamanders than frogs seem to approach the known maximum.

In general, larger species appear to live longer than smaller ones. Among salamanders, the large aquatic species seem to have the edge on their smaller semiaquatic or terrestrial relatives. Whether this reflects the true condition is difficult to say with certainty. Although it is probably purely coincidental, it is interesting to note that an aquatic neotenic larva of the Tiger Salamander (*Ambystoma tigrinum*) has lived longer (25 years) than any transformed adult (16 years) of that species. Since the larger species usually attract more attention because of their size and since they are more frequently kept in zoological parks and aquariums, we have more information on their length of life. However, it seems clear that there is a general correlation between large size and long life within a given group.

Among the turtles the long-lived Box Turtle is definitely an exception to the general rule that larger forms reach greater ages. The longest-lived of all turtles are the very large land tortoises of

TABLE 14

Maximum Length of Life

(Including only records of more than ten years. All except those marked with an asterisk (*) are based on animals in captivity.)

Species		*Known Age in Years*
SALAMANDERS		
Hellbender (*Cryptobranchus alleganiensis*)		29
Amphiuma (*Amphiuma means*)		27
Great Siren (*Siren lacertina*)		25
Spotted Salamander (*Ambystoma maculatum*)		25
Tiger Salamander (*Ambystoma tigrinum*)	Neotenic larva	25
	Adult	16
California Newt (*Taricha torosus*)		21
FROGS		
American Toad (*Bufo terrestris americanus*)		31
Bullfrog (*Rana catesbeiana*)		16
Marine Toad (*Bufo marinus*)		15
Green Frog (*Rana clamitans*)		10
TURTLES		
Eastern Box Turtle (*Terrapene c. carolina*)		138*
Alligator Snapping Turtle (*Macrochelys temmincki*)		58
Wood Turtle (*Clemmys insculpta*)		58
Common Musk Turtle (*Sternotherus odoratus*)		53
Spotted Turtle (*Clemmys guttata*)		42
Common Mud Turtle (*Kinosternon subrubrum*)		38
Atlantic Loggerhead Turtle (*Caretta c. caretta*)		33

TABLE 14 (Continued)

Species	*Known Age in Years*
Soft-shelled Turtle (*Trionyx ferox*)	25
False Map Turtle (*Graptemys pseudogeographica*)	21
Desert Tortoise (*Gopherus agassizi*)	18
Western Painted Turtle (*Chrysemys picta belli*)	11
CROCODILIANS	
American Alligator (*Alligator mississippiensis*)	56
American Crocodile (*Crocodylus a. acutus*)	13
LIZARDS	
Gila Monster (*Heloderma suspectum*)	20
Desert Iguana (*Dipsosaurus dorsalis*)	10
SNAKES	
Water Moccasin (*Ancistrodon piscivorous*)	21
Corn Snake (*Elaphe g. guttata*)	21
Northern Pacific Rattlesnake (*Crotalus viridis oreganus*)	20* (17)
Northern Copperhead (*Ancistrodon contortrix mokeson*)	18
Western Diamondback Rattlesnake (*Crotalus atrox*)	18
Louisiana Milk Snake (*Lampropeltis doliata amaura*)	18
San Diego Gopher Snake (*Pituophis catenifer annectens*)	15
Massasauga Rattlesnake (*Sistrurus catenatus*)	14
Pilot Black Snake (*Elaphe o. obsoleta*)	13
California Boa (*Lichanura roseofusca*)	12
Western Coachwhip (*Masticophis flagellum testaceus*)	10

the Galápagos Islands and islands in the Indian Ocean. But the Box Turtle is small compared with these giants or even with some of our fresh-water species. There are, of course, other exceptions.

Passing from the long life span of the turtles to the opposite extreme, we find that there are a few species whose members have an average life span of less than one year. In northern Florida, during a three-year period, I had occasion to study 200 marked Green Anolis (*Anolis c. carolinensis*) living on a two acre area. It was found that 98 per cent of the marked animals were not living a year after the date they were first marked and none survived more than 16 months. On the other hand, this lizard has been known to live for as long as four years in captivity. Of 100 Southern Fence Lizards (*Sceloporus u. undulatus*) that were marked and studied at the same time, 94 per cent lived less than one year. Two lived almost two years. Thus in both of these lizards there is an almost complete turnover of the population in approximately a year's time. Henry S. Fitch found a somewhat similar condition in his field study of the Western Fence Lizard (*Sceloporus occidentalis*) in the vicinity of Berkeley, California. In this lowland locality less than one-fifth of his marked animals were present a year later. It seems likely that when other small species living in warm areas are studied in detail, some, like the small geckos, will be found to have an even shorter life span.

Our present information on longevity under natural conditions is too incomplete to reveal inherent differences between related species. However, interesting variations are indicated for related forms living under different environmental conditions. These appear to be associated primarily with differences in temperature and length of annual activity periods. Ectothermal animals living in warm regions where they are active throughout the year appear to live fewer calendar years than related forms living in cooler areas where they are inactive for part of the year. This condition can be readily understood if we assume the simple hypothetical example that a given species lives for 365 activity-days. In the southern end of its range the temperature is high enough for the species to be active all year and thus it lives a single calendar year. However, in the northern end of its range, the temperature is so low in wintertime that the animal must hibernate for six months of the year. In the north the species would have to live two calendar years to live out its allotted 365 activity-days. This example greatly oversimplifies the phenomenon that is involved here, and the differences are not simple arithmetic ratios, but in general this is what is involved in the phenomenon referred to as Rubner's Hypothesis.

It can be illustrated by the Fence Lizard. In Florida 94 per cent of these lizards were found to live less than one year, and none lived for two years. The climate of northern Florida permits this lizard to be active every month of the year with only brief irregular periods of inactivity resulting from low temperatures. In Maryland, William H. McClellan found that the northern race of the Fence Lizard is active only seven months of the year and lives for more than four years, probably reaching a maximum age of eight years.

Charles M. Bogert has shown that all species of the genus (*Sceloporus*), to which the Fence Lizards belong, keep their body temperatures at approximately the same level regardless of where they live—in the south or north, at sea level or up in the mountains. This basic similarity in body temperature is an important aspect of the temperature-activity relationships of Rubner's Hypothesis. Robert C. Stebbins and Harry B. Robinson studied the Sierra Pine Lizard (*Sceloporus graciosus gracilis*) in California at an elevation of 6,000 feet where it had an activity period of five to six months. They compared the results of their study with the findings of Henry S. Fitch on the Western Fence Lizard (*Sceloporus occidentalis*) in the lowlands of California, where this lizard had an activity period of eight months or more. These lizards belong to different species that are not closely related and exhibit many more distinctions than are present between the two races of the Fence Lizard. Several of the differences pointed out by Stebbins and Robinson are of interest here. One-third of the Mountain Scaly Lizards were alive after three years, and one out of every three of these lizards had a life expectancy of at least six years. The maximum length of life was over eight years. In contrast to this, less than one-fifth of the lowland Western Fence Lizards were present after one year, and a single lizard was thought to have approached six years of age.

A suggestive, but by no means definite, circumstance that may be related to this phenomenon is the maximum age of the Eastern Box Turtle. This turtle ranges from New England south through Georgia and west to Wisconsin, Illinois, and Mississippi. Other races of the species go farther south and west. The maximum age of this turtle has been discovered by the recapture of individuals bearing dates carved on their lower shells, or plastrons. Several such individuals have been found with dates more than one hundred years old at the time the turtles were found. Care must be used in accepting all such dated turtles as authentic, because of the occasional jests of pranksters who have carved such impossible dates as 1492 on the shell. Nevertheless, a number of these turtles have been reported with apparently unquestionable dates showing that they were 50 to 80 years old. A few of those with dates more than one hundred years old also seem authentic beyond any reasonable doubt. It is interesting that all those with reliable dates of more than one hundred years of age have been found in the northeastern part of the turtles' range. This may be mere chance; or perhaps New England Yankees were more given to carving turtles than their southern cousins.

The whole fascinating question of physiological differences under different environmental conditions requires a great deal more factual information than we have at the present time.

Maximum Size

Size, like longevity, is a subject with considerable popular interest and about which there is a good deal of erroneous information. Size, however, is a relatively simple matter to measure, and therefore one about which we have more precise information. There are a number of practical considerations concerning reliability of reports on large individuals: All measurements must be carefully made and recorded at the same time. Only straight-line measurements should be used in reports on maximum size. Only measurements on whole animals should be used, and no measurements of skins alone should be accepted. For example, it is impossible to remove the skin of a snake without stretching it, and in the case of the large snakes the increase may amount to 20 or 25 per cent of the total length.

Unfortunately the largest individuals are of such bulk that they are not readily measured and are not easily moved. Because of the trouble of preparing and storing them, extremely large individuals are not always kept for museum collections and hence do not get recorded. If the unusually large individual escapes the hunter or collector, he is strongly tempted to report an estimate of its size. In later years the qualification "estimate" is forgotten and the record assumes unwarranted authenticity. These are a few of the practical difficulties that face the herpetologist when he endeavors to evaluate the maximum size of amphibians and reptiles.

A number of biological considerations also enter into the picture. The size limits of any species are among the inherited characteristics that make up the primary attributes of that species. Thus we find pronounced differences in size from one species to another. Operating within the inherent size limits for the species are the environmental conditions which have a tremendous influence on growth and ultimate size. Under one set of environmental conditions, individuals of a given species may attain a size of, say, 24 inches total length, whereas under different environmental conditions individuals with the same inherited capabilities may not exceed 12 inches in total length. Extremely large individuals are relatively rare, and thus a large number of specimens must be measured accurately to indicate the upper size limits of the population being studied. Laurence M. Klauber, in his extensive studies on the Rattlesnakes, calculated that extremely large individuals represent between 2 and 4 per cent of the population. Even then such individuals might not indicate the greatest possible size for the species. It is well known that where a species occurs over a wide geographic area there are usually differences in the average and maximum size in different localities. Sometimes there are marked differences in size within even a small geographic radius. Along the east coast of Florida the Green Anolis (*Anolis c. carolensis*) attains a total length of 6¾ inches, whereas 60 miles inland the population reaches a maximum length of only 6 inches. Sometimes the differences in size occur at random within the range of the species, but more often the variation changes progressively in a clear geographic gradient or cline. For example, in the eastern United States the Two-lined Salamander (*Eurycea b. bislineata*) shows an increase in total length from south to north. A number of other amphibians and reptiles exhibit this same phenomenon. A few change in the opposite direction, becoming smaller in size toward the north. Sometimes the gradients run from east to west or west to east. Because of this geographic variation in size, it is impossible to know the approximate size for the species until it has been thoroughly studied in all parts of its range.

Table 15 has been prepared within these limitations. It lists the known maximum lengths for representatives of each family of amphibians and reptiles. Where two or more species of a family

TABLE 15

MAXIMUM SIZE

Family and Species	*Known Maximum Length (in inches)*
AMPHIBIANS	
SALAMANDERS	
	Total length
Family Cryptobranchidae	
Hellbender (*Cryptobranchus alleganiensis*)	27
Family Proteidae	
Dwarf Mudpuppy (*Necturus punctatus*)	6 3/16
Mudpuppy (*Necturus m. maculosus*)	17
Family Sirenidae	
Broad-striped Mud Siren (*Pseudobranchus s. striatus*)	5 7/8
Great Siren (*Siren lacertina*)	36
Family Ambystomidae	
Mole Salamander (*Ambystoma talpoideum*)	3 7/8
Eastern Tiger Salamander (*Ambystoma t. tigrinum*)	13
Family Salamandridae	
Striped Newt (*Diemictylus perstriatus*)	3 1/16
Crater Lake Newt (*Taricha torosus*)	8 7/8
Family Amphiumidae	
Three-toed Amphiuma (*Amphiuma means tridactylum*)	39 1/2
Family Plethodontidae	
Pygmy Salamander (*Desmognathus wrighti*)	1 7/8
Mountain Purple Salamander (*Gyrinophilus d. danielsi*)	8
FROGS	
	Snout-vent length
Family Ascaphidae	
Tailed Frog (*Ascaphus truei*)	2
Family Pelobatidae	
Central Plains Spadefoot (*Scaphiopus bombifrons*)	2 1/4
Great Plains Spadefoot (*Scaphiopus couchi*)	3 1/2

TABLE 15 (Continued)

Family and Species	*Known Maximum Length (in inches)*
	Snout-vent length
Family Leptodactylidae	
Camp's Frog (*Syrrhopus campi*)	1
Robber Frog (*Eleutherodactylus latrans*)	3½
Family Bufonidae	
Oak Toad (*Bufo quercicus*)	1¼
Colorado River Toad (*Bufo alvarius*)	7
Family Hylidae	
Least Tree Frog (*Hyla ocularis*)	⅝
Cuban Tree Frog (*Hyla septentrionalis*)	5⅛
Family Brevicipitidae	
Great Plains Narrow-mouthed Toad (*Microhyla carolinensis olivacea*)	1⅛
Mexican Narrow-mouthed Toad (*Hypopachus cuneus*)	1⅝
Family Ranidae	
Eastern Wood Frog (*Rana s. sylvatica*)	2¼
Bullfrog (*Rana catesbeiana*)	7¼
REPTILES	
TURTLES	
	Shell length
Family Chelydridae	
Common Snapping Turtle (*Chelydra s. serpentina*)	17½
Alligator Snapping Turtle (*Macrochelys temmincki*)	26
Family Kinosternidae	
Striped Mud Turtle (*Kinosternon b. bauri*)	3¾
Mississippi Musk Turtle (*Sternotherus c. carinatus*)	5⅞
Family Emydidae	
Muhlenberg's Turtle (*Clemmys muhlenbergi*)	4
Suwannee Turtle (*Pseudemys floridana suwannensis*)	16⅜

TABLE 15 (Continued)

Family and Species	*Known Maximum Length (in inches)*
	Shell length
Family Testudinidae	
Berlandier's Tortoise (*Gopherus berlandieri*)	8½
Desert Tortoise (*Gopherus agassizi*)	14⅛
Family Cheloniidae	
Atlantic Ridley Turtle (*Lepidochelys olivacea kempi*)	27⅝
Atlantic Green Turtle (*Chelonia m. mydas*)	48
Family Trionychidae	
Southern Soft-shelled Turtle (*Trionyx f. ferox*)	17¾
Family Dermochelidae	
Atlantic Leatherback Turtle (*Dermochelys c. coriacea*)	96
CROCODILIANS	
	Total length
Family Crocodilidae	
American Alligator (*Alligator mississippiensis*)	228
LIZARDS	
	Total length
Family Gekkonidae	
Reef Gecko (*Sphaerodactylus notatus*)	2⅛
Banded Gecko (*Coleonyx variegatus*)	5⅝
Family Iguanidae	
Texas Tree Uta (*Uta o. ornata*)	4⅝
Chuckawalla (*Sauromalus obesus*)	16½
Family Anguidae	
Northern Alligator Lizard (*Gerrhonotus coeruleus principis*)	9⅝
Eastern Glass Lizard (*Ophisaurus ventralis*)	37½
Family Helodermatidae	
Gila Monster (*Heloderma suspectum*)	21¾
Family Anniellidae	
Black Footless Lizard (*Anniella pulchra nigra*)	9

TABLE 15 (Continued)

Family and Species	*Known Maximum Length (in inches)*
	Total length
Family Xantusidae	
Yucca Night Lizard (*Xantusia vigilis*)	4⅜
Island Night Lizard (*Xantusia riversiana*)	7⅞
Family Teidae	
Devil's River Race Runner (*Cnemidophorus perplexus*)	8⅜
New Mexican Race Runner (*Cnemidophorus sacki stictogrammus*)	15⅝
Family Scincidae	
Little Brown Skink (*Lygosoma laterale*)	4¾
Greater Five-lined Skink (*Eumeces laticeps*)	12⅜
Family Amphisbaenidae	
Florida Worm Lizard (*Rhineura floridana*)	11⅛
SNAKES	
	Total length
Family Leptotyphlopidae	
Texas Blind Snake (*Leptotyphlops d. dulcis*)	10⅝
Desert Blind Snake (*Leptotyphlops humilis cahuilae*)	15½
Family Boidae	
Rubber Boa (*Charina b. bottae*)	28
California Boa (*Lichanura r. roseofusca*)	36
Family Colubridae	
Slender Flat-headed Snake (*Tantilla g. gracilis*)	9
Indigo Snake (*Drymarchon corais couperi*)	103
Family Elapidae	
Arizona Coral Snake (*Micruroides euryxanthus*)	19½
Coral Snake (*Micrurus f. fulvius*)	47½
Family Crotalidae	
Arizona Twinspotted Rattlesnake (*Crotalus p. pricei*)	22⅝
Eastern Diamondback Rattlesnake (*Crotalus adamanteus*)	96+

occur in the United States and Canada, the species with the smallest maximum size and the species with the largest maximum size are listed. This has been done to show something of the size range within each family, the maximum size of both the smallest and largest forms providing comparable limits. It should be emphasized that the dimensions listed are not necessarily the maximum possible for any species, but rather the maxima that are known today. In the case of several species of approximately the same size, I have selected the one for which the greatest number of measurements are available. The figures listed thus give the known extreme upper limit of size for each species. The average adult size is usually nowhere near this figure, but frequently approximates one-half to two-thirds of the maximum.

The table shows that the Three-toed Amphiuma (*Amphiuma means tridactylum*) is the longest of our salamanders, reaching a maximum length of 39½ inches. The Hellbender (*Cryptobranchus alleghenіensis*) is not so long, attaining a length of 27 inches, but is probably our heaviest salamander. The smallest salamander is appropriately called the Pygmy Salamander (*Desmognathus wrighti*) and gets to be only 1⅞ inches in total length.

The Bullfrog (*Rana catesbeiana*) is our largest frog with a known length of 7¼ inches. The Colorado River Toad (*Bufo alvarius*) approaches this size closely, with a length of 7 inches. I do not have figures to indicate which of these is heavier, but a very large Bullfrog may weigh as much as 20 ounces. The Marine Toad (*Bufo marinus*) is often listed as our largest frog and as a species it does reach a large size, with a maximum length of 9 inches, but this maximum size is attained only in South America by a race that is not the same as that occurring in the southern United States, where the maximum size is less than that of the Colorado River Toad. Our smallest frog, the Least Tree Frog (*Hyla ocularis*) is a real Lilliputian that never exceeds ⅝ of an inch in length. It is one of the tiniest vertebrate animals known, possibly being exceeded in minuteness by a slightly smaller frog from Cuba.

The Alligator (*Alligator mississippiensis*) is our longest reptile, and possibly the heaviest. The longest measured specimen had a length of 19 feet 2 inches. The weight of this individual was not recorded, but must have been well over 1,000 pounds. Alligators 10 and 11 feet in length usually weigh more than 500 pounds, and as they grow in size the increase in weight is several times more rapid than the increase in length. The American Crocodile (*Crocodylus a. acutus*) has been reported to attain a maximum length of 23 feet, but no individuals anywhere near that length have been found in the United States.

Archie Carr, in his recently published *Handbook of Turtles*, has summarized the information on the maximum size of our largest turtle, the Leatherback Turtle (*Dermochelys coriacea*). Different subspecies occur in the Atlantic and Pacific Oceans. The Pacific race appears to attain a somewhat larger size and weight. The longest straight-line carapace length is 8 feet for the Atlantic race, but the greatest weight, 1,902½ pounds, is recorded for the Pacific form. Among the fresh-water and land turtles of this country, the Alligator Snapping Turtle (*Macrochelys temminicki*) is unquestionably the largest, with a shell length of 26 inches. An extreme weight of 403 pounds has been reported for this creature. However, this record requires confirmation because it is so much more than the usual maximum of 200 pounds. This is the largest fresh-water turtle in the world. Our smallest turtle is the Striped Mud Turtle (*Kinosternon b. bauri*), with a shell length of 3¾ inches.

The longest lizard in North America is the Eastern Glass Lizard (*Ophisaurus ventralis*), with a length of 37½ inches. The heaviest is the Gila Monster (*Heloderma suspectum*), which is known to reach a maximum length of 21¾ inches and a weight of 4 pounds 12 ounces. The smallest lizard is the Reef Gecko (*Sphaerodactylus notatus*), which has a maximum length of 2⅛ inches.

It is in reports on snakes that we find the greatest tendency to exaggerate length. This is not entirely owing to an American fondness for hyperbole, but is partly a result of the elongate serpentine body, which gives an optical illusion of great length, particularly when the snake is in motion. Many honorable and able persons who can estimate the size and weight of hogs, cattle, or human beings fail miserably in their efforts to judge the length of a snake. Many erroneous maximum lengths have been based on the measurement of skins. As one illustration of this, there is a recorded length of 8 feet 9 inches for the Eastern Diamondback Rattlesnake (*Crotalus adamanteus*). This size is listed in a number of books on reptiles or snakes. Charles M. Bogert investigated the original source of this report and found that it was obtained by measuring the skin only.

There are at least five species of snakes in the United States that are reported to have attained a total length of more than eight feet.

These are the Eastern Diamondback, 8 feet 9 inches; the Coachwhip (*Masticophis f. flagellum*), 8 feet 2 inches; the Pilot Blacksnake (*Elaphe o. obsoleta*), 8 feet 5 inches; the Indigo Snake (*Drymarchon corais couperi*), 8 feet 7½ inches; and the Common Bull Snake (*Pituophis catenifer sayi*), 9 feet. The Eastern Diamondback Rattlesnake does attain a great length, but according to Laurence M. Klauber, the foremost student of rattlesnakes, the maximum authentic record is a length just over eight feet. The measurements given for the Whipsnake, the Blacksnake, and the Indigo Snake were all based on actual measurements of unusually large individuals. The reported length of nine feet for the Bull Snake is a suspiciously general statement that requires confirmation. If this doubtful record is excluded from the table, the Indigo Snake, with a known maximum length of 8 feet 7½ inches, becomes the longest snake in the United States. The Eastern Diamondback Rattlesnake, with a maximum weight of more than 20 pounds, is the heaviest. It is also one of the heaviest, but not the longest, venomous snakes in the world. These maxima, like all the maxima in the table, are the longest authentic records known at the present. It is certain that some of them will be exceeded as additional data are brought to light and as more specimens are measured.

CHAPTER 13

Amphibians and Reptiles as Pets

MANY AMPHIBIANS AND REPTILES make excellent pets, interesting to study and relatively easy to keep. No part of the United States is without suitable native species, so that pets can be acquired readily. Some harassed parents may frequently feel that pets of this type are too easily obtained. The widespread popularity of turtles, baby Alligators, and the "American Chameleons" in the commercial pet trade adequately attests to the appeal of these animals.

Amphibians and reptiles can be considered as curio-ornamental pets rather than companion-cuddly or economical pets. They are kept as objects of interest, primarily to be observed and exhibited, with varying amounts of affection bestowed on them. Because of their many interesting habits and ease of maintenance, they are often kept as classroom pets in schools. A great deal can be learned through studying them.

Which species are most suitable to keep as pets? A number of factors must be considered: availability, size, housing requirements, environmental needs, feeding requirements, and hardiness and temperament of the animals. Many species will be eliminated from the list of potential pets simply because they do not meet these requirements satisfactorily. For example, the Florida Worm Lizard (*Rhineura floridana*) does not make a suitable pet because it is difficult to obtain, remains hidden underground most of the time, and has specialized food requirements, feeding primarily on termites.

Exotic species, especially from the tropics, have a great attraction for many people and sometimes are sought to the exclusion of our native amphibians and reptiles. All too frequently these ventures end in failure, chiefly because of the difficulty involved in providing tropical species with the necessary conditions and care required for survival in captivity. A large number of our native forms are more easily kept and make more interesting pets than most exotic species. Beginners should confine their interests to a few local species until they are able to keep these successfully.

The decision on which species are most desirable as pets will depend in part on the tastes of the individual. In general, diurnal species of medium size, gentle disposition, and simple food requirements are likely to be most satisfactory and easiest to keep. The place in which the pets are to be kept will also affect the selection of the species. If kept in a small city apartment, the possible choices will be more limited than if the animals are to be kept in a large outdoor enclosure.

Once the decision has been made, all preparations for the pet's proper housing and care should be attended to *before* obtaining the animal. Of course, it will not always be possible to do this beforehand, especially when the animal is obtained in the wild. In such cases, suitable temporary quarters should be provided and a permanent cage should be made as quickly as possible. Most reptiles and many amphibians are fairly hardy animals that can endure temporary treatment for a longer period than most mammals and birds, but this is no excuse for neglecting them. The keeping of any pet involves a large measure of responsibility for the owner.

Adequate preparations for the arrival of a pet and for its care once it is acquired should include looking up information on the animal's habits, its habitat, its food, its life history, and any unusual characteristics that might be of interest. This information is necessary to meet all of the animal's needs and will make for a more interesting pet. Most books on pets do not contain adequate information about amphibians and reptiles. The handbooks listed in the "Recommended References" at the end of this book are the best source of information about a given species.

Pet stores, aquarium shops, and some amusement halls in our larger cities often sell five or six native species. The most frequently seen are the American Alligator (*Alligator mississippiensis*); the Red-eared Turtle (*Pseudemys scripta elegans*), also called "Cumberland or Troost's Turtle"; the False Map Turtle (*Graptemys pseudogeographica*), also called "Mississippi Map Turtle"; the Green Anolis (*Anolis c. carolinensis*), also called "American Chameleon"; and one or two species of Eastern Newts. Additional forms that might be desired can be obtained by local collecting, by purchase from one of the large reptile dealers or biological supply houses, or by exchange with other interested persons in different parts of the country. All these methods have been successfully employed by amateur herpetologists.

A few of the more reliable dealers from whom amphibians and reptiles can be purchased are—

Quivira Specialties Company
4204 W. 21st Street
Topeka, Kansas

Ross Allen's Reptile Institute
1112 N. Miami Ave.
Miami 32, Florida

General Biological Supply House
8200 S. Hoyne Ave.
Chicago 20, Illinois

Tarpon Zoo
P. O. Box 847
Tarpon Springs, Florida

Otto Martin Locke
P. O. Drawer 731
New Braunfels, Texas

Names of people interested in exchanging amphibians and reptiles can frequently be obtained by writing to some of the organizations whose members are interested primarily in these animals. One of them is The Herpetologists League, Route 1, Box 80, Escondido, California.

"The Naturalists' Directory," published by the Cassino Press of Salem, Massachusetts, contains names of many who are interested in exchanging specimens of this type. From time to time small groups of interested amateurs are organized to further the exchange of animals and observations on their habits in captivity. Printed or mimeographed notices of their activities are sometimes circulated to stimulate interest. However, most of these groups have had a rather short existence.

A word of advice should be included for those who become tired or dissatisfied with their pet. Do not turn it loose in the nearest vacant lot, park, or countryside. If the pet is one that you caught yourself, take it back to the spot where you found it *but* be sure that the weather is suitable for its release. If it is a pet that you bought, acquired by exchange, or caught at a distant location, take the animal to the nearest zoo or museum. Animals kept in captivity for long periods or obtained from another region should not be released in a new and strange habitat. Such released animals usually die. The few that manage to survive may seriously upset the local animal populations. The animals turned over to the zoo or museum can be properly housed or sent on to other institutions that can take care of them adequately. At the New York Zoological Park we annually receive hundreds of such former pets. For example, during the past ten years we have been given 555 baby American Alligators alone. Most of these are sent on to other zoos, chiefly in Europe.

Housing

One of the advantages of amphibians and reptiles as pets is that they require relatively small space for housing. They do not appear to need the large areas for exercise that many mammals and birds require. This advantage is particularly important since in most parts of the country amphibians and reptiles should be kept indoors, at least during cold weather. A glass aquarium tank makes a versatile enclosure that is readily adapted for the keeping of many different amphibians and reptiles (Figures 71 and 72). It can be arranged to make suitable quarters for either aquatic or terrestrial species, depending on the amount of standing water that is placed in it. Filled with two to three inches of water and a few exposed rocks, it makes an excellent container for aquatic turtles, Alligators, many frogs, and aquatic salamanders. Set up with earth, living land plants, and a small, submerged dish of water, the tank becomes an attractive terrarium for the keeping of small land turtles, lizards, snakes, terrestrial salamanders, and the more terrestrial frogs, such as the toads. A half-and-half arrangement should be made for semiaquatic species.

When turtles and small Alligators are kept in tanks that are two or three inches higher than the animal's length, no cover is required. For frogs and salamanders, a piece of glass that completely covers the top of the tank makes a suitable cover; it can be propped up slightly at one end by a small piece of rubber tubing. When lizards and snakes are kept in an aquarium tank, the top should be made with a tight-fitting metal or wooden frame that fits down over the side of the tank and is covered with mosquito netting or ordinary window screen. Larger lizards (five inches or more in length) and most snakes should be kept in well-ventilated cages that have at least two sides or a side and top covered with screen instead of wood or glass. All joints and all parts of the access opening must be tightly fitted to prevent escape. These animals possess amazing abilities for escaping through tiny openings.

All animals require shelter areas where they can find seclusion.

FIG. 71. Glass tank set up as terrarium (above) for land-dwelling amphibians and as aquarium (below) for aquatic species.

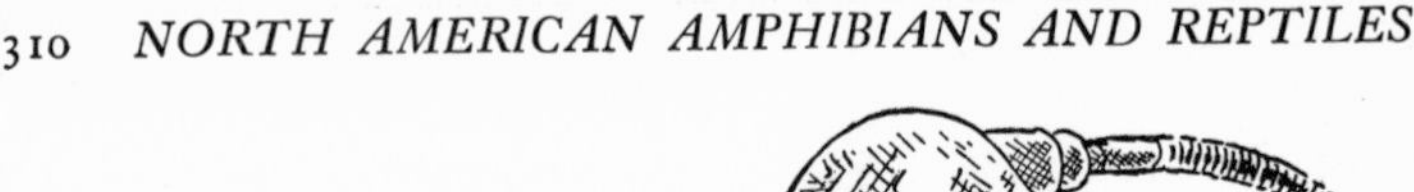

FIG. 72. Upper, glass tank set up to house fresh-water turtles. Lower, snake cage with glass front, wire top and sides and door with snaplock.

In the case of small amphibians or reptiles, this can be provided by a piece of bark, a thick plant, a hollow log, or stones arranged to form a cavelike retreat. Snakes readily take to small cardboard boxes turned upside down, and with a small opening cut in the front to serve as an entrance. Some species will feed only when provided with an adequate retreat of this sort.

The most important factors in the successful care of amphibians and reptiles are temperature, light, and moisture. These elements are important in the lives of the animals under natural conditions; animals meet their needs for them through behavioral responses. It is usually necessary to provide captive animals with some variation in these factors, and some freedom in the selection of different conditions of temperature and moisture. This cannot be emphasized too strongly, because of the apparent need for different conditions at different times. Again, species differ in the amount of variation that is required or that can be tolerated. There are some exceptions to the following generalizations, but usually aquatic species require less variable conditions than terrestrial forms; reptiles require and can tolerate greater variations in moisture conditions than amphibians; reptiles require and can tolerate higher temperatures and stronger light than amphibians; and, conversely, amphibians require and can tolerate lower temperatures and less light than reptiles. In Chapter 9 specific figures are given to indicate the limits of toleration for several species.

Temperature and light requirements can be provided in several ways. The least expensive source is the use of sunlight. In many parts of the country, however, this is not a satisfactory source of heat, and it *always* must be used with care. Where sunlight is used as a source of heat, the animals must be provided with an adequate, readily accessible shelter area in the shade. Amphibians should never be placed in strong, direct rays of the sun. However, the weak sunlight of the early morning, late fall, winter, or early spring in the northern part of the country is not harmful. Except where used with considerable care or in large outdoor enclosures, sunlight is not a satisfactory source of heat. Many pet reptiles and amphibians have been killed by overexposure to sunlight.

One of the easiest and safest methods of providing heat and light is through the use of regular household incandescent lights. Here the amount of heat and light can be varied easily by using light bulbs of different sizes and strength. If the light is placed over the top at one side or end of the cage, the animal can move directly under the light or away from it. The shelter area should usually be located on the opposite side from the light, providing a complete retreat from light and heat. By a little experimentation, the proper size of bulb can be determined. In general, amphibians require little or no light, rarely more than a 40-watt bulb. If a stronger light is used only to provide heat for amphibians, it should be placed at the side or back of the enclosure and masked. For reptiles, a 60-watt bulb or larger will be needed, depending in part on the size of the cage and the kind of reptiles being kept. Some desert lizards may require 100- or 120-watt bulbs to provide them with the necessary heat. With these species, infrared lamps may also be used to advantage.

Several types of electric heating units are now available and can be used to advantage with a number of species. These include aquarium heaters for aquatic species and regular dry heaters for terrestrial species. In using dry heaters, keep the heating unit enclosed so that the animals cannot come in direct contact with it and locate the unit so that it does not heat the entire cage. Too much heat will burn or desiccate the animals.

Some species, particularly desert forms, appear to need ultraviolet light in small amounts. Unfortunately we do not know what this requirement involves or how it can best be provided. The incandescent sunlamp bulbs on the market are convenient to use for this purpose. An exposure of five to twenty minutes per day at a distance of about two feet seems to give a necessary amount of this light. Some lizards and turtles appear to eat better when given small daily exposures to this light.

Moisture conditions can be varied in a crude fashion by varying the amount of water in the cage, by the use of plants, by the ventilation of the cage, and by the amount of heat supplied. Aquatic species will obviously be kept in an aquarium with only small basking and resting areas out of the water. Semiaquatic reptiles and amphibians should be kept in aquaria in which about half of the available area is built up into a rock or land area, with or without plants. In cages that are largely dry, the size of the water dish will depend on the habits of the species being kept. Some species of desert reptiles do not require water dishes in the cage, obtaining their moisture from the food they eat. Some species of lizards habitually lap drops of water off plants and will not take water from a dish. Virtually all snakes should be provided with a water dish that is of sufficient size to permit them to submerge completely. Plastic refrigerator storage dishes of different sizes make excellent water dishes for reptiles. Needless to say, they should be low enough to allow the animal easy access to them.

Various types of material can be used for the floor covering of the cage. Aquatic species, such as aquatic turtles and Alligators, may be kept in aquaria without any bottom covering, or the bottom may be covered with sand or gravel, as is usually done for newts and other aquatic salamanders. If living plants are kept in the aquarium, the bottom usually should be covered to provide attachment for the plants. The terrarium setup for keeping semiaquatic or terrestrial salamanders, many frogs and toads, and some lizards and snakes, should include a partial covering of earth or leaf mold built up at one end or around a water dish. Small live plants, such as mosses and ferns, make the appearance of the terrarium more attractive and help to keep it moist. Land turtles and many lizards and snakes can be kept on earth, leaf litter, sawdust, decayed wood, old newspapers, or sand. Newspapers make an excellent bottom cover that is dry and easily changed. In general, sand or fine gravel is best only for a few desert species and should be bridged with large flat stones. Actually, any cage for lizards and snakes is improved by having large rocks, logs, or branches added to the bottom covering.

Food

The problem of feeding pet amphibians or reptiles will frequently prove the deciding factor in determining which species make suitable pets. Species that feed only on living food are generally less suitable as pets for most people than those forms that can be kept on diets that are easily obtained. For example, the Eastern Garter Snake (*Thamnophis s. sirtalis*), which takes readily to a diet of cut raw fish, is far easier to keep than a Hog-nosed Snake (*Heterodon*), which feeds on toads and occasionally frogs. During the winter months most people will find it impossible to procure toads. It is primarily the difficulty of feeding that makes the attractive little Green Anolis or "American Chameleon" (*Anolis c. carolinensis*) an unsatisfactory pet in most homes. Thousands of these lizards are sold weekly as pets during the spring and summer, but few of them survive more than a few weeks because of improper care, chiefly a lack of acceptable food.

Success in getting animals to feed is often a matter of patience, ingenuity, and the availability of time to spend with the newly acquired pet. It is surprising how quickly animals can learn to feed at regular times and in a set manner, providing regular attention is given them in the beginning. Regularity is an important factor in the conditioning of an animal to a desired type of feeding.

For ease in keeping a tank clean in the case of aquatic species, it is wise to train the animals to eat in a separate smaller tank or bowl. By this method the pets can be fed individually, in pairs, or in any number desired, and the uneaten food can be disposed of easily without contaminating the tank in which they live. For example, two baby turtles that were regularly kept in a four-gallon aquarium tank were fed in a small 6″ x 4″ x 3″ plastic refrigerator dish filled with water. The meat or fish was put in the water in the refrigerator dish, and then the two turtles were put in. Beginning with the second time this was done the turtles fed regularly whenever placed in this dish. When they had finished feeding, they were rinsed in lukewarm water and returned to their home tank. The method of feeding the animals in a separate tank keeps the main tank cleaner and with fewer odors. This method is also recommended for aquatic salamanders and even for terrestrial species that feed on fish. In fact, the separate feeding enclosure appears to warrant much wider use for both aquatic and terrestrial species of all types of amphibians and reptiles. Its use should be tried wherever it might reduce objectionable odors in the home cage or where there is difficulty in feeding more than one individual in the home cage.

Some foods require additional vitamins and calcium in order to maintain the pet in good health. Young animals especially need calcium for proper bone growth. This can be added most easily by rubbing a small amount of bone meal into the food before it is offered. Cod-liver oil, for vitamin D, should be added to the food in small quantities about once every week or two. This should not be given to the animal directly, but should be put on or into the food. When placed on raw meat, it should be rubbed into the flesh. A good method of supplying calcium for aquatic turtles has been reported by Arthur Loveridge. He found that a small ball of hardened plaster of Paris in an aquarium tank will dissolve slowly, adding calcium to the water as it dissolves. A ball with the diameter of a half-dollar coin will last for several weeks in a small- to moderate-sized tank and will provide ample calcium for a number of turtles.

All salamanders and adult frogs are meat eaters, feeding on a variety of small animals. Some species will accept ground, cut, or chopped meat, but many forms require live, moving insects or worms. Meat can be dropped in the water for some aquatic species or placed on a broom straw and moved gently in front of the animal. Larval insects, such as grubs, caterpillars, and meal worms; or adult moths, flies, small grasshoppers, and whole or cut earthworms make suitable food for most amphibians. They may be placed in front of the animal being fed. Large frogs, such as the Bullfrog (*Rana catesbeiana*), the Green Frog (*Rana clamitans*), or the Leopard Frog (*Rana pipiens*), will quickly learn to take food morsels offered on tweezers or with the fingers.

Tadpoles are both vegetable feeders and meat eaters. On emerging from the eggs, they feed on microscopic plant life, such as green algae. In an aquarium they can be given small amounts of algae or can be fed boiled spinach. If algae are not readily available from a nearby body of water, a good growth of this kind of plant may be obtained by filling a glass jar with water from a pond and letting it stand exposed to the sunlight for a week or two. The inside of the jar will become covered with algae that can be scraped off when needed. When the tadpoles are several weeks old, this diet will have to be augmented with protein in the form of small quantities of raw meat or hard-boiled egg. Dead insects or worms may also be offered as food. Care should be taken to avoid overcrowding the tadpoles and to remove any sickly or dead individuals, since some tadpoles are cannibalistic.

Aquatic turtles and Alligators can be kept successfully on a diet of raw ground meat or raw fish. When fed mostly on raw meat, bone meal and cod-liver oil should be added. Turtles and Alligators should be fed two or three times per week, and the food should be placed in the water in front of them. The raw meat or fish diet can be varied by offering small table scraps of cooked meat or the white of a hard-boiled egg. Turtles should not be kept solely on a diet of dried insects or insect pupae (called "eggs"), which constitute the bulk of the prepared "turtle foods" sold in pet shops. An Alligator is sometimes slow to feed voluntarily and must have the food put into its mouth until it learns to take food readily. If the food is put in tweezers and rubbed along the edges of the jaws, or if the jaws are tapped gently with the food, an Alligator can be stimulated to open its mouth so that the food can be placed inside. Care must be used to prevent the animal from shutting its mouth quickly and injuring itself on the metal tweezers.

Terrestrial and semiaquatic turtles are chiefly vegetable eaters, taking a variety of fruits and raw vegetables, including lettuce. This vegetable diet should be supplemented with varying amounts of raw or cooked meat. The quantity of meat will depend on the species and age of the individual turtle, and can be determined with a little experimentation. Turtles should be fed about three times a week, and a supplement of calcium and cod-liver oil should be provided in the case of young turtles. It is advisable to put the food in a low dish or pan to facilitate cleaning the cage after the feeding.

Most lizards are carnivorous, feeding on insects and other small animals. A few species, like the Chuckawalla (*Sauromalus obesus*) and the Desert Iguana (*Dipsosaurus dorsalis*), are primarily vegetarian in their diet, but even these lizards will eat some insects. Very few of our native lizards voluntarily feed on raw meat, and a diet of live insects must be provided. A few can be conditioned to eat raw meat, but this is exceptional. The successful keeping of most lizards depends to a large degree on being able to get a constant source of suitable live insects. Most lizards should be fed two or three times per week.

In the warmer sections of the United States a good supply of insects can be obtained with a little ingenuity and collecting ability. Many insects can be kept for several weeks in containers filled with fresh leaves and placed in a cool (60° to 70° F.) location. Meal worms, which are larval Black Beetles (*Tenebrio molitor*), can be purchased in some of the larger pet stores or raised in any quantity desired. Directions for culturing meal worms and other insects may be found in a number of books on invertebrate animals or may be obtained by writing to the General Biological Supply House, 8200 S. Hoyne Ave., Chicago 20, Illinois. Stock for the starting of a culture can be purchased from this supply house, some large pet stores, or one of the large commercial raisers of these insects, such as the Sure-Live Worms Company, 22536 Halldale Avenue, Torrance, California.

Meal worms are widely used as food for lizards and large amphibians because of the ease with which they can be reared. However, some species will not take this food, and some have difficulty eliminating the chitinous hard parts of the older meal worms and do not do well if fed solely on meal worms. Small Orthopteran insects, such as grasshoppers, crickets, cockroaches, and praying mantises, make excellent supplementary food items for lizards and the larger amphibians. Several species of crickets are reared commercially for use as fish bait and can be bought at all times of the year. Two sources of crickets are Armstrong Cricket Farm, Glenville, Georgia; and Lucky Lure Cricket Farm, Leesburg, Florida.

Small praying mantises may be secured by collecting the egg masses of the large species. These can be kept for months in a cool (40° to 50° F.) place, and the hatching can be forced by moving them into a warm (75° to 80° F.) location. By collecting large numbers of such egg masses in the late summer and storing them in the bottom of a large refrigerator, one lizard fancier in the northeastern states feeds mantids to his pets all year round.

The Horned Lizards of our southwestern states are widely sold as pets. In their native habitats these lizards feed chiefly on various species of ants. In captivity some individuals will accept meal worms, crickets, and small grasshoppers, but they do not seem to thrive on such a diet and seldom live for more than a few months. Even when fed on some kinds of ants, they do not do very well. This is an interesting problem for one of our herpetologists in the southwestern states—to find out how to keep Horned Lizards successfully for more than a year.

All snakes are carnivorous, feeding on a wide variety of animal life. Some species are highly restricted in diet and will feed on a single kind of animal, whereas others will eat almost any animal they can swallow. There is a widespread belief that snakes will eat only live food. This notion is far from the truth; actually, a majority of the snakes in many zoological parks are fed solely on dead animals. This is the easiest and safest way to feed them since the food can be handled more readily and the snakes are not damaged in seizing the food. The late E. G. Boulenger, former Curator of Reptiles of the London Zoo, experimented for four years on the readiness with which snakes accept dead or live animal food. He concluded from a study of more than 300 snakes "that, with possible rare exceptions, a snake that refuses to feed on dead animals is not more likely to accept these if alive." One point that cannot be overstressed is that reptiles and amphibians must be kept under suitable environmental conditions in order for them to eat voluntarily.

Animals in captivity quickly modify their behavior and often alter their activity in a marked fashion. The presentation of live food to a snake in a cage sometimes disturbs the snake to the point that it tries to escape from the food animal. Under these conditions live rodents may inflict serious wounds or even kill snakes when left in cages with them. This is particularly true of wild mice and rats. It is something of a shock to go to a cage in which a live, wild mouse has been left overnight as food for a snake, only to find that the snake, even though venomous, has been killed and partly eaten by the mouse.

A number of methods have been used to induce reluctantly feeding snakes to eat. Charles H. Lowe, Jr., has suggested an effective method of placing mice and rats in a simulated nest box with only a small entrance hole for the snake. The box can be made of wood or simply by modifying a cardboard milk or ice-cream container. The entrance hole can be varied in size by fixing a triangular piece of cardboard across the hole to give an opening of the desired size. The food animals are placed inside the box, and this is placed in the snake's cage. The effectiveness of this method is increased if some used nesting material is also placed in the box. Apparently this increases the odor that stimulates the snake to feed. Snakes that refuse food offered any other way will frequently feed with this method. Individuals that have been fed regularly in this fashion generally become conditioned to feeding as soon as the box is placed in the cage. This method has proved most effective in the case of those species that feed on rodents or birds.

Odor seems to be the primary feeding stimulus in snakes. As was shown in Chapter 10, blindfolded snakes easily follow a trail marked by odor alone and quickly locate hidden food. They may search for and seize food as a result of optical stimulation, but the proper olfactory conditions must be present for swallowing to take place. The strength of the olfactory stimulus for eating has been utilized in the case of captive snakes with specialized, hard-to-get food requirements. Marlin Perkins succeeded in feeding a Mud Snake (*Farancia abacura*) by rubbing long, slender strips of horse meat with a dead Amphiuma (*Amphiuma means*) that he kept in a freezer for this purpose. The snake was sufficiently stimulated by the odor of its normal food so that it swallowed the horse meat.

Wade Fox performed a number of interesting experiments in the feeding of Pacific Coast Garter Snakes, indicating the primary importance of odor in the feeding habits of those snakes. He induced them to feed on unnatural foods merely by implanting the odor of their normal food item. This technique has useful applications in the keeping of pet snakes and emphasizes the necessity of knowing something of the habits of the species in the wild state. It has been shown that superficially similar species of snakes may possess quite different food habits.

Conditioning is an important part of the successful feeding of animals. It may require considerable patience, time, and ingenuity, but a well-conditioned pet is always a healthy pet. Regularity in the feeding routine and patience are the necessary keys to conditioning. Once a successful method has been found for presenting the food to the snake, continue the same method at the same time so that a regular pattern of feeding is established. Many pet snakes and many snakes in zoological parks have become highly conditioned to feeding in a particular fashion. Although some will take their food anywhere, others will eat only from a certain dish, from the fingers of their keeper, from forceps held by their keepers, from a particular spot in the cage, or from a small feeding box; and some will take their food only when they are transferred to another cage or box in which they are regularly fed. The important point is that they have all learned to eat under a particular set of circumstances and will eat readily whenever these circumstances are present.

Snakes usually should be fed once a week to keep them healthy. Larger individuals that eat sizable food animals may eat less frequently, and others may feed less often during the cooler months of the year. Snakes kept at lower temperatures usually eat less frequently and in smaller amounts than those kept at warmer temperatures. Gravid females generally eat more frequently and in larger quantities than males and nongravid females.

The snakes most often kept as pets because of their size, colorful patterns, and ease of handling are generally rodent eaters. This group includes the King Snakes (*Lampropeltis getulus*), the Rat Snakes (*Elaphe*), Gopher Snakes (*Pituophis catenifer*), and Indigo Snakes (*Drymarchon corais*). For most of the snakes in these groups, rodents are usually acceptable and the most easily obtained food. However, the provision of a constant supply of rodents may be something of a major problem for the city dweller. White mice and white rats can be raised without much difficulty only if adequate space is available. They can also be purchased from pet stores and biological supply houses, but this is the most expensive method of procuring them for food. Often arrangements can be made in large cities to secure, at little or no expense, small numbers of excess laboratory mice and rats from hospitals and medical laboratories.

Caution must be used to insure that such rodents have not been exposed to ailments or treatments that might prove detrimental to the snakes.

Wild mice and other rodents can be trapped, either dead or alive, by those pet owners who live in open areas. Wild rodents should usually be offered only as dead food, since they often inflict serious wounds on snakes when seized. They should never be left alive overnight in a cage with a snake.

Because of the ease of feeding and the constant availability of a food supply, the fish-eating snakes are the easiest species to keep. This group includes most Water Snakes and Garter Snakes. The primary objection to these snakes as pets is their objectionable habit of defecating and ejecting the contents of the cloacal glands when excited. The larger Water Snakes are capable of inflicting a painful bite and must be handled with care until they become tame. With patience and gentle handling these snakes will quickly lose the objectionable characteristics and become gentle pets that can be handled with complete freedom. They will learn to take fish from tweezers or from the hand. Virtually any kind of fish may be used to feed them, and it may be fed whole, if small enough, or cut in pieces if large. If cut fish is offered, the pieces should be approximately twice the size of the snake's head and four or five pieces should be provided for each snake. The fish can be placed on small, flat dishes or pans and put in the cage.

Small snakes, such as DeKay's Snakes (*Storeria dekayi*), Lined Snakes (*Tropidoclonion lineatum*), or Ringnecked Snakes (*Diadophis*) can be fed on earthworms or small slugs. Occasionally they will accept insect larvae, small adult insects, small lizards, or small salamanders. Most of the small species of snakes are difficult to keep, but do make attractive study specimens if one has a lot of patience and imagination.

Handling the Pet

In handling amphibians and reptiles care must be exercised to avoid injury to the animal and to the person handling it. An animal that is not accustomed to being handled may react strongly when first picked up. Most forms simply try to escape and must be forcefully retained. Some may try to defend themselves from such treatment, whereas others merely assume a passive defensive posture. When the animal's resistance to handling is violent, much time, patience, and gentle attention are required to get the animal conditioned. Some specimens never make this adjustment and therefore can be kept only without being handled. The effects of handling on amphibians and reptiles is unknown. Many species are not disturbed in any noticeable manner, and some individuals appear to enjoy it, speaking anthropomorphically. In more scientific jargon, some individuals show a definitely positive response to gentle handling. Others show a negative response to any handling, even of the most gentle nature. No animals will respond favorably to being handled roughly or to being held incorrectly. Therefore it is important to learn to handle your pet correctly, if it is to be handled at all (Figures 73 and 74).

Whenever possible, avoid sudden and quick movements. When picking an animal up, do so as gradually and gently as possible, being careful to support the animal's body. If the animal struggles to escape when seized, hold it firmly but gently. Do not squeeze it tightly by the neck, since this will cause it to struggle more. Do not handle any animal within an hour or two after it has eaten. Unless absolutely necessary, do not disturb snakes for a day or two after they have fed. Never grab a lizard by the tip of the tail or a frog by the leg or foot only. The lizard's tail will usually break off in your hands; and you run a good change of breaking the frog's leg.

Small aquatic amphibians, especially larvae, should be dipped up in a small net and not picked up by hand. If close examination is necessary, the animal may be placed in a closed vial with water or in a small dish of water for a short time. A suitable handling net can be made with a wire frame and covered with cheesecloth, or such nets can be purchased in pet shops.

Adults of the larger species of frogs and salamanders should be picked up by the body, grasping it firmly behind the front legs. Large frogs and toads may be held by the waist or by the lower legs, if held firmly so that they cannot twist. There is no danger of being bitten by any of our native amphibians, except the large aquatic species. Some of these, such as Amphiuma (*Amphiuma*), Siren (*Siren*), or the Hellbender (*Cryptobranchus*), can inflict a painful, but nonvenomous wound with the teeth. The secretions of the skin glands of some amphibians can cause painful irritation if brought in contact with the eyes, lips, or tongue. Care should be

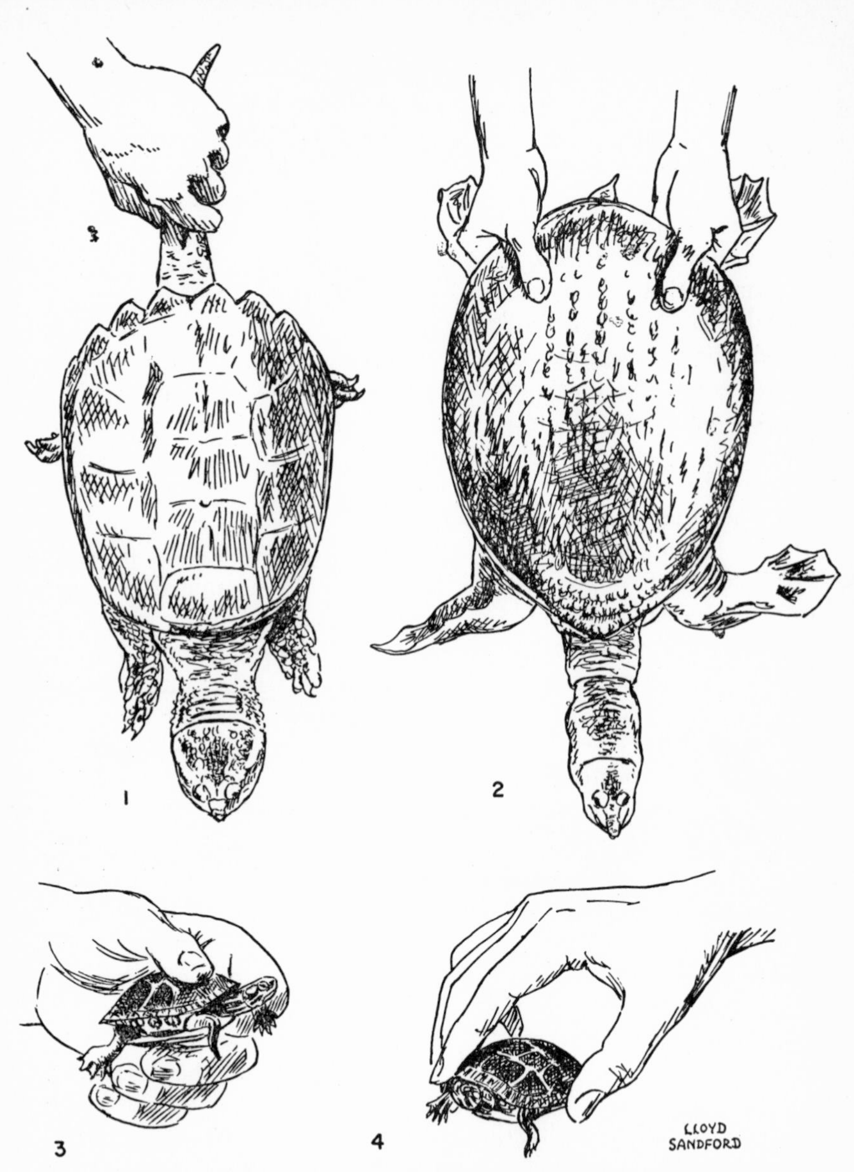

FIG. 73. Sketches illustrating the proper way to handle large and small turtles. 1. Species with a long tail like the Snapping Turtle (*Chelydra serpentina*) can be handled safely by pulling them up by the tail. 2. Short-tailed species like the Soft-shelled Turtle (*Trionyx ferox*) should be picked up by the rear of the shell. 3 and 4. Small turtles can be held in either fashion shown, but care must be used not to put pressure on the shell.

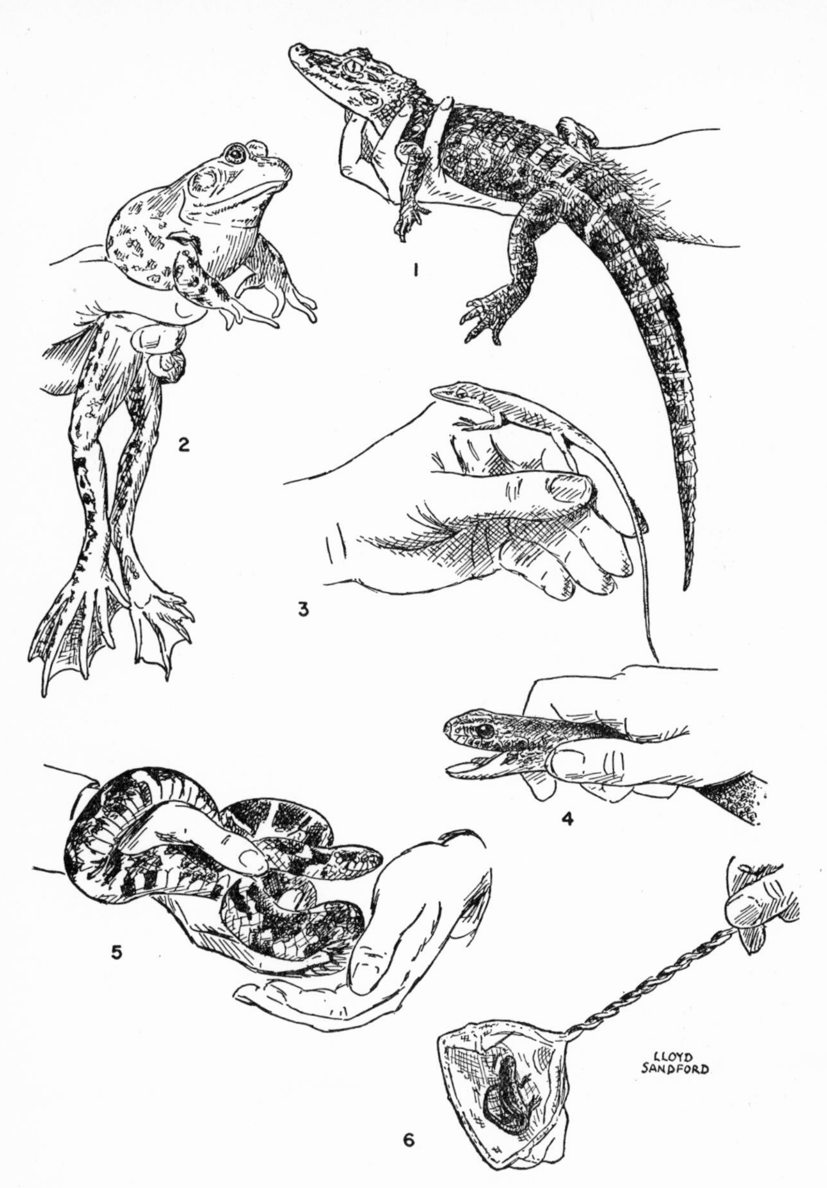

Fig. 74. Sketches showing the proper method of handling amphibians and reptiles. 1. Crocodilians and large lizards can be held safely in this manner or by reversing the position of the hand so that the animal is held from above. 2. Large frogs should be held like this or by gripping them immediately back of the front legs. 3. Small lizards and large salamanders can be held in this manner for close examination. 4. Wild or nervous snakes that are apt to bite should be held gently behind the neck. 5. Tame snakes can be held in this fashion with the body gently supported from below. 6. Small aquatic amphibians should be handled in a small net. Picking them up in the hand is likely to result in harm unless done with extreme care.

used not to rub the eyes or mouth accidentally with the hands while handling these animals.

Alligators and most lizards may be picked up by grasping around the body in front of or astraddle of the forelegs. Specimens longer than twelve inches in total length should be supported around or under the base of the tail. The tail of an Alligator may be grabbed without danger of breaking it, but with very few exceptions a lizard's tail should not be seized except at the base. Lizard's tails are generally fragile and are broken easily. The skin of geckos is easily torn by rough handling.

Alligators bite if not tame, and even a baby can inflict a painful wound. The larger the individual, the more serious the bite. Fortunately, Alligators become tame quickly. If kept properly, they soon grow too large to handle or to house adequately. Individuals two feet or more in total length not only have sharp teeth but can use their tails as effective defensive weapons. Care should be used to grasp the tail as well as the forward part of the body, when picking up one of these larger specimens.

Virtually any lizard may try to bite, but only the Gila Monster (*Heloderma suspectum*) and its close relative, the Mexican Beaded Lizard (*Heloderma horridum*), are venomous. Lizards with a head-body length of more than three inches can bite hard enough to break the skin, but none of our native nonvenomous species inflicts a dangerous wound. In picking up small lizards care must be used to avoid squeezing the animal too hard. A good method to use in handling young or very small lizards is to pick the individual up by the body, grasping it gently with the fingers of your right hand. Then place it lengthwise on the index finger of your left hand so that the lizard's head points toward your wrist. You can hold the little lizard safely by gently pressing your left thumb down on the lizard's left hind leg. This method may also be used to handle some small frogs and some salamanders.

Small turtles may be picked up by taking the shell gently between your thumb and index finger, but care should be used not to squeeze too hard on the shell of a small turtle. Larger turtles may be picked up in the same way. Snapping Turtles (*Chelydra* and *Macrochelys*) have sufficiently long and sturdy tails to be picked up by the tail; in fact, this is the safest way to pick up a Snapping Turtle of any size. Soft-shell Turtles (*Trionyx*) are best picked up by grasping the rear of the upper shell (carapace). The sharp, strong jaws of large turtles can inflict a painful bite. No turtle is venomous, but a large Snapper or Soft-shell Turtle must be handled with considerable care.

Venomous snakes do not make good pets because of the constant danger of a serious, perhaps fatal, bite. The physical risk and mental turmoil caused to others is too great to warrant the keeping of these snakes except by mature and experienced herpetologists. On the other hand, many nonvenomous species make admirable pets that can be handled easily and safely. Tame, harmless snakes may be picked up gently by any part of the body. They should not be pinched or squeezed too tightly. An individual that is still wild and apt to bite should be picked up in back of the head, close enough so that it cannot turn and bite. A firm but gentle grip is sufficient (it is not necessary to grasp the snake so tightly that it may be injured). After holding the snake this way for a few minutes, allow it to push its head and neck gradually forward several inches from the hand. Then allow it to crawl slowly over the hands, gently restraining it from time to time, or slowly moving the hands as the snake crawls so that its body is constantly supported by your hands. By repeated gentle handling in this fashion, most snakes gradually become tame and can be handled without concern. In handling very excitable snakes, you may wear a pair of soft leather gloves during the preliminary periods of the taming process. By wearing gloves, you are not so apt to squeeze the snake hard enough to hurt it and may hold it with less concern about being bitten.

Studying the Pet

The keeping of amphibians and reptiles as pets can be a fascinatingly interesting hobby. The successful care of these animals requires some knowledge of them and their habits. Much information can be obtained from careful reading about the ones you choose to keep, but you can learn a great many additional points of interest from the careful study of your own pets. It is thrilling to discover new facts about the habits and life of your pets. Often these facts are not mentioned in the books you read. Sometimes they may not be known for the species that you have.

It will make your pets more interesting if you keep a record for each individual and note all the interesting things that you find out about it: when is it active; when does it rest; how does it rest; does it stay hidden or in the open, in water or on land; how often does it eat; what does it eat; how much does it eat; how does it shed its skin; how often does it shed it; does it eat the shed skin; how fast does it grow in weight and length. These and many others questions may be answered by careful study of your pets. The more you know about them, the more interesting they will be to you. Record all this information in a notebook, keeping a separate section for each individual pet. You'll be surprised to see exactly how your pets are progressing. Note all changes in their habits.

The intelligent and critical study of amphibians and reptiles as a hobby holds many fascinating pleasures and may yield information of value to the professional herpetologists. This applies equally to the animals in captivity and those in the wild. Actually the two types of studies complement each other. Both are of value only when performed carefully and critically, however. To be of value, all observations must be written into the record at the time, or immediately after, the observation is made. Care must be used in interpreting all observations accurately. If you call your pet turtle each time that you regularly feed it and it comes quickly over to take the food from your fingers, it is *not* correct to assume that the turtle has learned to come when you call. Actually the turtle may have become conditioned to feeding at a regular time and may come at that time if you move to the feeding position and do not call. Try calling it from a position where it cannot see you. Does it come when you call from such a position? Try approaching the tank at feeding time *without* calling. Does it still come to be fed? Simple experiments such as these will teach you a lot about your pet.

If you are fortunate enough to live where amphibians and reptiles occur close by in the wild, you may enjoy the experience of making pets of wild individuals. This can be a rewarding and happy hobby. Helen T. and Frederick M. Gaige, the beloved biologists and teachers who formerly guided the Museum of Zoology of the University of Michigan, have always had a varied assortment of wild animals pets wherever they have lived. In the Florida retreat where they live during the winter amphibians and reptiles are well represented among their pets. On one visit with them my wife and I watched the hand feeding of their wild lizard friends and marveled at the Green Anolis (*Anolis c. carolinensis*) that habitually came over as if to hear the weather broadcasts on the radio! Other people have made pets of wild aquatic turtles, lizards, and frogs by regularly feeding them. One of the most unusual wild pets of this sort is that of an elderly lady living near New York City. This lady was formerly afraid of snakes, but she decided to overcome her fear by observing the snakes around her country place. She now regularly feeds a large Northern Water Snake (*Natrix s. sipedon*) that lives in a stump beside her duck pond. This is probably the only feeding station in the country operated exclusively for a snake. Incidentally, her interest in the habits of these animals has completely replaced her fear of them.

Glossary

ALLANTOIS. An embryonic membrane arranged to enable the developing embryo to breathe and dispose of waste products.

AMINO ACID. An organic acid involved in the formation of proteins or produced when proteins are broken into their simplest components.

AMNION. An embryonic membrane forming a sac that surrounds the embryo in reptiles, birds, and mammals.

AMPHIGONIA RETARDATA. The storage of viable sperm by females in some species of reptiles.

AMPLEXUS. The sexual embrace in amphibians.

ANTERIOR. At or toward the front of the body.

ANUS. The opening of the vent; it marks the external division between the body and the tail.

AXOLOTL. An Aztec word used for the large aquatic larvae of Ambystomid salamanders.

BAROTROPISM. A reaction to atmospheric pressure.

BIPEDAL. Locomotion on only two legs.

BIOTIC PROVINCE. A major ecologic division of a continent that covers a continuous geographic area.

CARAPACE. The upper shell of a turtle.

CARUNCLE. The horny tubercle on the snouts of embryonic turtles and crocodilians used in slitting the egg shells at hatching.

CAUDOCEPHALIC WAVES. Wave-like flexions of the body beginning at the tail and traveling forward to the head.

CHEMOTROPISM. A reaction to a chemical.

CLOACA. A single passageway to the outside through which the intestine, kidneys and sexual organs of an animal discharge.

CREPUSCULAR. Active at twilight or dusk.

CRYSTALLINE GUANINE. A pigment substance found in the eyes of some animals that enables them to shine at night by reflecting light.

DIURNAL. Active during the daytime or in daylight.

DORSOLATERAL FOLD. A glandular fold running along the side of the back or upper side of the body.

ECTOTHERMIC. Regulating the body temperature by means of outside sources of heat.

EGG TOOTH. A true tooth on the premaxillary bone in the roof of the mouth in embryonic lizards and snakes, used in slitting the egg shell at hatching.

ENDOTHERMIC. Regulating the body temperature by means of internal heat and internal regulating mechanisms.

ENZYME. A chemical agent that brings about or speeds up a specific chemical reaction.

ENVIRONMENTAL FORCE. A general designation for a number of environmental factors or functions too diverse to permit their ready classification into major groups.

ESTIVATION. Prolonged inactivity during periods of high temperature or deficient moisture.

FOETUS. Embryo of live-bearing animal in latter stages of development.

GEOGRAPHIC RANGE. The particular geographic area in which any species or subspecies lives.

GEOTROPISM. A reaction to gravity.

GESTATION. The period of development or carrying of embryos by the female in live-bearing species.

GILLS. Respiratory structures for removing oxygen from water; found in aquatic larvae and a few adult amphibians.

HABITAT. The physical, climatic and biotic setting in which a species or subspecies lives.

HEAD-BODY LENGTH. The straightline length of the animal, measured from the tip of the snout to the posterior edge of the anus.

HEDONIC GLANDS. Glands that function in courtship or mating to attract or stimulate.

HEMOTOXIC. Affecting the blood and circulatory system.

HEMIPENIS. One of the paired male intromittent organs in lizards and snakes. Plural: hemipenes.

HERPETOLOGY. The study or science of amphibians and reptiles.

HIBERNATION. A prolonged, regular inactivity during periods of low temperatures.

HOME RANGE. The area in which the individual animal carries on all of its activities.

HORMONES. Chemicals that are secreted by glands of the body and that produce certain reactions in other organs or systems of the body.

HYDROTROPISM. A reaction to humidity or moisture.

HYPOPHYSIS. An important gland of internal secretion located on the underside of the brain.

JACOBSON'S ORGAN. A sensory organ located in the roof of the mouth and used to perceive odors and chemical substances.

LARVA. An immature stage of life between egg and adult.

LATERAL LINE ORGANS. A series of sensory organs located in the skin in a row along the side of the body and used to perceive vibrations in the water.

METABOLISM. A term used for all of the physical and chemical processes required in the operation of an organism.

METAMORPHOSIS. The change in body form and way of life that ends the larval stage; also called transformation.

MUCOUS GLANDS. Glands located in the skin and secreting slippery or sticky, sometimes toxic, substances.

NEOTENY. Retaining the larval body form throughout life but capable of reproduction.

NEUROTOXIC. Affecting the nerves and nervous system.

NICHE. The particular position or situation that a species or subspecies occupies within a habitat.

NOCTURNAL. Relating to activity at night or during darkness.

ONTOGENETIC. Pertaining to the life cycle of the individual.

OVIPAROUS. Reproducing by means of eggs that develop outside of the body of the female.

PARIETAL EYE. A sensory structure, usually with little or no function, located in the top of the head behind the eyes and on the midline of the head.

PAROTOID GLAND. A large, external glandular mass located in the skin on each side of and in back of the head in toads of the genus *Bufo*.

PAROTID GLAND. An internal gland located on each side of the head behind the eye. This is one of the salivary glands and in venomous snakes is modified to produce venom.

PHOTOTROPISM. A reaction to light.

PLASTRON. The lower shell of a turtle.

POSTERIOR. At or toward the rear of the body.

PROTEROGLYPH. A venomous snake with relatively immovable front fangs.

RHEOTROPISM. A reaction to current.

RUBNER'S HYPOTHESIS. A theory that postulates a longer life span for species inactive part of the year than for species active continuously.

SHELL LENGTH. The straightline length of a turtle's upper shell or carapace, measured along the midline of the shell.

SNOUT-TO-VENT LENGTH. (Also called snout-vent length.) The straightline length of the animal, measured from the anterior tip of the snout to the posterior edge of the vent.

SOLENOGLYPH. A venomous snake with movable front fangs.

SPERMATOPHORE. A gelatinous mass of male sperm with a stalk or pedicel.

SPERMATOZOA. A ripe male sperm cell.

TADPOLE. The larva of a frog or toad.

TERRITORY. An area defended against intruders of the same species.

THERMOTROPISM. A reaction to heat.

THIGMOTROPISM. A reaction to touch or contact.

THYROID. An important gland of internal secretion.

TITILLATING. The rapid fanning or tapping of the claws of the male's front legs near or on the face of the female during courtship in some turtles.

TOTAL LENGTH. The maximum straightline length of an animal, measured from the anterior tip of the snout to the posterior tip of the tail.

TRICUSPID. A tooth with three points or cusps.

TROPISM. A reaction to a particular stimulus.

UMBILICAL SCAR. The remains of the opening in the body where the embryo was attached to the yolk sac or to parent during development.

VENT. The posterior opening of the body.

VIVIPAROUS. Reproduction by means of living young instead of eggs that develop outside of the female's body.

Recommended References

The following books are recommended for the identification of our native amphibians and reptiles, as well as for additional information about the forms. The serious student will find many detailed reports listed in the bibliographies of these works.

BISHOP, SHERMAN C.

1943. *Handbook of Salamanders. The Salamanders of the United States, of Canada, and of Lower California.* Comstock Publishing Co., Ithaca, N. Y., xiv + 555 pp., 144 figs., 54 maps.

CARR, ARCHIE

1952. *Handbook of Turtles. The Turtles of the United States, Canada, and Baja California.* Comstock Publishing Associates, Ithaca, N. Y., xviii + 542 pp., 82 pls., 37 figs., 22 maps, 15 tables.

CONANT, ROGER AND ISABELLE CONANT

(In Press.) *A Field Guide to Amphibians and Reptiles.* The Peterson Field Guide Series, Houghton Mifflin Company, Boston, Mass.

LOGIER, E. B. S.

1952. *The Frogs, Toads and Salamanders of Eastern Canada.* Clarke, Irwin and Co., Ltd., Canada, xii + 127 pp., 5 pls., 57 figs.

MILLS, R. COLIN

1948. *A Check List of the Reptiles and Amphibians of Canada.* *Herpetologica,* vol. 4, second supplement, 15 pp.

SCHMIDT, KARL P.

1953. *A Check List of North American Amphibians and Reptiles.* Sixth Edition. American Society of Ichthyologists and Herpetologists, University of Chicago Press, Chicago, Ill., viii + 280 pp.

SCHMIDT, KARL P. AND D. D. DAVIS

1941. *Field Book of Snakes of the United States and Canada.* G. P. Putnam's Sons, New York, xiii + 365 pp., 34 pls., 103 figs.

SMITH, HOBART M.
1946. *Handbook of Lizards. Lizards of the United States and Canada.* Comstock Publishing Co., Ithaca, N. Y., xxii + 557 pp., 135 figs., 41 maps.

STEBBINS, ROBERT C.
1954. *Amphibians and Reptiles of Western North America.* McGraw-Hill Book Company, Inc., New York, xiv + 529 pp., 104 pls., 52 figs.

WRIGHT, ALBERT H. AND ANNA A. WRIGHT
1949. *Handbook of Frogs and Toads of the United States and Canada.* Comstock Publishing Co., Ithaca, N. Y., xiv + 640 pp., 126 pls., 37 maps.

WRIGHT, ALBERT H. AND ANNA A. WRIGHT
(In Press.) *Handbook of Snakes of the United States and Canada.* Comstock Publishing Co., Ithaca, N. Y.

Index

Abastor. *See* Rainbow Snake
Abastor erythrogrammus. *See* Rainbow Snake
Acanthophis antarcticus. *See* Death Adder
Acris gryllus. *See* Cricket Frog
Activity: factors affecting, 126; daily, 131-134
Adhesive pads: of lizards, 94, Fig. 15
Adrian, E. D., 163
Agamidae: body temperature, 140; tooth structure, 181
Algae: on turtle shells, 147; in amphibian egg, 147
Allee, W. C., 157
Allen, Ross, 20, 119, 239, 307
Alligator: economic importance, 19-21, 26; protected by law, 29; family representative, 58; distribution, 75; distribution effected by man, 76; seasonal movements, 80; den, 81; territoriality, 82; speed, 100, 102; movements, 108; hibernation, 122; head, 161; hearing, 163; changes in food habits, 174; catching birds, 180; food consumed, 208; bellowing, 212-213; egg, 238; nest and care of eggs, 239; reproduction data, 241; nest and temperature, 248-249; nest and care of young, 251, 254; slow rate of growth, 266-267; sexual difference in size and growth, 268; time of sexual maturity, 278; growth rate, 279; reproductive age, 284; maximum age, 293; maximum size, 300, 302; as pet, 306, 308; diet in captivity, 315; holding, 323-324
Alligator Lizards: economic importance, 27; family representative, 61-62; walking, 86; defensive position, 152; food consumed, 203; shedding skin, 285
Alligator mississippiensis. *See* Alligator
Alligator Snapping Turtle: family representative, 54; movements, 109; lure on tongue, 181; maximum age, 292; maximum size, 303
Ambystoma gracile. *See* Northwestern Salamander
Ambystoma jeffersonianum. *See* Jefferson's Salamander
Ambystoma macrodactylum. *See* Long-toed Salamander
Ambystoma maculatum. *See* Spotted Salamander
Ambystoma opacum. *See* Marbled Salamander
Ambystoma talpoideum. *See* Mole Salamander
Ambystoma tigrinum. *See* Tiger Salamander
Ambystoma tigrinum californiense. *See* California Tiger Salamander
Ambystoma tigrinum tigrinum. *See* Eastern Tiger Salamander
Ambystomidae: representatives, 44
American Crocodile: protected by law, 29; family representative, 57-58; maximum age, 293; maximum size, 303

American Toad: family representative, 46; home range, 80; breeding movements, 105; movements of young, 106; food consumed, 197; sex ratio, 215; eggs, 232; reproduction data, 236; incubation and larval period, 262; time of sexual maturity, 277; buried in boxes, 288; maximum age, 292
Amphibian: definition, 41; Orders, 41-43; locomotion, 84-89
Amphibian egg, 232; hatching, 255
Amphigonia Retardata, 213
Amphisbaenidae: representatives, 63-65
Amphiuma: family representative, 42; movement by lateral undulation, 85, 89; estimated speed, 96; temperature relations, 141; food consumed, 192; maximum age, 292; used as food, 318; bite, 321
Amphiuma means. See Amphuima
Amphiuma means tridactylum. See Three-toed Amphiuma
Amphiumidae: representatives, 45
Amplexus: 227-229
Amusement: use in, 24-25
Anderson, Paul, 120
Aneides aeneus. See Green Salamander
Aneides hardyi. See Sacramento Mountain Salamander
Aneides flavipunctatus. See Black Salamander
Aneides lugubris. See Arboreal Salamander
Anguidae: representatives, 61-62
Anguids: chemical reception, 167
Ancistrodon contortrix. See Copperhead
Ancistrodon piscivorous. See Water Moccasin
Ancistrodon piscivorous leucostoma. See Western Cottonmouth
Anniella pulchra. See Footless Lizard
Anniellidae: representatives, 62
Anolis: adhesive pads, 94-95
Anolis carolinensis. See Green Anolis
Antivenins: manufacture, 23
Aquarium tank: for pets, 308-310
Arboreal Salamander: occurrence in habitat, 79; competition and food habits, 154; reproduction data, 234
Arizona Coral Snake: family representative, 67; maximum size, 301
Arizona Twinspotted Rattlesnake: maximum size, 301
Armstrong Cricket Farm: 317
Aronson, Lester, R., 227-228
Ascaphidae: representatives, 47
Ascaphus truei. See Tailed Frog
Atlantic Green Turtle: maximum size, 300
Atlantic Leatherback Turtle: maximum size, 300
Atlantic Loggerhead: number of eggs, 240; reproduction data, 241; maximum age, 292
Atlantic Ridley Turtle: maximum size, 300
Atmospheric pressure: effects of, 144
Auffenberg, Walter, 77
Axolotl: 210

Bahaman Slider Turtle: reported parental care, 252
Bailey, Reeve M., 119-120
"Balls of snakes," 124
Banded Gecko: family representative, 60; territoriality, 82; territories and mating, 214; sex recognition, 216; courtship, 224; maximum size, 300
Barbour, Thomas, 36
Barking Frog: tadpole, 261; number of eggs and size, 235
Basiliscus. See Basilisks
Basilisks: running on hind legs, 90
Bathysiredon. See Axolotl

Batrachoseps attenuatus. See Worm Lizard
Batrachoseps wrighti. See Western Four-toed Salamander
Beach, Frank, 213
Beck, William, 144
Berlandier's Tortoise: maximum size, 300
Biotic environment: 136, 146-148
Biotic province: definition, 71; mapped, Fig. 9
Biotic provinces of North America: 71-72
Bipedal running, 90
Birth, 253-259
Bisexual reproduction, 210-215
Bishop, Sherman C., 215, 220, 231, 275, 277
Black-banded Skink: nest and temperature, 249
Black Beetles: larval meal worms, 316
Black-bellied Salamander: distribution aided by man, 77
Black Footless Lizard: maximum size, 300
Black Racer: economic importance, 28; movements, 113; feeding, 177; food consumed, 206; courtship, 226
Black Salamander: jumping, 87
Black-spotted Newt: sexual difference in size, 269
Black Toad: body temperature, 139
Blair, Albert P., 78, 105, 212, 214-216
Blanchard, Frank N., 112, 121, 230, 240, 248, 277, 282, 284
Blanchard, Frieda Cobb, 230, 248
Blind Snake: family representative, 64
Blue Racer: hibernation, 124
Blue-tailed Skink: folklore, 5-6
Bogert, Charles M., 100, 107, 137-142, 152, 212, 295, 303
Bohnsack, Kurt, 122
Boidae: representatives, 66
Boids: rectilinear locomotion, 91
Boreal Toad: altitudinal occurrence, 78
Bothrops. See South American Pit Viper
Boulenger, E. G., 141, 317
Box Turtle: protected by law, 29; family representative, 52, 55; occurrence as individuals, 81; fighting of males, 83; hibernation, 118, 122; burrowing in mud, 125; hearing range, 163; courtship, 223; mating, 229; caruncle, 256; do not shed horny plates, 285; long lived, 291, 294
Brady, M. K., 222
Bragg, Arthur N., 106, 190, 212, 244, 262-263, 278
Brattstrom, Bayard H., 132
Bray, C. W., 163
Breckenridge, W. J., 105, 121, 249, 282
Breder, Charles M., 108
Breder, Ruth, 220
Brimley, Clement S., 130
Broad-striped Mud Siren: maximum size, 298
Brooding: by pythons, 253
Buckland: experiments on burying live toads, 288
Bufo. See Toads
Bufo alvarius. See Colorado River Toad
Bufo boreas. See Boreal Toad
Bufo cognatus. See Plains Toad
Bufo marinus. See Marine Toad
Bufo punctatus. See Red-spotted Toad
Bufo quercicus. See Oak Toad
Bufo terrestris americanus. See American Toad
Bufo t. terrestris. See Southern Toad
Bufo woodhousei fowleri. See Fowler's Toad
Bufonidae: representatives, 48
Bullfrog: economic importance, 17-18, 25, 29; transportation by

man, 27; protected by law, 29; family representative, 49; distribution aided by man, 76; in jumping contests, 97; jumping ability, 97-99; movements, 107-108; hibernation, 117; refused as food, 178; reproduction data, 236; relation to temperature and reproduction, 247; longest larval period, 263; sexual difference in eardrum, 270; growth rate, 276-277; maximum age, 292, 299, 302; feeding in captivity, 315
Bullock, Theodore H., 165
Bull Snake: economic importance, 28; hibernation, 124; seasonal incidence, 128-129; digestion of food, 187; courtship, 226; maximum size, 304
Butler's Garter Snake: speed, 101-102; 113; food habits, 156

Caecilians, 31, 39, 43
Cagle, Fred R., 109, 126-127, 191, 205, 221-222, 240, 254, 278, 284, 290
Caiman: economic importance, 21
Caiman crocodilus. See Caiman
California Boa: family representative, 64, 66; speed, 101-102; maximum age, 293; maximum size, 301
California King Snake: movement, 113; reproduction data, 243
California Newt: estivation, 143; protection, 150-151; reproduction data, 234; sexual differences in skin texture, 273; maximum reproductive age, 284; maximum age, 292
California Tiger Salamander: family representative, 44
California Yellow-legged Frog: reproduction data, 236
Callisaurus draconoides gabbi. See Common Gridiron-tailed Lizard
Camp, Charles C., 103
Camp's Frog: maximum size, 299
Canebrake Rattlesnake: movements, 114
Cannibalism, 148
Care of eggs, 249-253
Care of young; 249-253
Caretta caretta. See Loggerhead Turtle
Carpenter, Charles C., 101, 112-113, 154
Carr, Archie, 19, 150
Caruncle: in turtles and crocodilians, 256
Caterpillar locomotion, 91
Caudocephalic waves: 225-226
Cave Salamander: seasonal incidence, 126
Cemophora coccinea. See Scarlet Snake
Central Plains Spadefoot Toad: maximum size, 298
Chadwick, L. E., 152
Chain King Snake: occurrence as individuals, 81; large meal, 191
Chameleons: Old World, 182
Charina bottae. See Rubber Boa
Check List of North American Amphibians and Reptiles, 36
Chelonia mydas. See Green Turtle
Chelonidae: representatives, 56
Chelydra serpentina. See Snapping Turtle or Common Snapping Turtle
Chelydridae: representatives, 54-55
Chemical reception, 166-167
Chemicals: effect of, 144-145
Chicken Snake: climbing, 95-96
Childs, V. L., 208
Chionactis occipitalis. See Shovel-nosed Snake
Chrysemys. See Painted Turtle
Chrysemys picta. See Painted Turtle
Chrysemys picta marginata. See Midland Painted Turtle
Chuckawalla: high temperatures, 137, 140; maximum size, 300; diet in captivity, 315

Clanton, Wesley, 215
Clark, H. Walton, 18
Clark, Robert F., 206-207
Clarke, T. E., 206
Classification: categories of, 31-35
Clausen, H. J., 123, 157, 214
Clemmys insculpta. See Wood Turtle
Clemmys muhlenbergi. See Muhlenberg's Turtle
Climbing: amphibians, 87-89; reptiles, 94-96
Clouded Tiger Salamander: altitudinal occurrence, 79
Cnemidophorus. See Race Runner
Cnemidophorus perplexus. See Devil's River Race Runner
Cnemidophorus sacki stictogrammus. See New Mexican Race Runner
Cnemidophorus sexlineatus. See Eastern Race Runner or Six-lined Race Runner
Coachwhip: folklore, 11-12; moisture loss, 142; escape from enemies, 149; maximum size, 304
Cobra: and "snake charmers," 10-11; family representative, 67; fangs, 184
Cole, Lamont C., 137-138
Coleonyx variegatus. See Banded Gecko or Banded Ground Gecko
Collared Lizard: family representative, 60; running on hind legs, 87, 90
Colonies: occurrence, 81
Colorado Desert Whipsnake: speed, 101-102
Colbert, Edwin H., 100
Colorado River Toad: relation to humidity, 136; warning croak, 212; maximum size, 299, 302
Coluber. See Racer
Coluber constrictor. See Black Racer
Coluber constrictor flaviventris. See Yellow-bellied Racer
Coluber constrictor foxi. See Blue Racer
Coluber constrictor mormon. See Western Racer
Coluber constrictor priapus. See Florida Racer
Colubridae: representatives, 66-67
Colubrid: male combat "dance," 217-218; courtship pattern, 225
Combat "dance" of snakes, 83, 217-218
Common European Adder; occurrence within Arctic Circle, 72
Common Garter Snake: movements, 112-113
Common Gridiron-tailed Lizard: speed, 102-103; movements, 112; sexual differences in color, 272-273
Common Mud Turtle: poorly concealed eggs, 252; maximum age, 292
Common Musk Turtle: economic importance, 27-28; reproduction data, 241; eggs laid in shallow excavations, 252; time of sexual maturity, 278; growth rings on shell, 290; maximum age, 292
Common Snapping Turtle: speed, 99; digestion, 187; geographical variation in number of eggs, 245; delayed hatching, 248; caruncle, 256; maximum size, 299
Common Tree Frog: occurrence in habitat, 79
Common Water Snake: family representative, 64
Common Western Skink: altitudinal occurrence, 79
Conant, Roger, 127, 130
Concertina locomotion, 91
Cooperation, 157-158
Cope, James B., 113
Competition: 153-157; reduced by food habits, 154
Copperhead: economic importance, 27; family representative, 67
Compton, L. V., 152

Copulatory organ: crocodilians, 229; turtles, 229; lizards and snakes, 229-230

Coral Snake: family representative, 64, 67; fangs, 184; reproduction data, 243; maximum size, 301

Corn Snake: climbing, 96; eaten by King Snake, 191; maximum age, 293

Cottam, C., 206

Cottonmouth: venom used for hemophilia, 23

Cotylosaurs, 39

Courtship: definition, 218; salamanders, 219-222; frogs, 222; crocodilians, 222; turtles, 221-223; lizards, 222-225; snakes, 225-226

Cowles, Raymond B., 27, 100, 122, 137-142, 165, 259

Crater Lake Newt: competition and food habits, 154-155; sexual differences in size, 268; maximum size, 298

Crickets: as food, 317; sources of, 317

Cricket Frog: family representative, 46, 49; jumping ability, 97-99; sexual differences in color, 271

Criddle, Stuart, 123

Crocodilians: folklore, 5; definition, 58; walking and track, 90; sleeping, 134; hearing, 163; food consumed, 199-201, 208; bellowing, 213; nest and young, 239-240; care of young, 251

Crocodylus acutus. See American Crocodile

Crossopterygians, 39

Crotalus. See Rattlesnake

Crotalus adamanteus. See Eastern Diamondback Rattlesnake

Crotalus atrox. See Western Diamond Rattlesnake

Crotalus cerastes. See Sidewinder Rattlesnake

Crotalus horridus. See Timber Rattlesnake

Crotalus horridus atricaudatus. See Canebrake Rattlesnake

Crotalus p. pricei. See Arizona Twinspotted Rattlesnake

Crotalus viridis. See Prairie Rattlesnake

Crotalus viridis oreganus. See Northern Pacific Rattlesnake

Crotalidae: representatives, 67-68

Crotalids: rectilinear locomotion, 91

Crotaphytus collaris. See Collared Lizard

Crotaphytus collaris baileyi. See Western Collared Lizard

Crowned Snake: digging, 81

Cryptobranchidae: representatives, 43-44

Cryptobranchus alleganiensis. See Hellbender

Crystalline guanine, 164

Cuban Tree Frog: family representative, 49; jumping ability, 98-99; maximum size, 299

Cumberland turtle, 306

Daily activity, 131-134

Death Adder: family representative, 67

DeKay's Snake: movements, 112; hibernation and winter mortality, 119-120; hibernation aggregation, 123; aggregations and cooperation, 157; chemical reception, 167; eaten by King Snake, 191; sensory perception in mating, 214; sex recognition, 216; as a pet, 320

Dendroaspis. See Mamba

Dens: hibernation, 122-125

Dermochelidae: representatives, 56-58

Dermochelys coriacea. See Leatherback Turtle

Desert Banded Gecko: daily ac-

tivity, 133; temperature relations, 140-141
Desert Blind Snake: maximum size, 301
Desert Iguana: running on hind legs, 90; high body temperature, 140; food consumed, 201; maximum age, 293; diet in captivity, 315
Desert Patchnosed Snake; speed, 101-102
Desert Spiny Lizard: temperature relations, 141; size and number of eggs, 240
Desert Tortoise: protected by law, 29; family representative, 56; seasonal movement, 80; speed, 99, 102; moving long distances, 104; movements, 110; winter den, 122; summer retreat, 125; seasonal incidence, 127; daily activity, 132; sex recognition, reproduction data, 241; growth rings on shell, 290; maximum age, 293; maximum size, 300
Desmognathus fuscus. See Dusky Salamander
Desmognathus quadramaculatus. See Black-bellied Salamander
Desmognathus wrighti. See Pygmy Salamander
Developmental stages: Wood Frog, 258
Devil's River Race Runner: maximum size, 301
Diadophis amabilis. See Western Ring-necked Snake
Diamondback Terrapin: economic importance, 18; retention of spermatozoa, 213; growth rings on shell, 290
Diamondback Water Snake: food consumed, 205; sexual differences in shape of tail, 271; chin tubercles and supraanal keels in males, 273-274
Dice, Lee R., 71-72
Dickson, John D. III, 244, 247
Diemictylus meridionalis. See Black-spotted Newt
Diemictylus perstriatus. See Striped Newt
Diemictylus viridescens. See Red-spotted Newt
Digestion: 186-189; in relation to temperature, 187-188
Dinosaurs, 39
Dipsosaurus. See Desert Iguana
Dipsosaurus dorsalis. See Desert Iguana
Distribution: 69-78; comparison of northern and southern species, 73; factors influencing, 75-78
Drymarchon corais couperi. See Indigo Snake
Drymarchon corais erebennus. See Texas Indigo Snake
Dusky Salamander: distribution aided by man, 77; tongue, 179
Dwarf Blind Snake: ability to move, 75-76; reproduction data, 243
Dwarf Mudpuppy: maximum size, 298

Eastern Box Turtle: movements, 110; reproduction data, 241; intermittent growth, 265; sexual differences in eye color, 272; time of sexual maturity, 278; growth rate, 280; maximum reproductive age, 284; longevity studied, 289; growth rings on shell, 290; maximum age, 292; longevity and activity, 295-296
Eastern Diamondback Rattlesnake: economic importance, 19; family representative, 67; maximum size, 301, 303-304
Eastern Four-lined Salamander: hibernation site, 121
Eastern Four-toed Salamander: occurrence, 69; reproduction data,

234; size and number of eggs, 235; females guarding eggs, 250; communal nests, 250
Eastern Garter Snake: hibernation, 117; hibernation site, 121; hibernation aggregation, 123; temperature relations, 141; food habits, 156; sex recognition, 217; mating, 230; period of embryonic development and temperature, 248; reproduction data, 243; reproduction in alternate years, 244; shedding skin in absence of growth, 286; diet in captivity, 313
Eastern Glass Lizard: length, 59; maximum size, 300, 303
Eastern Hog-nosed Snake: food, 205; reproduction data, 243
Eastern King Snake: hatching, 257
Eastern Milk Snake: egg, 238; egg tooth, 256
Eastern Newt: movement, 104
Eastern Painted Turtle: egg, 238
Eastern Race Runner: family representative, 60, 63
Eastern Ribbon Snake: speed, 101-102; food habits, 156
Eastern Ring-neck Snake: egg, 238; size and number of eggs, 240; maximum reproductive size, 284
Eastern Spadefoot Toad: representative, 46; occurrence in habitat, 79; reproduction data, 236
Eastern Tiger Salamander: family representative, 44; burrow, 81; mass movements, 105; hibernation site, 121; sexual differences in size, 268; time of sexual maturity, 277; maximum size, 298
Eastern Wood Frog: movement away from breeding site, 106; reproduction data, 236; maximum size, 299
Eckert, J. E., 176
Ecological niches, 79
Ecology: definition, 70
Ectothermic: definition, 137
Edgren, Richard A., Jr., 77
Eft: definition, 45
Egg tooth: amphibian, 255; lizards and snakes, 256
Eggs: amphibian, 230-237; salamander, 230-231, 233-235; frog, 232, 235-237; number in relation to size, 235, 240; reptiles, 237-245; crocodilians, 239-240; turtles, 241; lizards, 242; snakes, 243; care of, 249-253
Elaphe. See Rat Snake
Elaphe guttata. See Corn Snake
Elaphe o. obsoleta. See Pilot Black Snake
Elaphe obsoleta quadrivittata. See Four-lined Chicken Snake
Elaphe subocularis. See Trans-Pecos Rat Snake
Elapidae: representative, 67
Eleutherodactylus latrans. See Robber Frog
Eleutherodactylus ricordi planirostris. See Greenhouse Frog
Embryonic development: definition, 245, 245-249
Emory's Soft-shelled Turtle: distribution aided by man, 76
Emydidae: representative, 55
Endothermic: definition, 137
Enemies: 148-153: man as, 148-149; protection from, 149-153
Ensatina e. eschscholtzi. See Monterey Salamander
Ensatina eschscholtzi oregonensis. See Northern Pacific Red Salamander
Environmental Force: definition, 147
Enzymes: definition, 186
Eretmochelys imbricata. See Hawksbill Turtle
Estivation: definition, 116; 125
Eumeces. See Skinks
Eumeces fasciatus. See Five-lined Skink
Eumeces laticeps. See Greater Five-lined Skink

Eumeces skiltonianus. See Common Western Skink
European Common Lizard: occurrence within Arctic Circle, 72
European Water Snake: vision, 165
Eurycea b. bislineata. See Two-lined Salamander
Eurycea lucifuga. See Cave Salamander
Eurycea neotenes. See Neotenic Salamander
Evans, L. T., 223
External fertilization: definition, 210

Facial pit of Pit Viper: 165-166
False Map Turtle: maximum size, 293; as pet, 306
Fangs of snakes: 183-185
Farancia. See Mud Snake
Farner, Donald S., 154-155
Feeding: frequency, 190-192
Fence Lizard: classification, 33; sex recognition, 216
Ferhat-Akat, S., 162
Fertilization: external, 210; internal, 210
Finn, Huckleberry, 2, 14
Finster, E. B., 112
Fitch, Henry S., 111, 113-114, 129, 173-174, 191, 203, 207, 282-283, 287, 294-295
Fitch's Garter Snake: movements, 114
Five-lined Skink: family representative, 60; expansion and contraction of range, 78; female guards nest, 254
Florida Box Turtle: several clutches of eggs per year, 244; total number of eggs, 244; period of incubation, 247-248
Florida Cricket Frog: vision, 165
Florida Green Water Snake: maximum number of young, 243
Florida Racer: speed, 101-102
Florida Ribbon Snake: sleeping, 134
Florida Terrapin: courtship, 221-222
Florida Worm Lizard: family representative, 60, 63-65; occurrence in habitat, 79; reproduction data, 242; maximum size, 301; unsuitable pet, 305
Flury, Alvin G., 133
Food: amphibians and reptiles as, 16-19; types of, 169; factors determining kind of, 169-171; changes in, 171-175; methods of locating, 175-178; methods of obtaining, 178-186; digestion, 186-189; of pets, 313-320
Food habits: changes in, 171-175; examples, 192-208
Footless Lizard: family representative, 60, 62; crawling, 191; on fine-textured soil, 145
Fossil history, 37-40
Four-lined Chicken Snake: speed, 101-102
Fowler's Toad: hopping, 97-99; nightly movements, 106; homing ability, 107; hibernation, 122; daily activity, 132-133
Fox, Wade, 177, 318
Fringe-toed Lizard: "swimming" into sand, 94; speed, 102-103; on loose sand, 145
Frog Chorus, 209
Frog jumping contest, 96
Frog larvae, 259-261; adaptive types, 261; shortest period, 262; longest period, 263
"Frog Olympics," 24-25, 97
Frogs: rains of, 4; economic importance, 16-18, 22, 24; Order of, 31; North American representatives, 45-49; largest genus of, 50; largest species of, 50; hopping, 85-87; swimming, 89; movements, 105-108; relation to humidity, 141; defensive posture, 152; food consumed, 196-199; calling and breeding, 212; holding, 323-324

Gaige, Frederick M., 326
Gaige, Helen T., 326
Garter Snake: family representative, 67; coast to coast occurrence, 75; speed, 101-102; movements, 112-114; competition and food habits, 154, 156; chemical reception, 167; feeding, 177; digestion and elimination of food, 188; frequency of feeding, 192; as pet, 320
Geckos: adhesive pads, 94-95; eating shed skin, 285
Gekkonidae: representatives, 59-61
General Biological Supply House, 307, 316
Geographic range: definition, 70-71
Gerrhonotus. See Alligator Lizard
Gerrhonotus coeruleus palmeri. See Sierra Alligator Lizard
Gerrhonotus coeruleus principis. See Northern Alligator Lizard
Gila Monster: protected by law, 29; family representative, 60, 62; venom apparatus, 182; reproduction data, 242; maximum age, 293; maximum size, 300, 303; venomous, 324
Gilbert, Perry W., 147
Giles, L. W., 208
Glass Lizard: folklore, 6; family representative, 60, 62; crawling, 91; head, 162; eaten by King Snake, 191; guarding eggs, 252, 254
Glass, Byron P., 277
Gloyd, Howard K., 272
Goin, Coleman J., 108, 117, 255, 278
Goin, Olive B., 108, 117
Gopher Frog: burrow, 81; cooperation, 158
Gopher Snake: economic importance, 27; family representative, 67; speed, 101-102; as pet, 319
Gopher Tortoise: economic importance, 19; family representative, 52; speed, 99, 102; movements, 110; seasonal incidence, 127-128; daily activity, 132; cooperation, 158; frequency of feeding, 191; mating, 229; chin glands, 273
Gopherus agassizi. See Desert Tortoise
Gopherus berlandieri. See Berlandier's Tortoise
Gopherus polyphemus. See Gopher Tortoise
Gordon, Robert E., 104, 142, 250
Granit, R., 165
Gray Tree Frog: family representative, 46; reproduction data, 236; incubation and larval period, 262
Great Basin Gopher Snake: at den, 124
Great Basin Rattlesnake: at den, 124
Great Plains Garter Snake: hibernation and winter mortality; 119-120; hibernation aggregation, 123; seasonal incidence, 129; temperature relations, 141; period of embryonic development and temperature, 248; shedding skin and temperature, 286
Great Plains Narrow-mouthed Toad: incubation and larval period, 262; maximum size, 299
Great Plains Spadefoot Toad: movement of young, 106; maximum size, 298
Great Plains Toad: unsuccessful breeding, 244
Great Siren: family representative, 42; maximum age, 292; maximum size, 298
Greater Five-lined Skink: hibernation, 117-118; sexual dimorphism in color, 273; maximum size, 301
Green Anolis: protected by law, 29; territoriality, 82-83; "parachuting," 95; movements, 111-112; territories, 111-112; home range, 111-112; winter activity,

118-119; seasonal incidence, 128; daily activity, 133; sleeping, 134; frequency of feeding, 191; territory and mating, 214; sex recognition, 216; courtship, 224-225; reproduction data, 241; number of eggs per year, 244; sexual differences in size and growth, 268; secondary sexual character of dewlap, 273; time of sexual maturity, 278, 282; growth rate, 281; eats shed skin, 285; longevity, 294; size variation, 297; pet, 306; diet in captivity, 313; wild pet, 326
Green Frog: economic importance, 18; protected by law, 29; family representative, 46; hopping, 87; jumping ability, 98; movement to breeding site, 105; movements and homing ability, 108; hibernation, 122; feeding, 176; food consumed, 196; eating elm seeds, 197; relation to temperature and reproduction, 247; sexual differences in color, 271; maximum age, 292; feeding in captivity, 315
Green Salamander: movement, 104; hibernation site, 121; relation to moisture, 142; guarding eggs, 250
Green Tree Frog: over brackish water, 145; changes in food habits, 174; frequency of feeding, 190; frequency of shedding skin, 285
Green Turtle: economic importance, 18; family representative, 52, 56; speed, 100, 102; number of eggs, 240; eggs laid several times per year, 243
Greenberg, Bernard, 82, 216, 224
Greenhouse Frog: family representative, 48; jumping ability, 98; reproduction data, 236; egg tooth, 255; time of sexual maturity, 278
Grobman, Arnold B., 119
Grodzinska, N., 165
Ground Geckos: absence of adhesive pads, 94
Growth: 264-268; determinate, 265; indeterminate, 265; how studied, 265-266; individual variation, 267; sexual differences, 265, 268-269
Growth rings: in turtles, 290
Gyrinophilus d. danielsi. See Mountain Purple Salamander
Gyrinophilus porphyriticus. See Purple Salamander

Hagen, Charles W., 112
Hamilton, William J., Jr., 176, 192, 194-197, 248, 256, 278
Hamlett, George W. D., 244
Hammond's Spadefoot Toad: tadpole, 261
Handling amphibians and reptiles, 320-325
Hardy, Ross, 80, 99, 110, 122, 127, 132, 216
Hartweg, Norman E., 248
Hatching: 253-259
Hawksbill Turtles: economic importance, 21; speed, 100
Head-bobbing: sex recognition, 216, 222
Hearing: 161-163
Hedonic glands: definition, 219; in male salamanders, 273
Hellbender: family representative, 42, 44; breeding migration, 105; reception of vibrations, 163; vision, 164-165; external fertilization, 210; no courtship, 219; internal fertilization, 227; eggs, 231; eggs in water, 233; reproduction data, 234; period of incubation, 245; male guards eggs, 250; longest larval period, 261; maximum age, 292; maximum size, 298, 302; bite, 321
Heloderma horridum. See Mexican Beaded Lizard
Heloderma suspectum. See Gila Monster

Hemidactylium scutatum. See Eastern Four-toed Salamander
Hemidactylus turcicus. See Turkish Gecko
Hemipenes, 229-230
Herpetologists League: 307
Heterodon. See Hog-nosed Snake
Heterodon nasicus. See Western Hog-nosed Snake
Heterodon platyrhinos. See Hog-nosed Snake
Hibernation: 115-125; definition, 116
Highlands Salamander: relation to moisture, 142
Hildebrand, Samuel, 213
Hissing, 151-152
Hodsdon, L. A., 252
Hog-nosed Snake: in folklore, 11; crawling and track, 86; bluffing and "playing dead," 151-152; diet, 313
Holzapfel, Ruth A., 116
Home range: 80-83; definition, 80
Home site: definition, 80-81
Horned Lizard: protection, 149-150; in captivity, 317
Horned Toad. *See* Horned Lizard
"Horned Toad": buried in cornerstone, 288
Hoop Snake: in folklore, 6-7
Hope, Lawrence, 121
Housing of pets, 308-313
Hoyt, J. Southgate, 101
Hubbard, Marian, 150
Humidity relations: 141-143
Hurter's Spadefoot Toad: movement of young, 106; shortest larval period, 262
Hydromantes platycephalus. See Mount Lyell Salamander
Hyla. See Tree Frog
Hyla cinerea. See Green Tree Frog
Hyla crucifer. See Spring Peeper
Hyla ocularis. See Least Tree Frog
Hyla regilla. See Pacific Tree Frog
Hyla septentrionalis. See Cuban Tree Frog
Hyla squirella. See Squirrel Tree Frog
Hyla versicolor. See Gray Tree Frog
Hylidae: representatives, 48-49
Hypopachus. See Narrow-mouthed Toad
Hypopachus cuneus. See Mexican Narrow-mouthed Toad

Ichthyosaurs, 39
Incubation: definition, 245; 245-249; period of in relation to temperature, 246-249
Indigo Snake: moisure loss, 142; maximum size, 301, 304; as pet, 319
Ingram, William M., 276-277
Internal fertilization: definition, 210
Iguanidae: representatives, 61
Iguanids: chemical reception, 167
Island Night Lizard: family representative, 62; reproduction data, 242; maximum size, 301
Isolating mechanisms, 212
Ives, J. D., 126

Jacobson's Organ: description and function, 166-167; used before swallowing, 186
Jameson, D. L., 133
Japanese Giant Salamander, 44
Jefferson's Salamander: hibernation site, 121; sex ratio, 215; eggs, 231; reproduction data, 234; time of sexual maturity, 277
Johnson, Richard M., 282
Jumping ability of frogs, 96-99

Kellogg, Remington, 174, 208
Kenyon, Walter A., 187-188
Kilby, John D., 174, 188-190, 285
King Snake: economic importance, 27; family representative, 67; coast to coast occurrence, 75; climbing, 95; eating Water Snake, 148; approaching Rattle-

snake, 152; eating, 183; food, 206-208; courtship, 226; as pet, 319
Kinosternidae: representatives, 255
Kinosternon. *See* Mud Turtle
Kinosternon bauri. *See* Striped Mud Turtle
Kirkland, A. H., 197
Kirtland's Water Snakes: reproduction data, 243
Klauber, Laurence M., 130, 132, 140, 240, 287, 297, 304
Klimstra, W. D., 99
Knowlton, George F., 27, 171-172, 176, 189, 202, 204
Komodo Monitor, 59

Laboratory: use in, 22-23
Labyrinthodonts, 39
Lacerta vivipara. *See* European Common Lizard
Lagler, Karl F., 27, 170, 191, 198-200
Lampropeltis. *See* King Snake
Lampropeltis doliata gentilis. *See* Western Milk Snake
Lampropeltis g. getulus. *See* Chain King Snake
Lampropeltis zonata multicincta. *See* Sierra Coral King Snake
Larvae of amphibians: 259-263
Lateral Line organs: 163-164
Latham, Roy, 122
Larva: of salamanders, 259-260; of frogs, 259-260; longest period of, 261; shortest period of, 262
Least Tree Frog: family representative, 48; number of eggs and size, 235; maximum size, 299, 302
Leatherback Turtle: family representative, 52, 54, 56-58; speed, 100; reproduction data, 241; maximum size, 303
Locomotion in amphibians, 84-89
Leopard Frog: economic importance, 19, 22; protected by law, 29; altitudinal occurrence, 79; jumping ability, 98; reaction to decreasing temperature, 120; hibernation site, 121-122; protection, 150; factors determining food, 170; sex recognition, 216; amplexus, 228; tadpole, 261; sexual differences in color, 273; feeding in captivity, 315
Lepidochelys olivacea. *See* Ridley Turtle
Lepidochelys olivacea remivaga. *See* Pacific Ridley Turtle
Leptodactylidae: representatives, 48
Leptodactylus labialis. *See* Mexican White-lipped Frog
Leptotyphlopidae: representatives, 65-66
Leptotyphlops dulcis. *See* Blind Snake
Leptotyphlops d. dulcis. *See* Texas Blind Snake
Leptotyphlops humilis. *See* Dwarf Blind Snake
Leptotyphlops humilis cahuilae. *See* Desert Blind Snake
Lichanura roseofusca. *See* California Boa
Light: effect of, 144
Linnaeus, Carolus, 33
Lined Snake: time of sexual maturity, 282; as pet, 320
Livezey, Robert, 237
Little Brown Skink: reproduction data, 242; time of sexual maturity, 282; maximum size, 301
Lizards: folklore, 5-6; definition, 59; venomous, 59; families, 59-65; running, 90; movements, 111-112, hibernation, 122-123; fragile tail and protection, 151; defensive posture, 152; hearing, 163; vision, 164-165; food consumed, 201-203
Lobe-finned fish, 39
Locomotion in reptiles, 90-96
Locke, Otto Martin, 307
Lockwood, Richard A., 191
Loggerhead Turtle: economic importance, 18; eggs, 238

Longevity: 288-296; methods of studying, 289; morphological aids to study, 290-291; relation to activity, 294-295
Long-toed Salamander: competition and food habits, 154-155
London Zoo, 317
Loveridge, Arthur, 130, 314
Louisiana Milk Snake: maximum age, 293
Lowe, Charles E., Jr., 143, 318
Lucky Lure Cricket Farm, 317
Lygosoma laterale. See Little Brown Skink
Lyon, Harold, 198

Macrochelys temmincki. See Alligator Snapping Turtle
Malaclemmys terrapin. See Diamondback Terrapin
Male combat "dance," 217-218
Mamba: family representative, 67; fangs, 184
Mangrove Water Snake: compressed tail, 93
Map Turtle: family representative, 55; movements, 109
Marbled Salamander: family representative, 44; eggs and nest, 230; reproduction data, 234; wintering over of larvae, 261
Margined Salamander: courtship, 222
Marine Toad: economic importance, 26-27; sense organs, 159; eating blossoms, 198; maximum age, 292; maximum size, 302
Mark Twain, 14, 25
Marine Turtles: moving long distance, 104; 110-111; in fresh water, 145
Martof, Bernard, 77, 106, 108
Mason, E. R., 254
Massasauga: nonfunctional egg tooth, 257; maximum age, 293
Masticophis flagellum. See Coachwhip
Masticophis t. taeniatus. See Striped Whip Snake
Materials: use of amphibians and reptiles as, 20-22
Mating: definition, 226; salamanders, 227; frogs, 227-229; crocodilians, 229; turtles, 229; lizards, 229-230; snakes, 230
Maturity: sexual, 269-284
Maximum size: 296-304
McClellan, William H., 295
McClure, H. Elliott, 106, 128
McIlhenny, E. A., 174, 200, 239, 249, 278
Meade, George P., 253-254
Meal Worms: as food, 316; sources of, 317
Medsger, Oliver P., 110, 253
Megalobatrachus japonicus. See Japanese Giant Salamander
Mesquite Lizard: reproduction data, 242
Metabolism, 168
Mexican Beaded Lizard: family representative, 62; venom apparatus, 182; venomous, 324
Mexican Narrow-mouthed Toad: maximum size, 299
Mexican Vine Snake: protection, 150
Mexican White-lipped Frog: reproduction data, 236
Microhyla. See Narrow-mouthed Toad
Microhyla carolinensis. See Narrow-mouthed Toad
Microhyla carolinensis olivacea. See Great Plains Narrow-mouthed Toad
Microhylidae: representatives, 49
Micruroides. See Coral Snake
Micruroides euryxanthus. See Arizona Coral Snake
Micrurus fulvius. See Coral Snake
Midland Painted Turtle: wintering over in egg, 248
Midland Soft-shelled Turtle: reproduction data, 241

Milk Snake: in folklore, 8-9
Miller, Charles M., 145, 282
Miller, Loye, 290
Mills, Colin, 71-72
Mississippi Map Turtle: 306
Mississippi Musk Turtle: maximum size, 299
Moccasin: sex recognition, 217
Mole Salamander: burrow, 81; maximum size, 298
Mohr, Charles E., 215
Monterey Salamander: competition and food habits, 154
Moore, John A., 246-247, 258
Moore, Joseph C., 240
Mosasaurs, 39
Mosauer, Walter, 100-101, 112
Mount Lyell Salamander: altitudinal occurrence, 78; use of tail in walking, 88; lays eggs, 251
Mountain Purple Salamander: maximum size, 298
Mountain Salamander: body temperature, 139; reproduction data, 234
Mountain Short-horned Lizard: number of young, 241; reproduction data, 242
Movements; 104-114
Mudpuppy; family representative, 42, 44; breeding migration, 105; reception of vibrations, 163; digestion, 187; food consumed, 193; breeding, 211-212; eggs, 231; eggs in water, 233; reproduction data, 234; growth rate, 275; time of sexual maturity, 277; maximum size, 298
Mud Snake: in folklore, 6-7; protection, 151; guarding eggs, 253-254; feeding in captivity, 318
Mud Turtle: family representative, 55
Muhlenberg's Turtle: family representative, 55; maximum size, 299
Museum of Zoology, University of Michigan, 326
Musk Turtle: family representative, 55; movements, 109

Naja. See Cobra
Narrow-mouthed Toad: family representative, 46, 49; burrow, 81; reproduction data, 236
Natrix. See Water Snake
Natrix kirtlandi. See Kirtland's Water Snake
Natrix natrix. See European Water Snake
Natrix rhombifera. See Diamond-back Water Snake
Natrix sipedon. See Common Water Snake
Natrix sipedon compressicauda. See Mangrove Water Snake
Naturalist's Directory: 307
Necturus maculosus. See Mudpuppy
Necturus punctatus. See Dwarf Mudpuppy
Neill, Wilfred T., 20, 114, 119, 239
Neoseps reynoldsi. See Sand Skink
Neotenic Salamander: neoteny, 210
Neoteny: definition, 210
Nest: alligator, 239; crocodile, 240
Netting's Dwarf Siren; reproduction data, 234; maximum number of eggs, 235
New Mexican Race Runner: maximum size, 301
Newt: reception of vibration, 164; secondary sex characters, 269; sexual differences, 274; as pets, 306
Nichols, John T., 110, 265, 278, 289
Nichols, Ray J., 107
Night Lizard: family representative, 62; assisting birth of young, 253, 259
Noble, G. K., 123, 157, 165-167, 214, 216, 219-221, 224, 228, 232, 252, 254
Norris, Kenneth S., 103, 140, 201

Northern Alligator Lizard: maximum size, 300
Northern Copperhead: log nest, 147; changes in food habits, 173-174; reproduction data, 243; maximum age, 293
Northern Fence Lizard: courtship, 224-225; reproduction data, 242
Northern Leopard Frog: response to low temperature, 116; hibernation aggregations, 121-122; temperature and reproduction, 247
Northern Pacific Rattlesnake: altitudinal occurrence, 78; movement, 113; seasonal incidence, 129; food habits, 173-174; frequency of feeding, 191; reproduction data, 243; time of sexual maturity, 282; growth rate, 283; frequency of shedding and number of rattles, 287; maximum age, 293
Northern Pacific Red Salamander: protection, 150-151
Northern Prairie Skink: time of sexual maturity, 282
Northern Purple Salamander: reproduction data, 234
Northern Side-blotched Uta: changes in food, 171-172; feeding, 176; estimated number per acre, 176; digestion, 189
Northern Spring Peeper: hibernation site, 121
Northern Dusky Salamander: hibernation site, 120
Northern Water Snake: hibernation, 123; food habits and availability of food, 171; frequency of feeding, 191; reproduction data, 243; fed in wild, 327
Northern Wood Frog: occurrence within Arctic Circle, 71; hibernation site, 121
Northwestern Salamander: reproduction data, 234
New York Zoological Park, 308

Oak Toad: eggs, 232; reproduction data, 236; maximum size, 299
"Old Rip," 288
Old World Vipers, 183
Ontogenetic change: in food habits, 174-175
Opheodrys aestivus. See Rough Green Snake
Opheodrys vernalis. See Smooth Green Snake
Ophiophagus. See Cobra
Ophisaurus. See Glass Lizard
Ophisaurus attenuatus. See Slender Glass Lizard
Ophisaurus ventralis. See Eastern Glass Lizard
Ornate Box Turtle: seasonal incidence, 129
Orton, Grace L., 259-261
Oviparous: definition, 239
Oxybelis aeneus auratus. See Mexican Vine Snake
Oxyuranus scutellatus. See Taipan

Pacific Fence Lizard: movements, 111
Pacific Garter Snake: feeding, 177; eating in captivity, 318-319
Pacific Gopher Snake: movement, 113; food consumed, 207
Pacific Ridley Turtle: aggregation, 111
Pacific Tree Frog: reproduction data, 236
Pack, H. J., 176
Painted Turtle: economic importance, 26-27; family representative, 55; coast to coast occurrence, 75; walking, 86; movements, 109; seasonal incidence, 127; hearing range, 163; digestion, 187; food consumed, 199; courtship, 222; elongate claws on male, 270; shedding outer horny plates, 285

"Parachuting": definition, 89; in Green Anolis, 95; in Southern Fence Lizard, 95
Parasites, 153
Parietal eye, 165
Parotid gland, 183
Parotoid gland, 150
Pearse, A. S., 193
Pelobatidae: representatives, 48
Peninsular Turtle: reproduction data, 241
Perkins, C. B., 217, 287
Perkins, Marlin, 318
Pest control: use in, 26-28
Pets: qualifications, 306; sources, 306-307; housing, 308-313; food, 313-320; handling, 320-325; studying, 325-327
Phrynosoma. See Horned Lizard
Phrynosoma cornutum. See Texas Horned Lizard
Phrynosoma douglassi hernandesi. See Mountain Short-horned Lizard
Phyllodactylus tuberculosus. See Tubercular Gecko
Physical environment: outlined, 135-137; reactions to, 145-146
Pickerel Frog: reproduction data, 236; relation to temperature and reproduction, 247
Pilot Black Snake: movements, 113; courtship, 226; egg, 238; reproduction data, 243; guarding eggs, 253; maximum age, 293; maximum size, 304
Pine Snake: sex recognition, 217
Pituophis. See Gopher Snake
Pituophis catenifer deserticola. See Great Basin Gopher Snake
Pituophis catenifer sayi. See Bull Snake
Pituophis m. melanoleucas. See Pine Snake
Pit Viper: facial pit, 165-166; listed, 183; male combat "dance", 217-218
Plains Toad: time of sexual maturity, 278
Plaster of Paris: in turtle tank, 314
Plesiosaurs, 39
Plethodon c. cinereus. See Red-backed Salamander
Plethodon glutinosus. See Slimy Salamander
Plethodon jordani. See Highlands Salamander
Plethodontidae: representatives, 45
Poison glands: in amphibians, 150
Pollister, Arthur W., 246, 258
Pond Terrapin: family representative, 55
Pope, Clifford H., 98, 277
Pope, Sarah H., 277
Prairie Garter Snake: movements, 112
Prairie Rattlesnake: family representative, 67; occurrence in habitat, 79; reaction to decreasing temperature, 120; cooperation, 158; courtship, 226; size and number of young, 240; reproduction in alternate years, 244
Protection from enemies, 149-153
Proteidae: representative, 44
Proteroglyphs, 184
"Proto-cooperation," 157
Pseudacris nigrita triseriata. See Western Chorus Frog
Pseudacris s. streckeri. See Strecker's Chorus Frog
Pseudemys. See Slider Turtle or Pond Terrapin
Pseudemys floridana. See Southern Terrapin
Pseudemys floridana suwannensis. See Suwannee Turtle
Pseudemys malonei. See Bahaman Slider Turtle
Pseudemys scripta elegans. See Red-eared Turtle
Pseudobranchus s. striatus. See Broad-striped Mud Siren
Pseudotriton ruber. See Red Salamander

Pterosaurs, 39
Purple Salamander: tongue, 179
Pygmy Salamander: maximum size, 298, 302

Quivira Specialties, 307

Race Runner: family representative, 63; digging, 81
Racer: economic importance, 27; family representative, 64, 67; coast to coast occurrence, 75; climbing, 95; eating, 183; sex recognition, 217
Rahn, Hermann, 152, 244
Rainbow Snake: folklore, 7; sexual differences in coloration, 272
Rana. See True Frogs
Rana aurora. See Red-legged Frog
Rana b. boyli. See California Yellow-legged Frog
Rana capito. See Gopher Frog
Rana catesbeiana. See Bullfrog
Rana clamitans. See Green Frog
Rana grylio. See Southern Bullfrog
Rana palustris. See Pickerel Frog
Rana pipiens. See Leopard Frog
Rana pipiens sphenocephala. See Southern Leopard Frog
Rana sylvatica. See Wood Frog
Rana sylvatica cantabrigensis. See Northern Wood Frog
Rand, A. Stanley, 97-99
Rand, Austin, 154, 175
Raney, Edward C., 107, 276-277
Ranidae: representatives, 49
Rat Snake: economic importance, 27; family representative, 67; as pet, 319
Rattlesnake: folklore, 12-15; use of venom, 23; economic importance, 27; family representative, 67; rattling, 152; defensive posture, 152; sex recognition, 217; shedding skin in relation to rattle, 287; frequency of shedding, 287; large sets of rattles, 287-288
Rattlesnake oil, 23
Rattlesnake rattles; and age, 287
Rattling: frequency, 152
Rectilinear locomotion: in snakes, 91
Red-backed Salamander: response to low temperature, 116; winter mortality, 119; hibernation site, 121; food consumed, 195; eggs, 231; eggs on land, 233; reproduction data, 234; time of sexual maturity, 277
Red-bellied Snake: hibernation aggregation, 123; reproduction data, 243; time of sexual maturity, 282
Red-eared Turtle: natural extension of range, 78; distribution aided by man, 76-77; seasonal incidence, 127; frequency of feeding, 191; courtship, 221; size and number of eggs, 240; reproduction data, 241; nest, 254; caruncle, 256; long claws of male, 277; time of sexual maturity, 278; maximum reproductive age, 284; shedding of plates with and without growth, 286; as pet, 306
Red-legged Frog: hibernation, 118; relation to humidity, 136
Red Salamander: distribution aided by man, 77; courtship, 220
Red Scaly Lizard, 33
Red-sided Garter Snake: northern occurrence, 71-72
Red-spotted Newt: economic importance, 26; distribution aided by man, 76; walking, 86; hibernation site, 121; sleeping, 134; reaction to high oxygen in water, 145; oxygen and breeding, 211-212; courtship, 220; eggs, 231; reproduction data, 234; starving individuals shed skin, 286

Red-spotted Toad: reproduction data, 236
Red-striped Garter Snake: feeding, 177
Reef Gecko: question of introduction, 59-61; egg, 238; reproduction data, 242; maximum size, 300, 303
Reptile: definition, 51; Orders, 51-52; largest Order, 68; largest family, 68; largest genus, 68; largest species, 68; locomotion, 90-96
Rhineura floridana. See Florida Worm Lizard
Rhyacosiredon. See Axolotl
Rhyacotriton olympicus. See Mountain Salamander
Rhyncocephalia, 51
Rhyncocephalians, 39
Ribbon Snake: climbing, 95; movements, 113
Ridley Turtle: economic importance, 18
Ring-necked Snake: protection, 151; as pet, 320
Richmond, Neil, D., 272
Risley, Paul L., 278
Robber Frog: family representative, 46; tadpole, 261; parental care, 235; maximum size, 299
Robinson, Harry B., 286, 295
Rose, Walter, 25
Rough Green Snake: sleeping, 134
Rough-skinned Newt; family representative, 42
Rubber Boa: family representative, 66; reproduction data, 243; maximum size, 301
Rubner's Hypothesis, 295

Sacramento Mountain Salamander: altitudinal occurrence, 79
Sagebrush Lizard: digestion, 189; food consumed, 202
Salamanders: relation to fire, 4-5; Order, 31; North American representatives, 42-45; largest genus, 50; largest species, 50; movements, 104-105; temperature control, 138; food consumed, 155, 195-197; hearing, 162-163; vision, 164-165; handling, 323
Salvadora hexalepis. See Desert Patchnosed Snake
Salyer, J. Clark II, 170, 191
Sand Skink: family representative, 63; "swimming" through sand, 94; on sandy soil, 145
San Diego Alligator Lizard: reproduction data, 242
San Diego Gopher Snake: maximum age, 293
"Sand-swimming": by lizards and snakes, 93-94
San Francisco Alligator Lizard: reproduction data, 242
Sauromalus obesus. See Chuckawalla
Sawyer, Tom, 2
Scaly Lizards: largest genus, 68; territoriality and mating, 214; sexual differences in size and growth, 268
Scaphiopus bombifrons. See Central Plains Spadefoot Toad
Scaphiopus couchi. See Great Plains Spadefoot Toad
Scaphiopus hammondi. See Western Spadefoot Toad
Scaphiopus holbrooki. See Eastern Spadefoot Toad
Scaphiopus holbrooki hurteri. See Hurter's Spadefoot Toad
Scarlet Snake: distribution extended by airplane, 77; food, 205
Sceloporus. See Scaly Lizard
Sceloporus g. graciosus. See Sagebrush Lizard
Sceloporus graciosus gracilis. See Sierra Pine Lizard
Sceloporus graciosus vandenburgianus. See Southern Mountain Lizard
Sceloporus grammicus disparilis. See Mesquite Lizard

Sceloporus magister. See Desert Spiny Lizard
Sceloporus o. occidentalis. See Pacific Fence Lizard
Sceloporus occidentalis taylori. See Yosemite Fence Lizard
Sceloporus u. undulatus. See Southern Fence Lizard
Sceloporus undulatus hyacinthinus. See Northern Fence Lizard
Schmidt, A., 165
Schmidt, Karl P., 17, 36, 71, 78
Schneck, J., 110
Schroder, Robert C., 123
Scientific name, 33-35
Scincidae: representatives, 63
Seasonal activity, 125-131
Secondary sexual characters: 269-277
Seibert, Henri C., 112
Senility, 284-285
Senses, 158-167
Serpentine locomotion, 91
Sex hormones: control secondary sex characters, 274, 278
Sex ratio, 214-215
Sex recognition, 215-217
Sexual difference: growth and size, 268-269; in Greek Anolis, 268; in Alligator, 268; in Scaly Lizard, 268; in Eastern Tiger Salamander, 268; in Crater Lake Newt, 268
Sexual maturity: 269-284; how studied, 269; secondary sexual characters in relation to, 269-277
Shakespeare, 3
Shasta Salamander: eggs on land, 233
Shaw, Charles E., 217-218, 240, 259
Shedding skin: related to growth, 285-288; factors influencing, 286
Shelford, V. E., 143
Shovel-nosed Snake: "swimming" through sand, 94; movements, 112; daily activity, 133
Sidewinder Rattlesnake: "sidewinding," 91-93; speed, 101-102; movements, 112; body temperature, 139-140; protection of rattling, 152
"Sidewinding" locomotion, 91-93
Sierra Alligator Lizard: altitudinal occurrence, 79
Sierra Coral King Snake: speed, 101-102
Sierra Pine Lizard: movements, 111; time of sexual maturity, 282; frequency of shedding skin, 286; longevity, 295
Silvery Footless Lizard: reproduction data, 242; time of sexual maturity, 282
Siredon. See Axolotl
Siren: swimming, 89; estimated speed, 96; external fertilization, 210, 227; eggs in water, 233; bite, 321
Sirenidae: representatives, 44
Siren intermedia nettingi. See Netting's Dwarf Siren
Siren lacertina. See Great Siren
Sistrurus. See Rattlesnake
Sistrurus catenatus. See Massasauga
Six-lined Race Runner: speed, 101-103; movements, 112; hibernation, 117, 122; daily activity, 133; reproduction data, 242
Size: and number of eggs, 235, 240; sexual differences, 268-269; maximum, 296-304; measurements, 296; biological factors influencing, 297
Skin: shedding, 285-288
Skink: largest genus, 68
Skull, 179
Slater, James R., 229
Sleeping, 133-134
Slender Flat-headed Snake: maximum size, 301
Slender Glass Lizard: family representative, 60
Slider Turtle: movements, 109; courtship, 222; laying eggs, 239; well-camouflaged nests, 252;

elongate claws on males, 270; sexual differences in color, 272; shedding outer horny plates, 285; growth rings on shell, 290
Slimy Salamander: family representative, 42; time of sexual maturity, 277
Smith, Charles C., 190
Smith, Hobart M., 235
Smith, Robert G., Jr., 165
Smooth Green Snake movements, 112; hibernation aggregation, 123
Snake-feeding station, 327
Snakes: folklore, 6-15; swallowing young, 7-8; milking cows, 8-9; "charming" prey, 9; "charming" of, 9-10; economic importance, 19, 21-24; definition, 65; families, 65-68; movements, 112-114; hibernation, 123-125; seasonal incidence, 129-131; defensive posture, 152; hearing, 163; vision, 164-165; venom apparatus, 183-185; food consumed, 204-208; holding, 323
Snapping Turtle: economic importance, 19, 27-28; family representative, 52, 54-55; geographic distribution, 71, movements, 109; defense, 151; walking, 190; food consumed, 198; egg, 238; reproduction data, 241; holding, 322, 324
Soft-shelled Turtle: economic importance, 19; family representative, 52, 56; movements, 109; defense, 151; food consumed, 200; maximum age, 293; holding, 322, 324
Solenoglyphs, 184
South American Coral Snake: family representative, 67
South American Pit Viper: use of venom, 23
Southern Bullfrog: economic importance, 18; protected by law, 29
Southern Fence Lizard: movements, 111-112; territories, 111-112; home range, 111-112; winter activity, 118-119; frequency of shedding skin, 191; differential growth, 266; time of sexual maturity, 282; longevity, 294-295
Southern Leopard Frog: digestion, 188-189; frequency of feeding, 190; incubation and larval period, 262
Southern Mountain Lizard: altitudinal occurrence, 79
Southern Soft-shelled Turtle: maximum size, 300
Southern Terrapin: family representative, 52
Southern Toad: homing ability, 107
Southhall, John B., 18
Spadefoot Toad: burrow, 81; movement of young, 106; relation to atmospheric pressure, 144; period of incubation, 245
Speed: 96-103; salamanders, 96; turtles, 99-100; alligator, 100; snakes, 100-103; lizards, 101-103
Spenser's "Faerie Queene," 7
Spermatophores, 227
Spermatozoa: retention, 213
Sphaerodactylus notatus. See Reef Gecko
Sphenodon punctatus. See Tuatara
Spotted Salamander: classification, 32; family representative, 42, 44; occurrence, 69; hibernation site, 120-121; geotropism, 146; eggs and algae, 147-148; breeding aggregation, 211; courtship, 220; sexual differences in color, 271-272; maximum age, 292
Spotted Turtle: maximum age, 292
"Spring lizards": as bait, 25; aiding distribution, 77
Spring Peeper: jumping ability, 98-99; call in spring, 209; eggs, 232; reproduction data, 235
Squirrel Tree Frog: family representative, 49; occurrence in habi-

tat, 79; "parachuting," 89; nightly station, 108
Stabler, Robert M., 286
Stebbins, Robert C., 88, 111, 137-139, 145, 220, 250-251, 254, 282, 285-286, 295
Stejneger, Leonhard, 36, 78
Stereochilus marginatus. See Margined Salamander
Sternotherus. See Musk Turtle
Sternotherus c. carinatus. See Mississippi Musk Turtle
Sternotherus odoratus. See Common Musk Turtle
Stickel, Lucille, 110
Stickel, William H., 113
Stille, W. T., 106-107, 132-133, 141
Storer, Tracy I., 118
Storeria dekayi. See DeKay's Snake
Storeria occipitomaculata. See Redbellied Snake
Strecker's Chorus Frog: incubation and larval period, 262
Striped Mud Turtle: family representative, 52, 55; maximum size, 299, 303
Striped Newt: maximum size, 298
Striped Whip Snake: at den, 124
Studying pet amphibians and reptiles, 325-327
Sure-Live Worm Company, 316
Suwannee Turtle: economic importance, 19; family representative, 55; speed, 99, 102; maximum size, 299
Syrrhopus campi. See Camp's Frog

Tadpole: definition, 46-47; adaptive types, 260-261
Tadpoles: relation to light, 144
Tailed Frog: family representative, 46-47; internal fertilization, 210, 227; sex recognition, 216; amplexus, 229; reproduction data, 236; tadpole, 261; maximum size, 298
Taipan: family representative, 67
Tanner, Wilmer W., 125
Tantilla. See Crowned Snake
Tantilla g. gracilis. See Slender Flat-headed Snake
Taricha granulosa. See Rough-skinned Newt
Taricha granulosa mazamae. See Crater Lake Newt
Taricha torosus. See California Newt
Tarpon Zoo, 307
Taste, 166-167
Teidae: representatives, 63
Teids: chemical reception, 167; tooth modification, 181
Temperature: relation to, 137-141; effect on incubation, 246-249; effect on embryonic development, 248-249
Terrapene. See Box Turtle
Terrapene carolina. See Box Turtle
Terrapene carolina bauri. See Florida Box Turtle
Terrapene ornata. See Ornate Box Turtle
Territory: 81-83; definition, 81-82
Tessellated Race Runner: food consumed, 204
Testudinidae: representatives, 55-56
Tevis, Lloyd, 112
Texas Blind Salamander; phototropism, 146
Texas Blind Snake: maximum size, 301
Texas Horned Lizard: family representative, 60; established in Florida, 77; egg, 238; reproduction data, 242
Texas Indigo Snake: frequency of shedding, 287
Texas Tree Uta: maximum size, 300
Thamnophis butleri. See Butler's Garter Snake
Thamnophis elegans. See Western Garter Snake

Thamnophis ordinoides. See Red-striped Garter Snake
Thamnophis ordinoides vagrans. See Wandering Garter Snake
Thamnophis radix. See Prairie Garter Snake
Thamnophis sauritus. See Ribbon Snake
Thamnophis sauritus sackeni. See Florida Ribbon Snake
Thamnophis sirtalis parietalis. See Red-sided Garter Snake
Three-toed Amphiuma: reproduction data, 234; female guards, eggs, 250; maximum size, 298, 302
Tiger Salamander classification, 31-35; coast to coast occurrence, 75; seasonal incidence, 128; larvae in alkaline water, 145; neotenic forms, 210; age of larva and adult, 291; maximum age, 292
Timber Rattlesnake: family representative, 64; local extermination, 75-76; hibernation, 117; log nest, 147; sexual differences in color, 272
Titillating, 221-222
Toads: in folklore, 2-4; and warts, 2-3; economic importance, 26-28; use of term, 47; distribution aided by man, 76; movement of young, 106; reaction to decreasing temperature, 120; hibernation, 122; response to decreasing moisture, 125; seasonal incidence, 128; temperature relations, 140; relation to humidity, 141; phototropism, 146; sense organs, 158-160; frequency of feeding, 190; sexual differences in color, 271; frequency of shedding skin, 286
Trans-Pecos Rat Snake: daily activity, 133
Tree Frog: family representative, 48; adhesive disks, 88; sleeping, 134; protection, 149-150
Trionychidae: representatives, 56
Trionyx. See Soft-shelled Turtle
Trionyx ferox. See Soft-shelled Turtle
Trionyx f. ferox. See Southern Soft-shelled Turtle
Trionyx ferox spinifera. See Midland Soft-shelled Turtle
Troost's Turtle, 306
Tropidoclonion lineatum. See Lined Snake
Tropism: definition and designation, 145-146
True Frog: family representative, 49; occurrence in colonies, 81; movement to breeding site, 105; seasonal incidence, 128; hearing range, 162; changes in food habits, 174; effect of temperature on incubation, 246-247
Tuatara, 53
Tubercular Gecko: adhesive pads, 94-95
Turkish Gecko; adhesive pads, 94
"Turtle oil," 23
Turtles: in folklore, 5; economic importance, 18-19, 24; North American representatives, 53-58; altitudinal occurrence, 79; swimming, 93; movements, 108-111; sleeping, 134; hatchlings and tropisms, 146; eating, 180-181; food consumed, 201-202; holding, 322, 324-325
Twain, Mark, 25
Two-lined Salamander: winter mortality, 119; hibernation site, 120-121; sense organs, 159; food consumed, 194; courtship, 219-220, 222; eggs, 231; size variation, 297
Typhlomolge rathbuni. See Texas Blind Salamander

Uhler, F. M., 206
Uma. See Fringe-toed Lizard
Uta o. ornata. See Texas Tree Uta
Uta s. stansburiana. See Northern Side-blotched Uta

Varanids: tooth structure, 181
Varanus komodoensis. See Komodo Monitor
Venom: Gila Monster, 182; snakes, 183-185
Vernberg, F. John, 116, 119
Vertebrates: relations among, 36-37
Vine Snake: binocular vision, 165
Vipera berus. See Common European Adder
Vision: 164-165; binocular, 165; color, 165
Viviparous: definition, 237

Walker, Charles F., 106
Walls, Gordon L., 164
Wandering Garter Snake: altitudinal occurrence, 78; reproduction data, 243
Water Moccasin: family representative, 67; courtship, 226; time of sexual maturity, 282; maximum age, 293
Water Snake: economic importance, 21; family representative, 66-67; occurrence in colonies, 81; sleeping, 134; preyed on by King Snake, 148; feeding, 177; as pet, 320
Western Coachwhip: maximum age, 293
Western Collared Lizard: reproduction data, 241
Western Cottonmouth: natural extension of range, 78
Western Chorus Frog: altitudinal occurrence, 79; hibernation site, 121
Western Diamondback Rattlesnake: family representative, 67; established in Wisconsin, 77; head, 162; number of rattles, 288; maximum age, 293
Western Fence Lizard, 294-295
Western Four-toed Salamander: female guarding eggs, 250-251; hatching process, 255
Western Garter Snake: number of subspecies, 68; attacking salamanders, 150-151
Western Hog-nosed Snake: family representative, 64; seasonal incidence, 128-129
Western Milk Snake: hibernation, 125
Western Painted Turtle: reproduction data, 241; maximum age, 293
Western Racer: at den, 124
Western Red-bellied Newt: sexual differences in color, 271
Western Ring-necked Snake: attacking salamanders, 150-151
Western Skink: reproduction data, 242
Western Spadefoot Toad: eggs, 232; reproduction data, 236
Western Toad: feeding, 176
Wever, E. G., 163
Whip Snake: abilities of movement: 75-76; climbing, 95; eating, 183; sex recognition, 217
Wickham, M. M., 109
Winter den: Alligator, 122; Desert Tortoise, 122; snakes, 123-125
Winter mortality, 119-120
Wood Frog: family representative, 49; coast to coast occurrence, 75; sex recognition, 216; eggs, 232; relation of period of incubation to temperature, 246-247; developmental stages, 258; sexual differences in web of foot, 270
Wood, John T., 231, 235, 251
Wood Turtle: protected by law, 29; head, 161; sexual differences in length of tail, 271; maximum age, 292
Woodbury, Angus M., 80, 99, 110, 122, 124, 127, 132, 216
Woodhouse's Toad: feeding, 176; warning croak, 212; maximum

number of eggs, 235; reproduction data, 236
Worm Salamander: locomotion, 85; protection, 151; eggs on land, 233
Wright, Albert H., 98, 232, 237
Wright, Anna A., 232, 237
Wyeth, Inc., 23

Xantusia. See Night Lizard
Xantusia riversiana. See Island Night Lizard
Xantusia vigilis. See Yucca Night Lizard
Xantusidae: representatives, 62-63

Yellow-barred Tiger Salamander: time of sexual maturity, 277
Yellow-bellied Racer: seasonal incidence, 128
Yellow-eyed Salamander: courtship, 220
Yosemite Fence Lizard: altitudinal occurrence, 79
Yosemite Toad: sexual differences in color, 270
Young: maximum number, 243; care of, 249-253
Yucca Night Lizard: family representative, 60; at high temperature, 137, 140; reproduction data, 242; maximum size, 301

Zoogeography: definition, 69
Zweifel, Richard G., 154